Homework and Problem Solving

Student Book

- Homework
- Leveled Problem Solving

Visit Education Place®
www.eduplace.com/kids

HOUGHTON MIFFLIN BOSTON

Printed in the U.S.A.

ISBN 10: 0-618-96123-2
ISBN 13: 978-0-618-96123-8

15 16 0982 16 15 14 13 12
4500377934

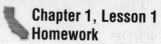

Name _______________ Date _________

Hands On: Numbers and Number Parts to 10

CA Standards
KEY NS 1.1, MR 1.2

Count and write the number.

There are three cups. ___3___

Count. Write the number.

1.  _____

2.  _____

3.  _____

4.  _____

Spiral Review (Grade K, Chapter 8, Lesson 2) **KEY K NS 1.0**

Circle the matching number.

5.  1 2

6. 1 2

Name ____________________ Date __________

CA Standards
KEY NS 1.1, MR 1.2

Hands On: Numbers and Number Parts to 10

Count. Write the number.

Jon has a fish tank like the one in the picture.

1. How many crabs does Jon have?

2. How many plants does Jon have?

3. How many sea horses does Jon have?

4. How many spotted fish does Jon have?

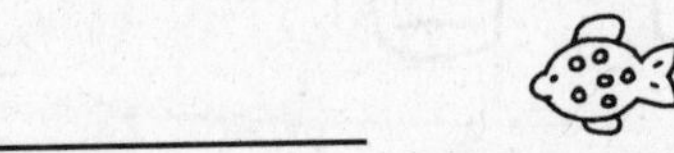

5. How many striped fish + spotted fish does Jon have?

6. How many crabs + plants does Jon have?

Name ______________ Date ________

Hands On: Numbers and Number Parts to 20

CA Standards
KEY NS 1.1, MR 1.2

Count and write the number.

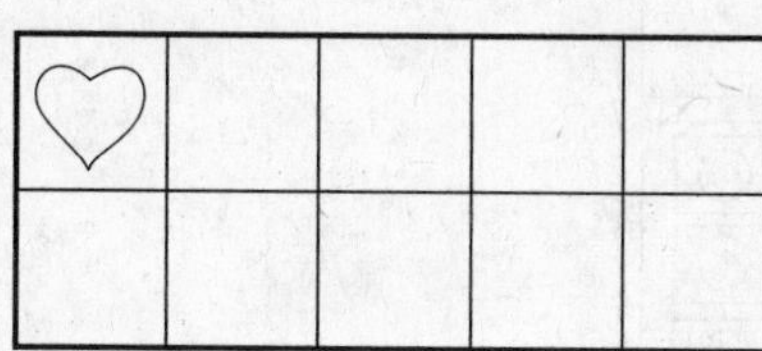

11

Count. Write the number.

1.

2. 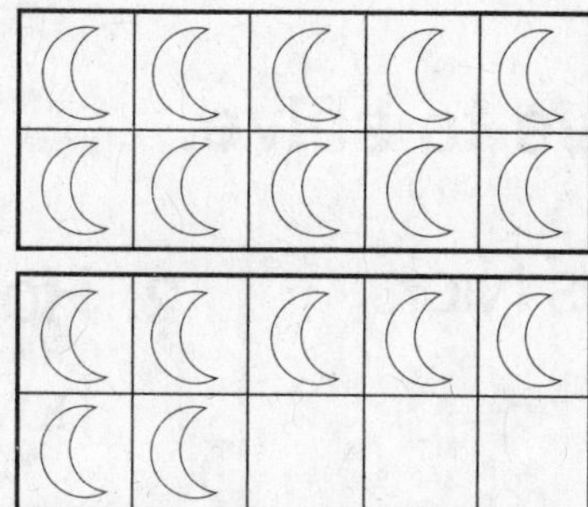

3. 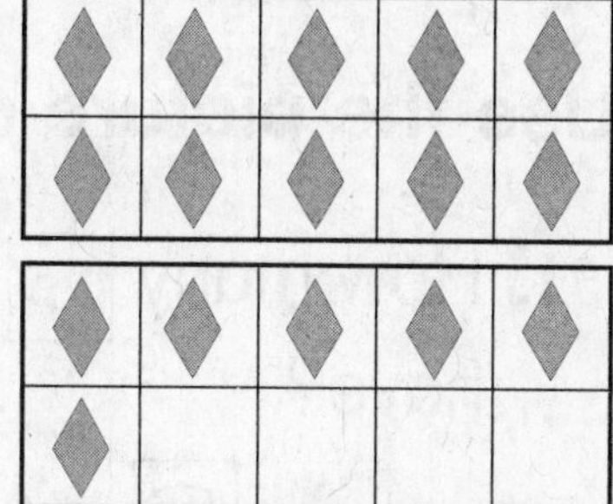

______ ______ ______

Spiral Review (Chapter 1, Lesson 1) **MR 1.2, KEY NS 1.1**

Count. Write the number.

4. 

5. 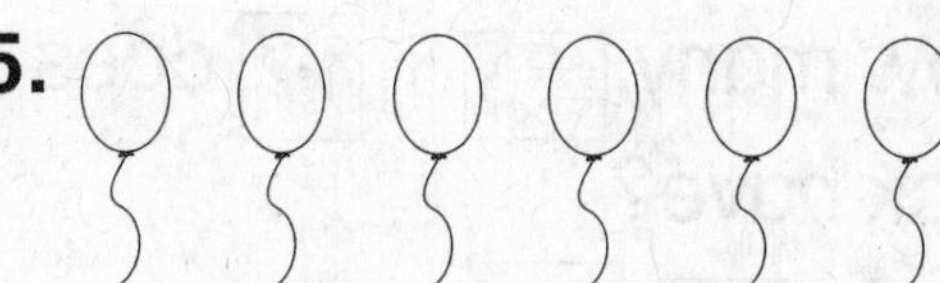

______ ______

Name ______________________ Date __________

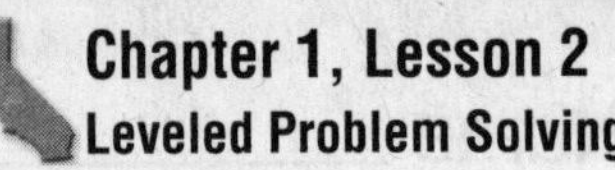

Hands On: Numbers and Number Parts to 20

CA Standards
KEY NS 1.1, MR 1.2

Nick's Stickers

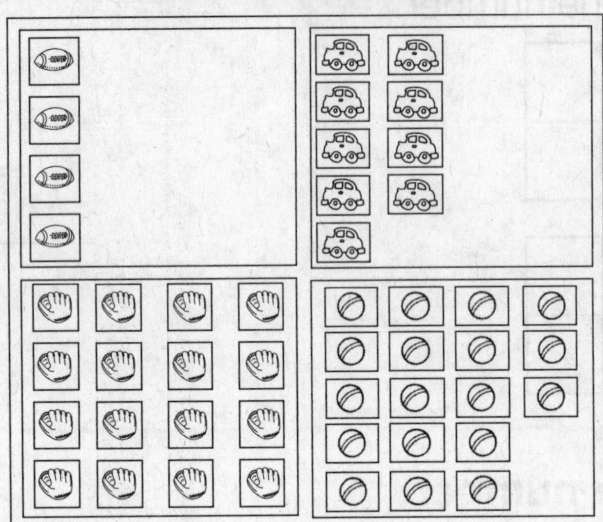

Use the picture above to solve.

1. How many 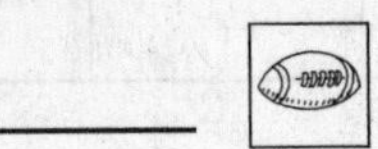 does Nick have?

   ______

2. How many does Nick have?

   ______

3. How many does Nick have?

   ______

4. How many  does Nick have?

   ______

5. How many  + does Nick have?

   ______

6. How many + does Nick have?

   ______

Name ____________________ Date __________

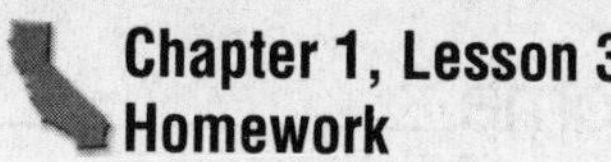

Before, After, Between

CA Standards
KEY NS 1.1, KEY NS 2.3

Number lines can help you put numbers in order.

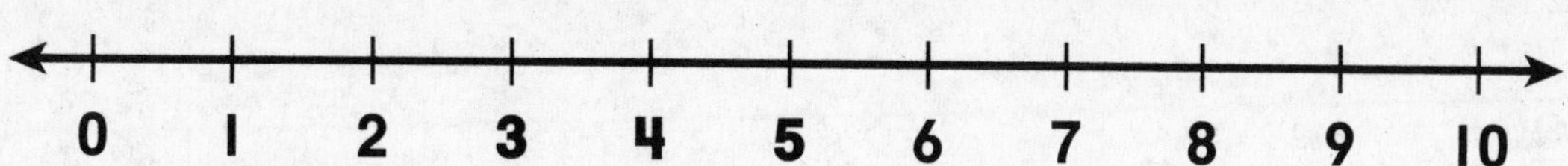

3 is just before 4.
5 is just after 4.
4 is between 3 and 5

Write the numbers.

1. Just after

5, 6, ________

2. Just before

________, 3, 4

3. Between

3, ________, 5

4. Just before and just after

________, 5, ________

Spiral Review (Chapter 1, Lesson 1) **MR 1.2, KEY NS 1.1**

Circle the matching number.

5. ● ● ● ● ● ●　　6　7

6. ● ● ●　　2　3

Before, After, Between

CA Standards
KEY NS 1.1, KEY NS 2.3

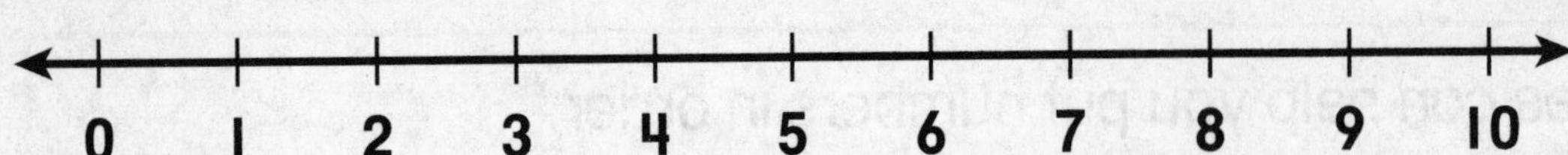

Solve.

1. Jan is looking for a number that is just before 5. Circle the number that is just before 5.

   2 4

2. Ryan is looking for a number that is just after 7. Circle the number that is just after 7.

   8 5

3. Rosa is looking for a number that is between 5 and 7. Write the number that is between 5 and 7.

   ____

4. Mike is looking for a number that is just before 4. Write the number that is just before 4.

   ____

5. Iisha is looking for a number that is 3 more than 3. Write the number that is 3 more than 3.

   ____

6. Mario is looking for a number that is 2 less than 9. Write the number that is 2 less than 9.

   ____

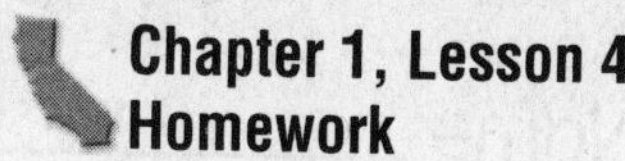

Count Forward and Backward

CA Standards
KEY NS 1.1, NS 1.0

Numbers get bigger when you count forward. 1, 2, 3, 4, 5
Numbers get smaller when you count backward. 5, 4, 3, 2, 1

Count forward. Write the numbers.

1. 5, 6, 7, ____
2. 13, 14, 15, ____
3. 9, 10, 11, ____
4. 17, 18, 19, ____

Count backward. Write the numbers.

5. 8, 7, 6, ____
6. 10, 9, 8, ____
7. 16, 15, 14, ____
8. 4, 3, 2, ____

Spiral Review (Chapter 1, Lesson 1) **MR 1.2, KEY NS 1.1**

Circle the matching number.

9. 6 8

10. 7 5

Name ____________________ Date __________

Count Forward and Backward

CA Standards
KEY NS 1.1, NS 1.0

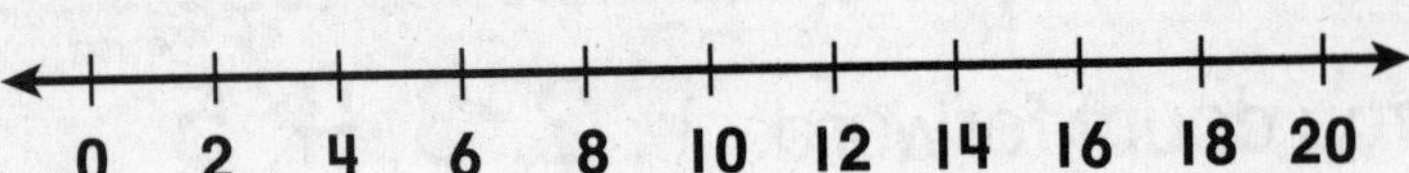

Solve.

1. Tara starts at the number 7. She counts forward 1 number. Circle her new number.

   2 8

2. Chu starts at the number 9. He counts backward 1 number. Circle his new number.

   8 3

3. Kyle starts at the number 12. He counts forward 3 numbers. What is his new number?

   ____

4. Michelle starts at the number 17. She counts backward 3 numbers. What is her new number?

   ____

5. Larry starts at the number 25. He counts backward 5 numbers. What is his new number?

   ____

6. Anita starts at the number 23. She counts forward 4 numbers. What is her new number?

   ____

Problem Solving: Find a Pattern

CA Standards
KEY NS 1.1, KEY SDAP 2.1

You can make a pattern with shapes.

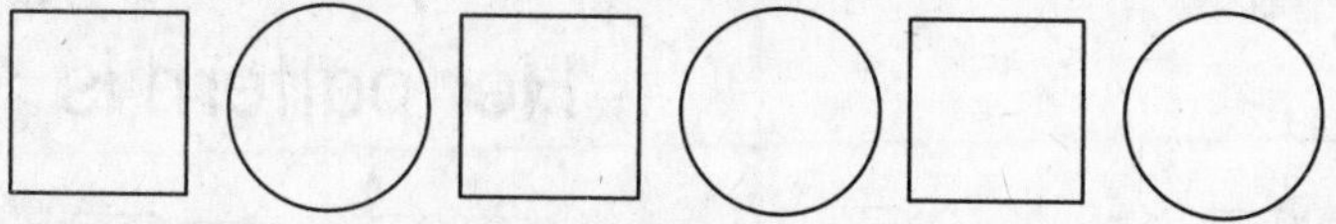

This is a square, circle, square, circle, square, circle pattern.
Circle the shape that comes next.

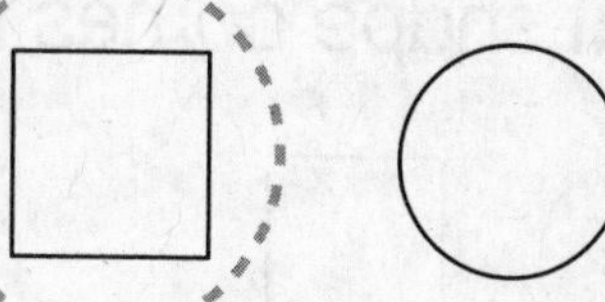

Circle the shape that is likely to come next in the pattern.

1.

2.

3.

4.

Spiral Review (Chapter 1, Lesson 1) **MR 1.2, KEY NS 1.1**

Circle the matching number.

5. 10 8

6. 7 9

Name ______________________ Date __________

Problem Solving: Find a Pattern

CA Standards
KEY NS 1.1, KEY SDAP 2.1

Solve.

1. Randy is making a belt.
His pattern is

What shape comes next?

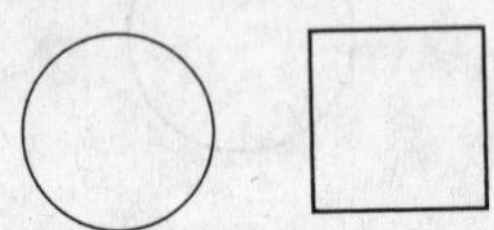

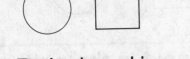

2. Suzy is making a necklace.
Her pattern is

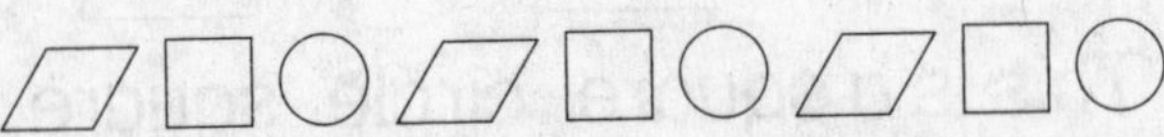

What shape comes next?

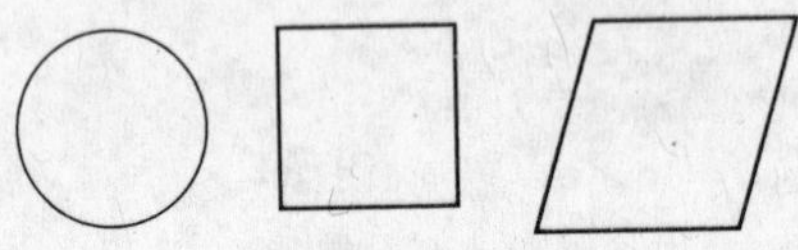

3. Pedro is making a quilt.
His pattern is

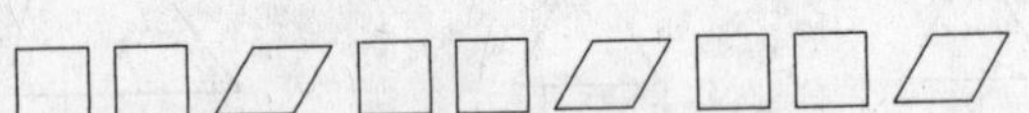

What shape comes next?

______

4. Kara is making a scarf.
Her pattern is

What shape comes next?

______

5. Trina is making a bracelet.
Her pattern is

She left out 1 shape.
Draw the missing shape.

6. Kent is making a belt.
His pattern is

He left out 1 shape.
Draw the missing shape.

Name ______________________ Date __________

Chapter 2, Lesson 1
Homework

Hands On: Numbers 11–19

CA Standards
KEY NS 1.1, NS 1.4

Regroup 12 ones as 1 ten and 2 ones.

Tens	Ones
	12 ones

→

Tens	Ones
1 ten	2 ones

12 ones

Solution: _1_ ten _2_ ones

Use small items such as coins or pasta to help you.

Show.	Make 1 ten. Write the tens and the ones.	Write the number.
1. 18 ones	____ ten ____ ones	____
2. 12 ones	____ ten ____ ones	____
3. 15 ones	____ ten ____ ones	____
4. 17 ones	____ ten ____ ones	____

Spiral Review (Chapter 1, Lesson 3) **KEY** NS 1.1, **KEY** NS 2.3

0 1 2 3 4 5 6 7 8 9 10

Write the numbers.

5. Between

5, _____, 7

2, _____, 4

6. Just before and just after

_____, 9, _____

_____, 4, _____

Name ______________________ Date __________

Hands On: Numbers 11–19

Solve.

1. Tara has 12 stickers.
Circle to show how many tens she has.

How many tens?

______ ten

How many ones are left?

______ ones

2. Mickey has 15 pencils.
Circle to show how many tens he has.

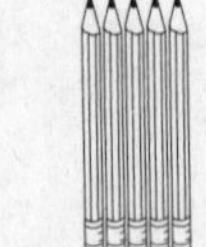

How many tens?

______ ten

How many ones are left?

______ ones

3. Jan has 18 football cards to put in albums.
Each album holds 10 cards.
How many tens can she put in each album? How many ones are left?

______ ten ______ ones

4. Brett has 13 rocks in his collection. His box holds 10 rocks.
How many tens can he put in the box?
How many ones are left?

______ ten ______ ones

5. Jamal has 6 small buttons and 8 large buttons. His button box will hold 10 buttons.
How many tens can he put in the box? How many ones are left?

______ ten ______ ones

6. Rosita has 6 small marbles and 5 large marbles. She is going to give 10 marbles away.
How many tens can she give away? How many ones are left?

______ ten ______ one

Use with text pp. 23–24

Name ____________________ Date __________

Read and Write Numbers to 50

CA Standards
KEY NS 1.1, NS 1.4

Show the number as tens and ones.

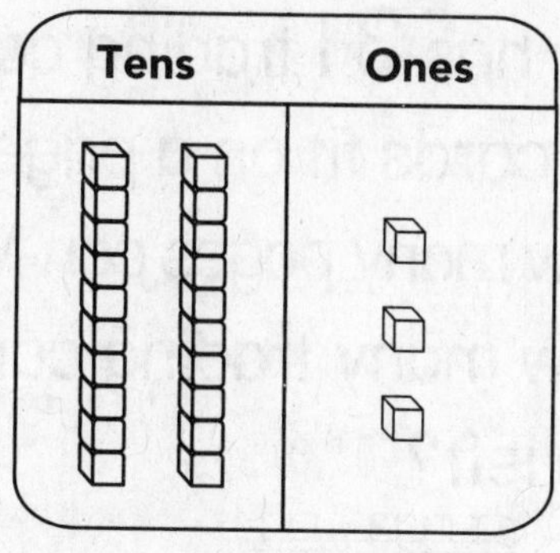

2 tens 3 ones 23
twenty-three

Write the number.

1\. 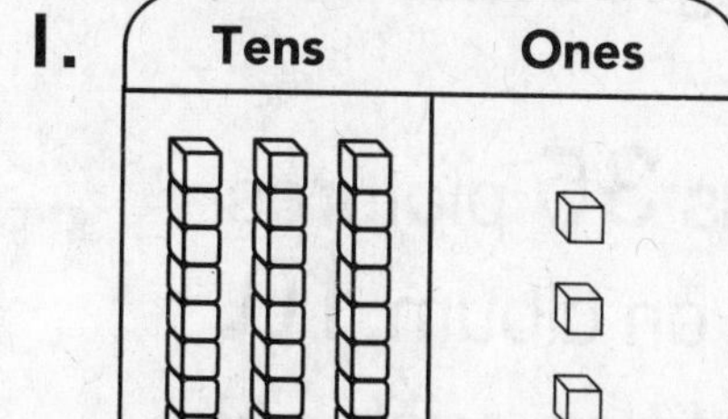

____ tens ____ ones ____
thirty-four

2\. 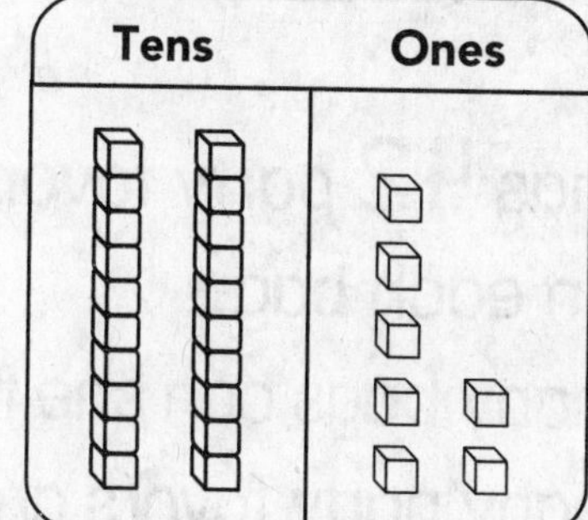

____ tens ____ ones ____
twenty-seven

Spiral Review (Chapter 1, Lesson 5) **KEY SDAP 2.1**

Circle the picture that comes next in the pattern.

3\.  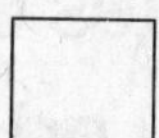  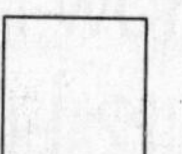  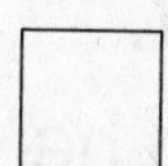 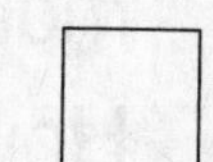

4\.  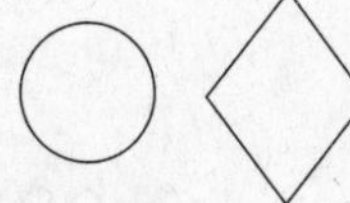 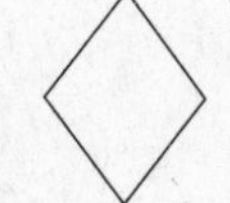 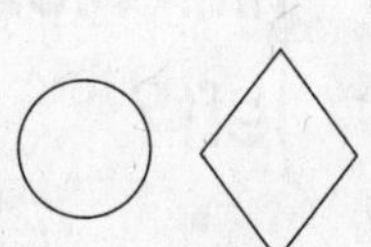

Name ____________________ Date __________

Read and Write Numbers to 50

CA Standards
KEY NS 1.1, NS 1.4

Solve.

1. Pablo has 27 hats in his store. 10 hats fit on a shelf. How many shelves can Pablo fill? How many hats are left?

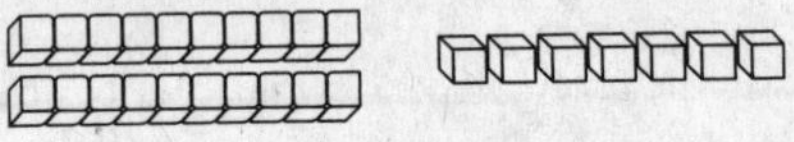

_____ shelves _____ hats

2. Mia has 31 trading cards. 10 cards fit on a page. How many pages can Mia fill? How many trading cards are left?

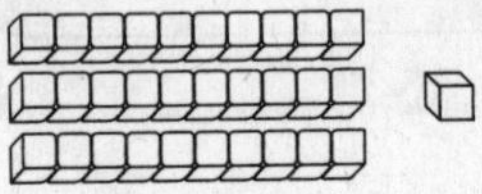

_____ pages _____ card

3. Alma has 42 party favors. 10 fit in each bag. How many bags can she fill? How many party favors are left?

_____ bags _____ favors

4. Dean has 35 pictures to put in an album. 10 pictures fit on each page. How many pages can he fill? How many pictures are left?

_____ pages _____ pictures

5. Joseph has 21 small marbles and 19 big marbles. He puts 10 marbles in each bucket. How many buckets can he fill? How many marbles are left?

_____ buckets _____ marbles

6. Pam has 23 crayons and 31 markers. She puts 10 art supplies in each box. How many boxes can she fill? How many art supplies are left?

_____ boxes _____ supplies

Name ______________________ Date __________

One More, One Less

CA Standards
KEY NS 2.3, KEY NS 1.1

18 19 Count forward to find 1 more.

21 22 Count backward to find 1 less.

Write the number that is 1 more or 1 less.

1. 18	____
2. 21	____
3. 13	____
4. 37	____
5. 42	____
6. 24	____

7. ____	13
8. ____	28
9. ____	45
10. ____	30
11. ____	32
12. ____	17

Spiral Review (Chapter 1, Lesson 3) **KEY** NS 1.1, **KEY** NS 2.3

Write the numbers.

13. Just after

6, 7, ____

14. Just before

____, 13, 14

One More, One Less

CA Standards
KEY NS 2.3, KEY NS 1.1

Solve.

1. How many [dog] does Mike have?

____

2. How many [bird] does Patty have?

____

3. There were 4 [cat] in the [basket]. Then 1 more jumps in. How many [cat] are in the [basket] now?

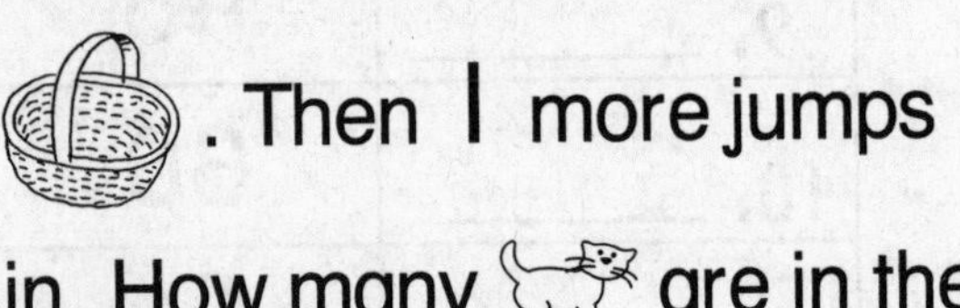

____

4. There were 9 [ladybug] on a [leaf]. Then 1 [ladybug] flies away. How many [ladybug] are on the leaf now?

____

5. Julius had 3 [Red crayon] and 6 [Yellow crayon]. He gets 1 more [Yellow crayon]. How many [Yellow crayon] does he have now?

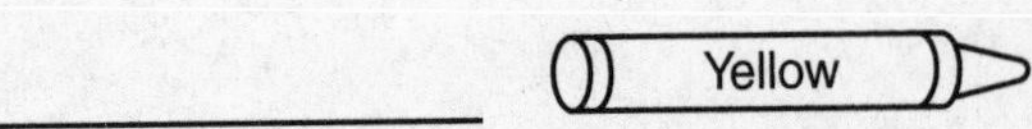

6. Marta had 13 [Blue crayon] and 17 [Orange crayon]. She gives 1 [Blue crayon] to a friend. How many [Blue crayon] does she have left?

______________ [Blue crayon]

Name ______________________ Date __________

Ten More, Ten Less

CA Standard
KEY NS 2.3

28 38	21 31
Add 1 to the tens place.	Take away 1 from the tens place.

Write the number that is 10 more.

1. 18	______
2. 11	______
3. 33	______
4. 37	______
5. 32	______
6. 24	______

Write the number that is 10 less.

7. ______	17
8. ______	29
9. ______	44
10. ______	19
11. ______	38
12. ______	36

Spiral Review (Chapter 1, Lesson 4) **KEY** NS 1.1, NS 1.0

Count backward. Write the numbers.

13. 15, 14, ____, 12

14. 29, 28, 27, ____, 25

Name ____________________ Date __________

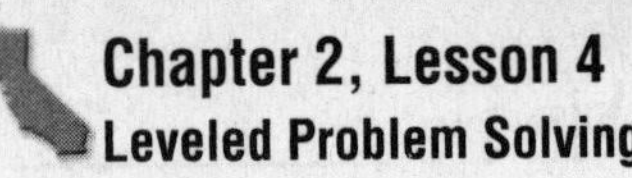

Ten More, Ten Less

CA Standard
KEY NS 2.3

Solve.

1. How many crayons does Tom have?

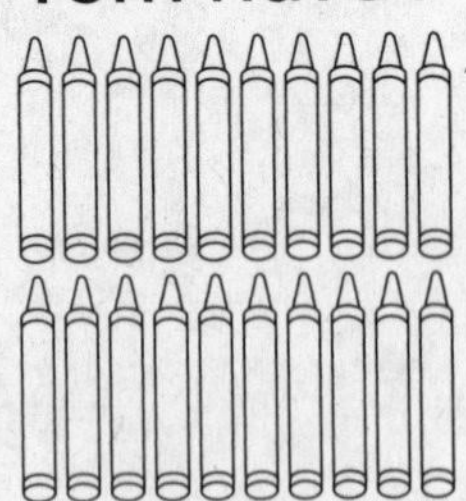

____

2. How many cars does Frank have?

____

3. Neva has 41 pencils. Dave has 10 more pencils than Neva. How many pencils does Dave have?

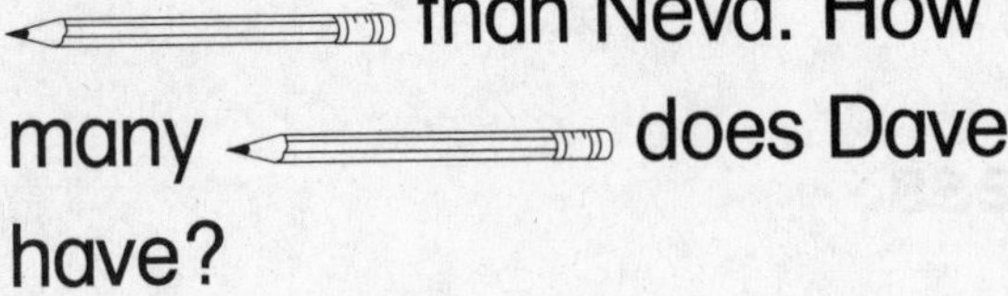

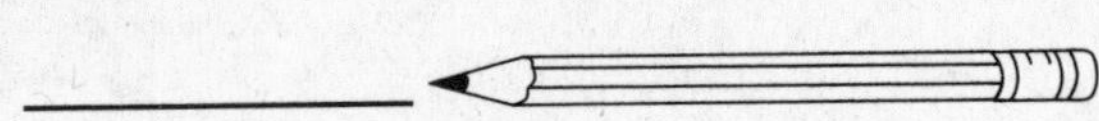

____

4. Ari has 36 shells. Geno has 10 less shells than Ari. How many shells does Geno have?

____________________ 

5. Adam had 25 red stickers and 17 blue stickers. He gives 10 red stickers to Sally. How many red stickers does Adam have now?

____________ red stickers

6. Chu had 34 big marbles and 19 small marbles. He gets 10 more small marbles. How many small marbles does Chu have now?

____________ small marbles

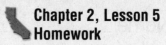

Problem Solving: Create and Solve

CA Standards
KEY NS 1.1, KEY NS 2.3

Count the balls in the picture.

Write the number. ___30___

What number is 10 less? ___20___

Color that many balls in the picture.

Count the balls again. Write the number. __________

What number is 10 more? __________

Draw a picture to show the number.

Spiral Review (Chapter 1, Lesson 4) **KEY** NS 1.0, **KEY** NS 1.1

What number is missing?

1. 18, 19, ____, 21

2. 33, 32, ____, 30

Problem Solving: Create and Solve

CA Standards
KEY NS 1.1, KEY NS 2.3

Solve.

1. How many (apple) are on the tree?

__________ (apple)

2. How many (bird) are in the nest?

__________ (bird)

3. There were 15 (duck) in the pond. 1 (duck) swims away. How many (duck) are left?

__________ (duck)

4. Mary counts 25 cows in the barn. Mark counts 10 more cows than Mary. How many cows does Mark count?

__________ cows

5. Callie sees 14 frogs and 17 ducks in the pond. Then 10 frogs hop away. How many frogs are there now?

__________ frogs

6. Terrell had 16 rocks and 18 shells. He finds 10 more shells. How many shells does Terrell have now?

__________ shells

Name ____________________ Date __________

CA Standard
NS 1.3

Hands On: Break a Number into Parts

There are different ways to show a number.
You can break a number into different parts.
Here are two ways to show 6.

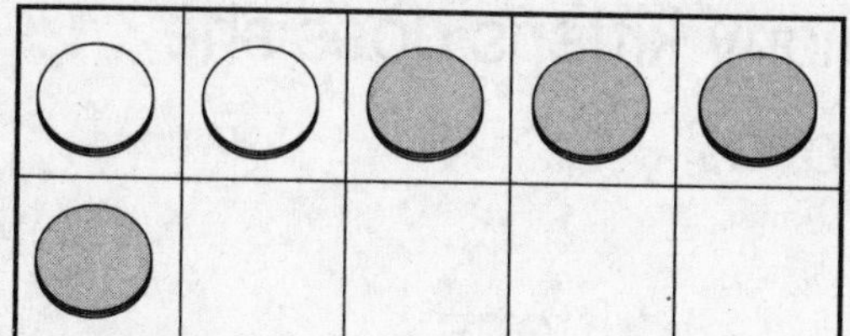

2 + 4

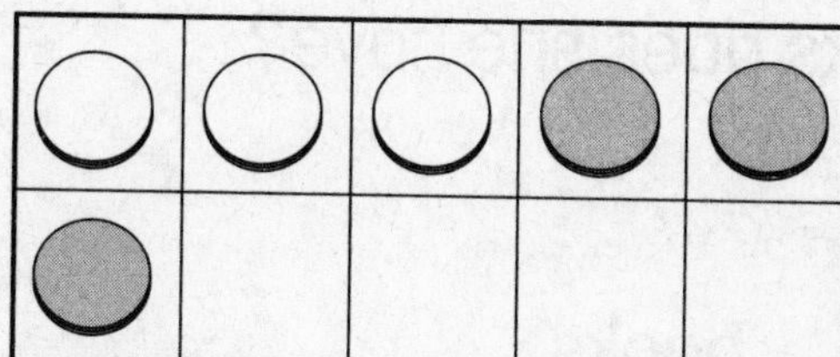

3 + 3

Use ●. Show ways to make 6.
Write the number sentence.

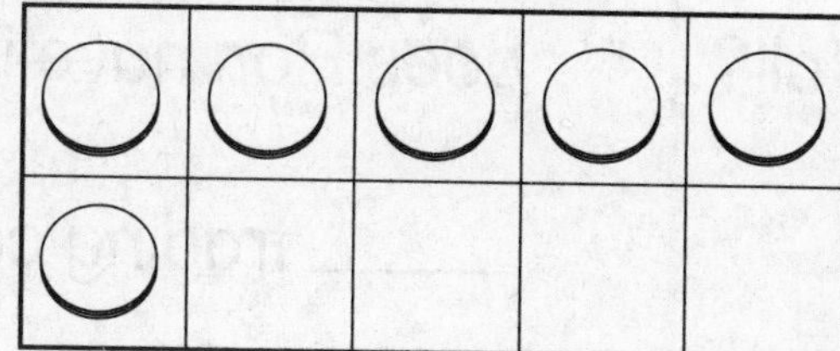

1. _____ + _____

2. _____ + _____

3. _____ + _____

4. _____ + _____

Spiral Review (Chapter 2, Lesson 1) **KEY NS 1.1, NS 1.4**

5. 17 ones _____ ten _____ ones

6. 12 ones _____ ten _____ ones

CA Standard
KEY NS 1.3

Hands On: Break a Number into Parts

Write the numbers. Use counters to help.

1. Jana has 1 math book and 1 science book. How many books does she have?

   ______ books

2. Kerri has 2 white kittens and 2 gray kittens. How many kittens does she have?

   ______ kittens

3. There are 3 plates on the table. Mel puts 2 more plates on the table. How many plates are there in all?

   ______ plates

4. Ron has 4 trading cards. His dad gives him 1 more. How many trading cards does Ron have in all?

   ______ trading cards

5. Kim has 4 apples and 6 grapes. Dan gives her 3 more apples. How many apples does Kim have in all?

   ______ apples

6. Pedro has 1 toy plane and 3 toy cars. Sam gives him 3 more toy cars. How many toy cars does Pedro have in all?

   ______ toy cars

Hands On: Model Addition

CA Standard
NS 1.3

You add the parts to find the whole.

Whole	
5	
Part	Part
3	2

Use small items such as buttons or coins to show the parts. Write the whole.

1. Dalia has 1 balloon.
A clown gave her 1 more.

Whole	
___	
Part	Part
1	1

2. Iris had 1 ball. She found 2 more.

Whole	
___	
Part	Part
1	2

3. Look in your room to find things you have in 2 different colors, for example, 3 green baseball caps and 3 red caps. Draw what you found.

Spiral Review (Chapter 2, Lesson 2) **KEY** NS 1.1, NS 1.4

4. 39 ones ______ tens ______ ones

5. 24 ones ______ tens ______ ones

Name ______________________ Date __________

Hands On: Model Addition

CA Standard
NS 1.3

Show the parts with counters. Write the whole.

1. Dan has 2 hats. Show the hats with ●.
Pat has 3 hats. Show the hats with ○.
How many hats are there in all?

_____ hats in all

2. Ali has 1 dog. Show the dog with ●.
Juan has 2 dogs. Show the dogs with ○.
How many dogs do they have in all?

_____ dogs

3. There are 2 apples in the box. Danny puts in 2 more apples. How many apples are there in all?

_____ apples

4. Lee has 1 blue pen. He got 4 red pens. How many pens does Lee have in all?

_____ pens

5. Tommy has 4 blue buttons and 3 red buttons.
He got 4 more blue buttons.
How many blue buttons does Tommy have in all?

_____ blue buttons

6. Abby has 5 yellow books and 4 red books.
She got 3 more red books.
How many red books does Abby have in all?

_____ red books

Name ________________ Date ________

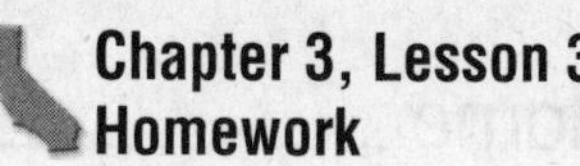

Draw to Add

CA Standards
KEY NS 2.1, NS 2.0

Jackie has 4 hats.
Josh has 3 hats.
How many hats do they have in all?

Solution: 4 + 3 = 7

You can draw a picture.

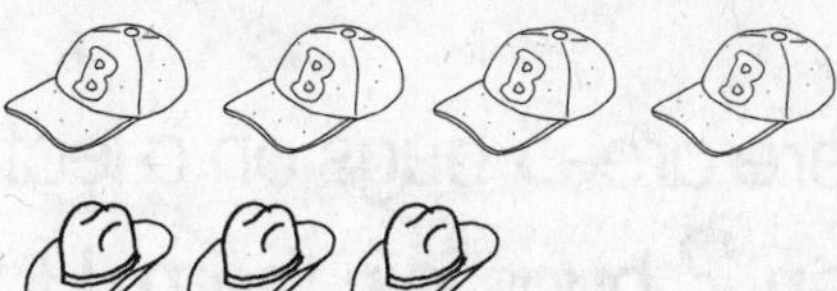

You can count how many in all. There are 7 hats in all.

Read the story.
Draw a picture on a separate sheet of paper to solve. Write the addition fact.

1. Marisol has 3 kittens.
Bali has 5 kittens.
How many kittens do they have in all?

___ + ___ = ___ kittens

2. Carlos has 4 turtles.
Enrique has 2 turtles.
How many turtles do they have in all?

___ + ___ = ___ turtles

3. Miguel has 6 toy cars.
Steve has 5 toy cars.
How many toy cars do they have in all?

___ + ___ = ___ toy cars

4. Sarah has 2 dolls.
Beth has 5 dolls.
How many dolls do they have in all?

___ + ___ = ___ dolls

Spiral Review (Chapter 2, Lesson 3) **KEY** NS 2.3, **KEY** NS 1.1

5. Write the number that is 1 more.

15, ____

6. Write the number that is 1 less.

____, 18

Draw to Add

CA Standards
KEY NS 2.1, NS 2.0

Solve. Draw pictures to help solve.

1. There are 3 bugs on a leaf. Then 2 bugs join them. How many bugs are there in all?

3 + 2 = _____ bugs

2. There are 4 kittens in the basket. Then 3 more kittens jump in. How many kittens are there in all?

4 + 3 = _____ kittens

3. There are 4 frogs in the pond. 5 more frogs go into the pond. How many frogs are there in all?

_____ + _____ = _____ frogs

4. Sally has 6 dolls. She gets 2 more dolls. How many dolls does Sally have in all?

_____ + _____ = _____ dolls

5. Junji has 2 blue stickers, 4 green stickers, and 6 red stickers. He finds 6 more green stickers. How many green stickers does Junji have in all?

_____ ◯ _____ ◯ _____ green stickers

6. Tasha has 9 blue markers, 5 yellow markers, and 8 green markers. She gets 5 more blue markers. How many blue markers does Tasha have in all?

_____ ◯ _____ ◯ _____ blue markers

Name ______________________ Date __________

Write Addition Number Sentences

CA Standards
AF 1.1, KEY NS 2.1

One step in solving a problem is to write an addition sentence.

Melissa has 3 football cards.
Jeff has 5 baseball cards.
How many cards do they have in all?

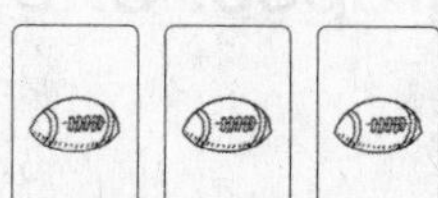

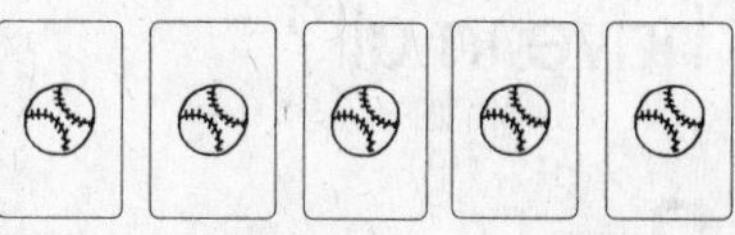

3 + 5 = 8

Write an addition sentence to solve.

1.  

There are 5 kangaroos in the grass. 2 more kangaroos join them. How many kangaroos are there in all?

_____ + _____ = _____

_____ kangaroos

2.  

There are 6 koala bears. 2 more join them. How many koala bears are there in all?

_____ + _____ = _____

_____ koala bears

Spiral Review (Chapter 2, Lesson 4) **KEY NS 2.3**

3. Write the number that is 10 more.

17, _____

4. Write the number that is 10 less.

_____, 45

Write Addition Number Sentences

CA Standards
AF 1.1, KEY NS 2.1

Solve.

1. Tami has 3 grapes. She gets 2 more.
How many grapes does Tami have in all?

3 + 2 = _____ grapes

2. Flo has 1 puzzle. She buys 2 more puzzles.
How many puzzles does Flo have in all?

1 + 2 = _____ puzzles

3. Bob has 6 books. He gets 7 more at the library.
How many books does Bob have in all?

_____ + _____ = _____
books

4. Suzy has 8 stamps. She finds 4 more.
How many stamps does Suzy have in all?

_____ + _____ = _____
stamps

5. Raúl has 9 big marbles and 5 small marbles. He finds 7 more big marbles.
How many big marbles does Raúl have in all?

_____ ◯ _____ ◯ _____
big marbles

6. Ted has 8 red blocks and 12 blue blocks. He gets 5 more blue blocks.
How many blue blocks does Ted have in all?

_____ ◯ _____ ◯ _____
blue blocks

Name ______________________ Date __________

Chapter 3, Lesson 5
Homework

Problem Solving: Act It Out

CA Standards
KEY NS 2.5, AF 1.1

There are 3 white dogs. There are 2 black dogs.
How many dogs are there in all?
Show the story with counters.

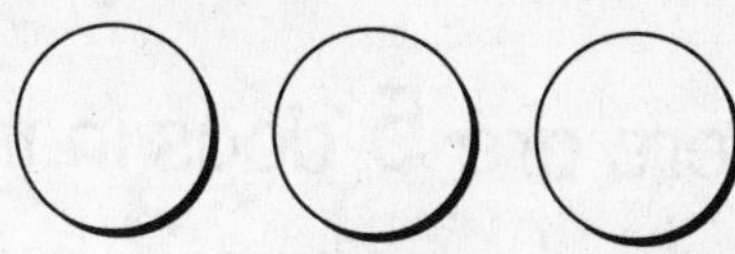

Write the addition sentence.

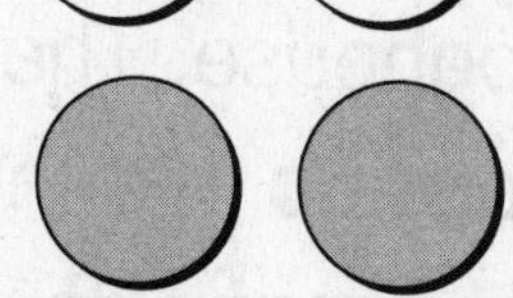

3 + 2 = 5 dogs

Act out the problem with counters. Write the answer. Write the addition sentence.

1. There are 4 ladybugs on the leaf. Then 1 ladybug joins them. How many ladybugs are on the leaf now?

   ___ ladybugs

   ___ + ___ = ___

2. There are 5 cows in the barn. There are 4 cows in the field. How many cows are there in all?

   ___ cows

   ___ + ___ = ___

Spiral Review (Chapter 2, Lesson 5) **KEY** NS 1.1, **KEY** NS 2.3

3. Count the balls in the picture. What number is 10 more?

   ___

4. Count the balls in the picture. What number is 10 less?

   ___

Problem Solving: Act It Out

CA Standards
KEY NS 2.5, AF 1.1

Act out the problem with counters. Write the answer. Write the addition sentence.

1. There are 5 dogs in the doghouse. Then 3 more dogs go into the doghouse. How many dogs are there now?

   5 + 3 = _____ dogs

2. There are 4 fish in the tank. Sam puts in 1 more fish. How many fish are in the tank now?

   4 + 1 = _____ fish

3. Haley has 7 rings. She finds 2 more rings. How many rings does Haley have now?

   _____ + _____ = _____ rings

4. Demoris picks 8 apples. Tad gives him 2 more apples. How many apples does Demoris have now?

   _____ + _____ = _____ apples

5. Adam has 6 green crayons and 7 red crayons. He gets 9 more red crayons. How many red crayons does Adam have now?

   _____ ○ _____ ○ _____ red crayons

6. Sari has 7 big shells and 8 small shells. She finds 8 more big shells at the beach. How many big shells does Sari have now?

   _____ ○ _____ ○ _____ big shells

Hands On: Ways to Make 7 and 8

CA Standard
NS 1.3

Use [white cube] and [gray cube] to make a sum.

Use [white cube] and [gray cube] to make 7.
Complete the addition sentence.

1. [6 white cubes, 1 gray cube] 6 + 1 = 7
2. [3 white cubes, 4 gray cubes] 3 + 4 = 7
3. [2 white cubes, 5 gray cubes] 2 + 5 = 7

1. Use [white cube] and [gray cube] to make 8. Complete each addition sentence.

[1 white cube, 7 gray cubes] _____ + _____ = _____

[2 white cubes, 6 gray cubes] _____ + _____ = _____

[3 white cubes, 5 gray cubes] _____ + _____ = _____

[4 white cubes, 4 gray cubes] _____ + _____ = _____

2. Use [white cube] and [gray cube] to make 7. Complete each addition sentence.

[1 white cube, 6 gray cubes] _____ + _____ = _____

[5 white cubes, 2 gray cubes] _____ + _____ = _____

Spiral Review (Chapter 3, Lesson 1) **NS 1.3**

Show different ways to make 10.
Write the number sentence.

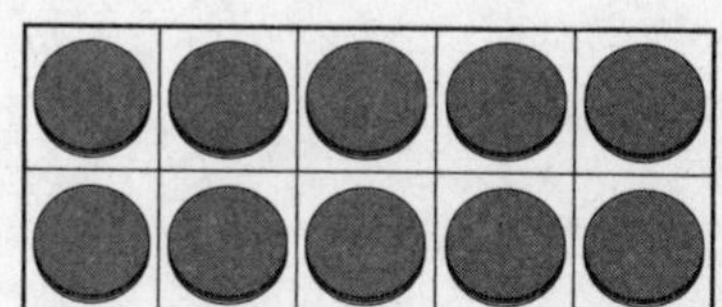

3. _____ + _____ = 10 4. _____ + _____ = 10

Hands On: Ways to Make 7 and 8

CA Standard
NS 1.3

Solve.

1. There are 3 green cubes. There are 4 blue cubes. How many cubes are there in all?

   3 + 4 = _____ cubes

2. There are 6 red cubes. There are 2 green cubes. How many cubes are there in all?

   6 + 2 = _____ cubes

3. There are 7 cubes in all. 5 cubes are red. The rest are blue. How many cubes are blue?

   _____ blue cubes

4. There are 8 cubes in all. 5 cubes are yellow. The rest are red. How many cubes are red?

   _____ red cubes

5. There are 8 cubes in all. 3 cubes are red. 2 cubes are blue. The rest are yellow. How many cubes are yellow?

   _____ yellow cubes

6. There are 7 cubes in all. 3 cubes are green. 2 cubes are blue. The rest are red. How many cubes are red?

   _____ red cubes

Name ______________ Date ________

Ways to Make 9 and 10

CA Standard
NS 1.3

There are many ways to make a number.
Here are two ways to make 10.

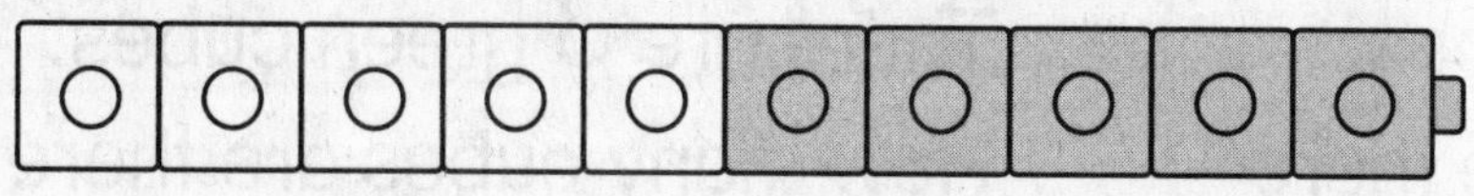

5 + 5 = 10

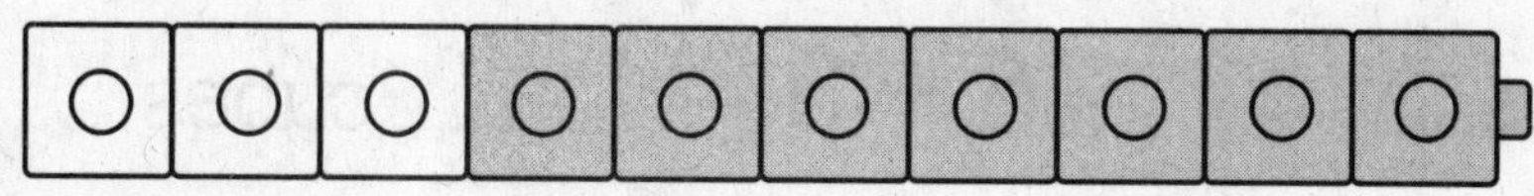

Solution: 3 + 7 = 10

Use two colors to show a way to make 9.
Complete the addition sentence.

1. ____ + ____ = ____

Use two colors to show a way to make 10.
Complete the addition sentence.

2. ____ + ____ = ____

Spiral Review (Chapter 3, Lesson 2) **NS 1.3**

Add the parts to find the whole.
Write the whole. Use counters to help.

3.

Whole	
____	
Part	Part
4	6

4.

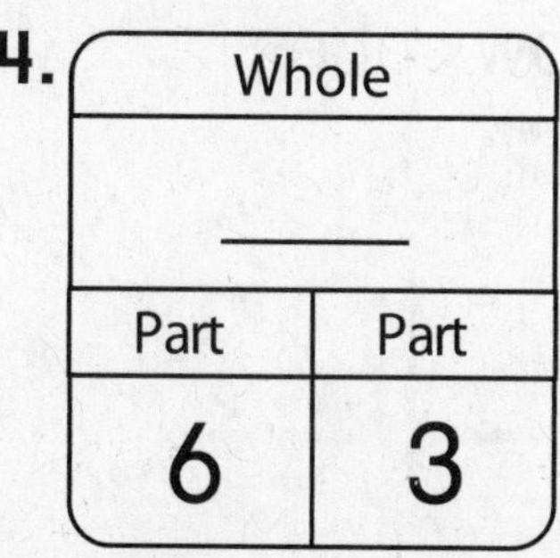

Whole	
____	
Part	Part
6	3

Ways to Make 9 and 10

CA Standard
NS 1.3

Solve.

1. There are 3 green cubes. There are 7 blue cubes. How many cubes are there in all?

   3 + 7 = _____ cubes

2. There are 6 red cubes. There are 3 green cubes. How many cubes are there in all?

   6 + 3 = _____ cubes

3. There are 9 cubes in all. 5 cubes are red. The rest are blue. How many cubes are blue?

   _____ blue cubes

4. There are 10 cubes in all. 5 cubes are yellow. The rest are red. How many cubes are red?

   _____ red cubes

5. There are 10 cubes in all. 5 cubes are red. 2 cubes are blue. The rest are yellow. How many cubes are yellow?

   _____ yellow cubes

6. There are 9 cubes in all. 3 cubes are green. 4 cubes are blue. The rest are red. How many cubes are red?

   _____ red cubes

Add in Vertical Form

CA Standard KEY NS 2.1, AF 1.1

You can write the same addition fact in two ways.

You can add across.

3 + 2 = 5

You can add down.

$$\begin{array}{r} 3 \\ +\,2 \\ \hline 5 \end{array}$$

Write the sum.

1. $\begin{array}{r} 4 \\ +\,2 \\ \hline \end{array}$
2. $\begin{array}{r} 5 \\ +\,1 \\ \hline \end{array}$
3. $\begin{array}{r} 8 \\ +\,0 \\ \hline \end{array}$
4. $\begin{array}{r} 3 \\ +\,3 \\ \hline \end{array}$
5. $\begin{array}{r} 2 \\ +\,1 \\ \hline \end{array}$
6. $\begin{array}{r} 4 \\ +\,0 \\ \hline \end{array}$
7. $\begin{array}{r} 7 \\ +\,1 \\ \hline \end{array}$
8. $\begin{array}{r} 2 \\ +\,5 \\ \hline \end{array}$
9. $\begin{array}{r} 1 \\ +\,6 \\ \hline \end{array}$
10. $\begin{array}{r} 3 \\ +\,5 \\ \hline \end{array}$

Spiral Review (Chapter 3, Lesson 3) **KEY NS 2.1, NS 2.0**

Read the story. Draw a picture.
Write the addition fact.

11. Ava has 2 goldfish.
Caleb has 3 goldfish.
How many goldfish are there in all?

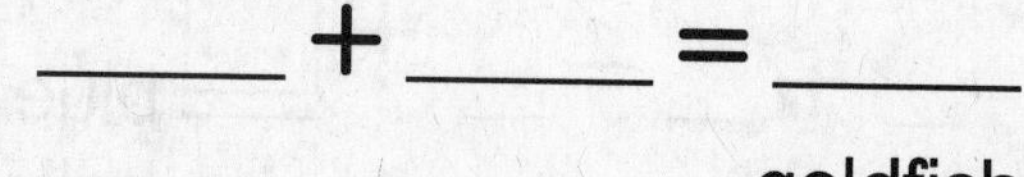

_____ + _____ = _____ goldfish

12. Marcos has 5 apples.
Sari has 4 apples.
How many apples are there in all?

_____ + _____ = _____ apples

Add in Vertical Form

CA Standard
KEY NS 2.1, AF 1.1

Write two addition sentences.
One goes across. One goes down.

1. There are 4 apples on the tree. There are 2 apples on the ground. How many apples are there in all?

$4 + 2 =$ __ + __ apples

2. Chou has 3 bananas. He gets 2 more. How many bananas does Chou have now?

$3 + 2 =$ __ + __ bananas

3. Eli gave his mother 3 roses and 4 daisies. How many flowers did Eli give his mother?

__ + __ = __ + __ flowers

4. Millie saw 5 yellow bugs and 3 red bugs. How many bugs did she see in all?

__ + __ = __ + __ bugs

5. Sofia has 5 red markers and 6 yellow markers. She gets 4 more yellow markers. How many yellow markers does she have in all?

__ + __ = __ + __ yellow markers

6. Luke has 4 blue balloons and 7 green balloons. Sam gives him 5 more blue balloons. How many blue balloons does Luke have in all?

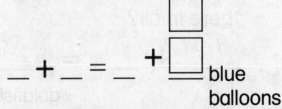

__ + __ = __ + __ blue balloons

Name ____________________ Date __________

Add With Zero

CA Standard
KEY NS 2.1

When you add zero to a number, the sum is that number.

3 + 0 = 3

Write the sum.

1. 2 + 0 = ____
2. 3 + 1 = ____
3. 0 + 7 = ____
4. 0 + 4 = ____
5. 6 + 0 = ____
6. 5 + 1 = ____
7. 2 + 2 = ____
8. 0 + 0 = ____
9. 0 + 5 = ____
10. 2 + 1 = ____

Spiral Review (Chapter 3, Lesson 4) **AF 1.1**

Write an addition sentence to solve.

11. There are 4 ducks in the pond.
Then 3 more ducks join them.
How many ducks are in the pond now?

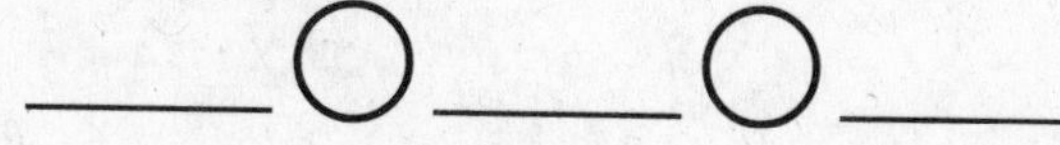

____ ducks

12. There are 6 cows in the field.
There are 3 cows in the barn.
How many cows are there in all?

____ ◯ ____ ◯ ____

____ cows

Name ________________ Date __________

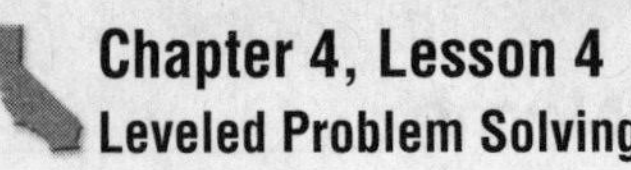

Add With Zero

CA Standard
KEY NS 2.1

Write the sum.

1. There are no flowers in the vase. Marco adds 3 flowers to the vase. How many flowers are there in all?

   0 + 3 = ____ flowers

2. There are 4 worms in the can. No more worms are added. How many worms are there in all?

   4 + 0 = ____ worms

3. There are 6 apples in one basket. There are no apples in the other basket. How many apples are there in all?

   ____ + ____ = ____ apples

4. Harry has 5 pennies in his bank. Kim has no pennies in her bank. How many pennies do they have in all?

   ____ + ____ = ____ pennies

5. Mia has 5 big shells. She has no small shells. Mia finds 9 small shells at the beach. How many small shells does Mia have now?

   ____ + ____ = ____ small shells

6. George has no toy trucks. He has 8 toy cars. George gets 7 toy trucks from a friend. How many toy trucks does George have now?

   ____ + ____ = ____ toy trucks

Problem Solving: Draw a Picture

CA Standard
KEY NS 2.5, MR 2.0

Seth has 4 kites.

Rosa has 2 kites.

How many kites do they have in all?

You can draw a picture.

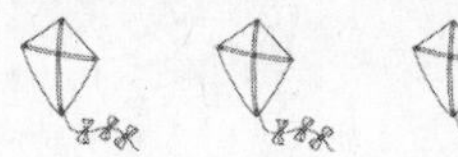

You can write a number sentence to solve.

Solution:     

4 + 2 = 6

Write a number sentence to solve.

1. A man has 5 bananas. He gets 3 more. How many bananas does he have now?

   ___ ◯ ___ ◯ ___

2. Sara has 2 dogs. Tom has 3 dogs. How many dogs do they have in all?

   ___ ◯ ___ ◯ ___

Spiral Review (Chapter 3, Lesson 5) **KEY NS 2.5, AF 1.1**

Act out the problem with counters. Write the answer. Write the addition sentence.

3. There are 6 bees in the hive. There are 2 more bees flying near the hive. How many bees are there in all?

   _____ bees

   _____ + _____ = _____

4. There are 4 frogs in the pond. Then 5 more frogs hop in the pond. How many frogs are in the pond now?

   _____ frogs

   _____ + _____ = _____

Problem Solving: Draw a Picture

CA Standard
KEY NS 2.5, MR 2.0

Draw a picture.
Write a number sentence to solve.

1. Myra picks 4 green grapes and 4 red grapes. How many grapes does she have in all?

   ____ ◯ ____ ◯ ____

2. Paul has 1 pencil on his desk and 6 in his supply box. How many pencils does he have in all?

   ____ ◯ ____ ◯ ____

3. Ben wrote 2 letters to relatives and 7 letters to friends. How many letters did he write in all?

   ____ ◯ ____ ◯ ____

4. Sienna had 6 pennies. She found 2 quarters. How many coins does she have in all?

   ____ ◯ ____ ◯ ____

5. Dora saw 7 birds in the park and 3 birds in her yard. How many birds did she see in all?

   ____ ◯ ____ ◯ ____

6. Greg went to 5 birthday parties in June and 5 birthday parties in July. How many birthday parties did Greg attend in all?

   ____ ◯ ____ ◯ ____

Name ______________________ Date __________

Hands On: Add in Any Order

CA Standard
NS 1.3

Look at the balloons.

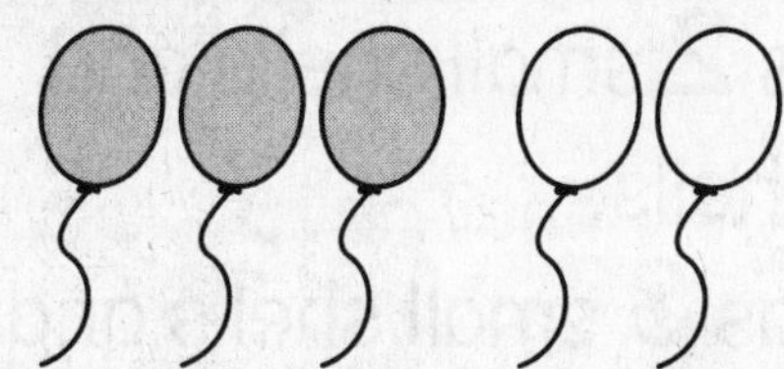

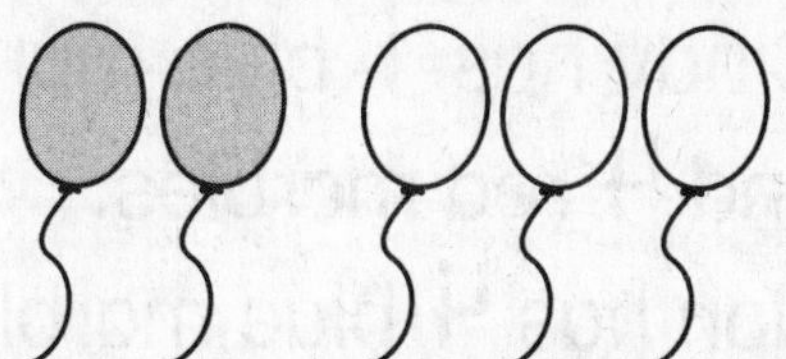

$3 + 2 = 5$ $2 + 3 = 5$

You can change the order of the addends and get the same sum.

Add. Then change the order of the addends and add.

1. $2 + 1 =$ ____

____ + ____ = ____

2. $4 + 2 =$ ____

____ + ____ = ____

3. $1 + 4 =$ ____

____ + ____ = ____

4. $0 + 6 =$ ____

____ + ____ = ____

Spiral Review (Chapter 4, Lesson 1) **NS 1.3**

5. Color to show 7.
Write the addends you used.

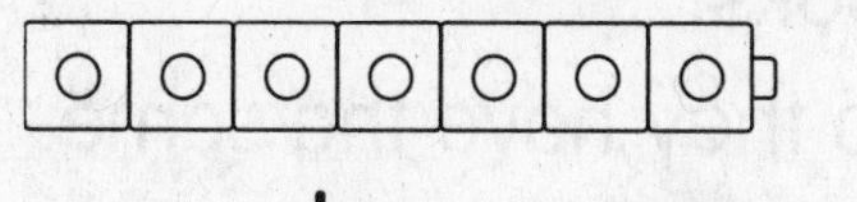

____ + ____ = ____

6. Color to show 8.
Write the addends you used.

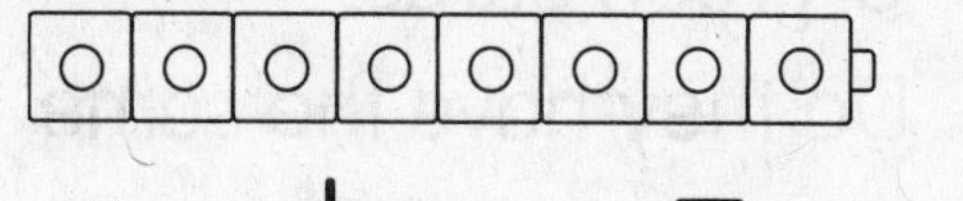

____ + ____ = ____

Name ____________________ Date __________

Hands On: Add in Any Order

CA Standard
NS 1.3

Solve.

1. Cindy has 1 blue marble and 4 red marbles. Nan has 4 blue marbles and 1 red marble. Do they have the same number of marbles?

   ____

2. Tim has 2 small shells and 4 big shells. Sally has 3 small shells and 2 big shells. Do they have the same number of shells?

   ____

3. Brett has 3 green apples and 2 red apples. Alice has 2 green apples and 2 red apples. Do they have the same number of apples?

   ____

4. Jorja picks 5 red flowers and 1 yellow flower. Dina picks 1 red flower and 5 yellow flowers. Do they have the same number of flowers?

   ____

5. Luke has 5 yellow cards, 4 blue cards, and 3 red cards. Sara has 6 blue cards and 6 green cards. Do they have the same number of cards?

   ____

6. Gwen has 4 green books and 5 red books. Kim has 5 red books, 3 blue books, and 2 yellow books. Do they have the same number of books?

   ____

Name ____________________ Date __________

Count On to Add

CA Standard
KEY NS 2.1

You can count on to add. Find 5 + 3.

Start with 5. Count on 3.

5, 6, 7, 8

5 + 3 = 8

Count on to add.

1. 4 + 2 = ____
2. 1 + 2 = ____
3. 4 + 3 = ____

4. 3 + 2 = ____
5. 6 + 2 = ____
6. 2 + 5 = ____
7. 8 + 1 = ____
8. 3 + 5 = ____

Spiral Review (Chapter 4, Lesson 2) NS 1.3

9. Use two colors to show a way to make 10. Write the addends you used.

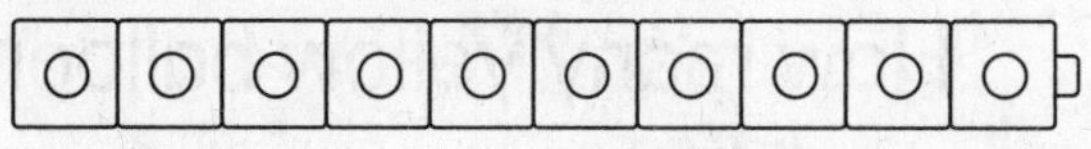

____ + ____ = ____

10. Use two colors to show a way to make 9. Write the addends you used.

____ + ____ = ____

Count On to Add

CA Standard
KEY NS 2.1

Read the problem.
Count on to add.

1. There are 5 bees in the hive. Then 2 bees join them. How many bees are there in all?

_____, _____

5 + 2 = _____ bees in all

2. There are 3 white roses in the vase. There is 1 red rose in the vase. How many roses are in the vase now?

_____

3 + 1 = _____ roses in all

3. There are 3 frogs in the pond. 3 more frogs jump in the pond. How many frogs are in the pond now?

_____ frogs in all

4. Ari finds 3 pink shells. Then she finds 4 white shells. How many shells does Ari have now?

_____ shells in all

5. Lora has 8 blue fish, 3 red fish, and 6 goldfish in the tank. She adds 5 more goldfish to the tank. How many goldfish are in the tank now?

_____ goldfish in all

6. Meg has 5 green balloons, 4 yellow balloons, and 6 red balloons. She finds 7 more yellow balloons. How many yellow balloons does Meg have now?

_____ yellow balloons

Name ____________________ Date __________

Use a Number Line to Add

CA Standards
KEY NS 2.1, MR 1.2

You can use a number line to add. Find 5 + 2.

Start with 5 on the number line. Count on 2 more numbers.

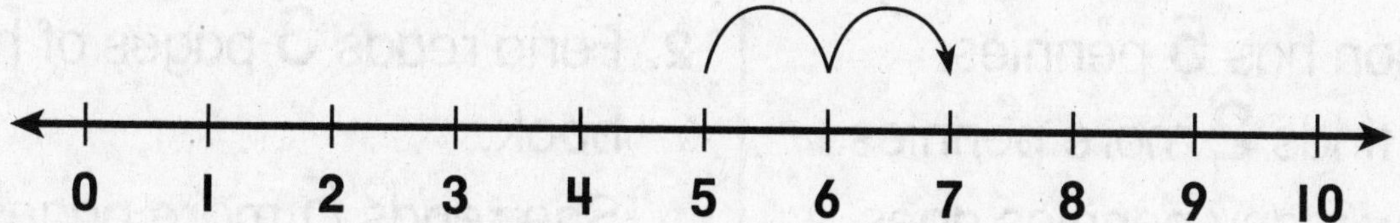

You end on 7, so 5 + 2 = 7

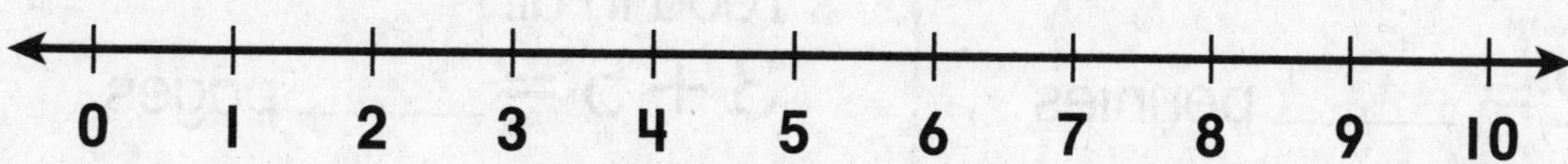

Use the number line. Find the sum.

1. 5 + 3 = ______

2. 2 + 5 = ______

3. $\begin{array}{r} 6 \\ +3 \\ \hline \end{array}$

4. $\begin{array}{r} 4 \\ +2 \\ \hline \end{array}$

5. $\begin{array}{r} 3 \\ +5 \\ \hline \end{array}$

6. $\begin{array}{r} 2 \\ +6 \\ \hline \end{array}$

7. $\begin{array}{r} 7 \\ +2 \\ \hline \end{array}$

8. $\begin{array}{r} 4 \\ +3 \\ \hline \end{array}$

Spiral Review (Chapter 4, Lesson 3) **KEY** NS 2.1, AF 1.1

Write the sum.

9. $\begin{array}{r} 4 \\ +4 \\ \hline \end{array}$

10. $\begin{array}{r} 1 \\ +6 \\ \hline \end{array}$

Use a Number Line to Add

CA Standards
KEY NS 2.1, MR 1.2

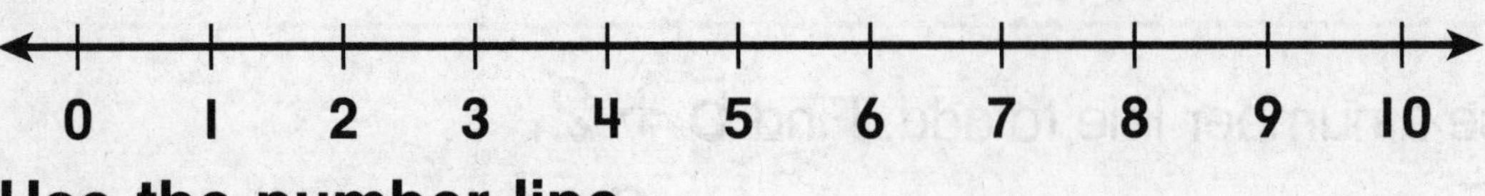

Use the number line.

1. Jason has 5 pennies.
He finds 2 more pennies.
How many pennies does Jason have now?

$5 + 2 =$ _____ pennies

2. Feria reads 3 pages of her book.
She reads 5 more pages after dinner.
How many pages does she read in all?

$3 + 5 =$ _____ pages

3. The team scores 2 goals in the first half of the game.
They score 3 goals in the second half.
How many goals do they score in all?

_____ goals

4. Nathan has 4 red balloons.
He has 3 blue balloons.
How many balloons does he have in all?

_____ balloons

5. Carly has 7 big books and 6 small books.
She gets 4 more small books at the library.
How many small books does Carly have now?

_____ small books

6. Devin has 3 red crayons and 5 green crayons.
He finds 6 more red crayons.
How many red crayons does Devin have now?

_____ red crayons

Use Doubles to Add

CA Standards
KEY NS 2.1, NS 2.0

You can use doubles to add.
This is a double.

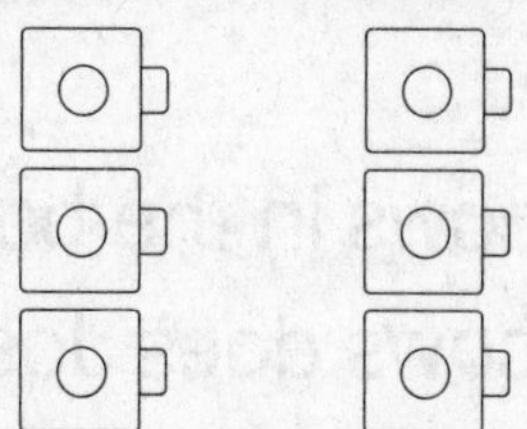

3 + 3 = 6
addend addend sum

A doubles fact has two addends that are the same.

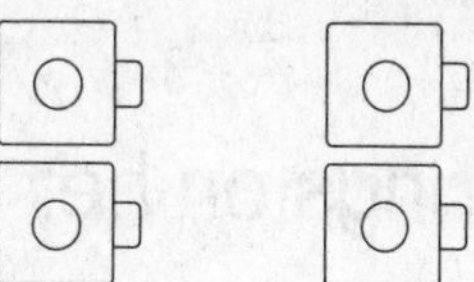

2 + 2 = 4
addend addend sum

Write the sum.

1. 1 + 1 = ____
2. 5 + 5 = ____
3. 3 + 3 = ____
4. 2 + 2 = ____
5. 1 + 1 = ____
6. 4 + 4 = ____
7. 4 children are playing in the park. 4 more children join them. How many children are there in all?

4 + 4 = ____ children

Spiral Review (Chapter 4, Lesson 4) **KEY** NS 2.1

Write the sum.

8. 0 + 5 = ____
9. 6 + 0 = ____

Name ______________________ Date __________

Use Doubles to Add

CA Standards
KEY NS 2.1, NS 2.0

Read to solve. Think about doubles.

1. Sally wears 2 rings on one hand.
She wears 2 rings on her other hand.
How many rings does Sally wear in all?

$2 + 2 =$ _____ rings

2. Josh sees 3 cows in the field.
He sees 3 cows in the barn.
How many cows does Josh see in all?

$3 + 3 =$ _____ cows

3. Demoris reads 5 books in the morning.
He reads 5 books at night.
How many books does Demoris read in all?

_____ books

4. Sofia packs 4 dishes in one box.
She packs 4 dishes in another box.
How many dishes does she pack in all?

_____ dishes

5. Ji Sun has 6 baseball cards and 9 football cards.
Harry has 6 baseball cards and 7 football cards.
How many baseball cards do they have in all?

_____ baseball cards

6. Delia has 8 red hair bows and 7 yellow hair bows.
Marta has 7 yellow hair bows.
How many yellow hair bows do they have in all?

_____ yellow hair bows

Problem Solving: Create and Solve

CA Standards
AF 1.1, AF 1.2

You can use a number sentence to solve a problem.

3 hop on a log. 7 more  hop on the log.

How many  are on the log now?

3  7  10

Write a number sentence to solve.

1. There are 4 black ants and 5 red ants. How many ants are there in all?

   ____ ○ ____ ○ ____

   ____ ants

2. Dalia has 6 crayons. Amit has 2 crayons. How many crayons do they have in all?

   ____ ○ ____ ○ ____

   ____ crayons

Spiral Review (Chapter 4, Lesson 5) **KEY** NS 2.5, MR 2.0

Draw a picture and write a number sentence to solve. Write the answer.

3. Tami sees 4 birds. Rosa sees 3 birds. How many birds do they see in all?

   ____ ○ ____ ○ ____

   ____ birds

4. Marco sees 6 cats. Ricky sees 4 cats. How many cats do they see in all?

   ____ ○ ____ ○ ____

   ____ cats

Problem Solving: Create and Solve

CA Standards
AF 1.1, AF 1.2

Solve.

1. Olivia has 2 books.
She gets 3 more at the library.
How many books does Olivia have in all?

2 + 3 = _____ books

2. Ross has 5 toy cars.
Sam gives him 3 more cars.
How many toy cars does Ross have now?

5 + 3 = _____ toy cars

3. Trevor feeds 3 cats.
Then he feeds 7 more cats.
How many cats does Trevor feed in all?

_____ ◯ _____ ◯ _____
cats

4. Becky picks 6 apples.
Sara picks 3 apples.
How many apples do they pick in all?

_____ ◯ _____ ◯ _____
apples

5. Joey sees 6 red birds and 7 blue birds in the tree.
Then he sees 4 more blue birds fly to the tree.
How many blue birds does Joey see in all?

_____ ◯ _____ ◯ _____
blue birds

6. Anita has 7 big shells and 5 small shells.
She finds 6 big shells at the beach.
How many big shells does Anita have in all?

_____ ◯ _____ ◯ _____
big shells

Name ____________________ Date __________

Hands On: Model Subtraction

CA Standards
KEY NS 2.1, KEY NS 2.5

If you know the whole and one of the parts, you can subtract to find the other part.

There are 10 pennies.
4 are heads up.
The rest are tails up.

How many are tails up? 6

Use 10 pennies.

1. Put 6 pennies heads up.
   Put the rest tails up.
   Write the missing numbers.
   I have ____ pennies.
   ____ are heads up.
   The rest are tails up.
   How many are tails up? ____

2. Put 8 pennies heads up.
   Put the rest tails up.
   Write the missing numbers.
   I have ____ pennies.
   ____ are heads up.
   The rest are tails up.
   How many are tails up? ____

Spiral Review (Chapter 5, Lesson 1) **NS 1.3**

Use Workmat 1. Use 10 ◯.

Add. Then change the order of the addends and add again.

3. 3 + 4 = ____

   ____ + ____ = ____

4. 0 + 5 = ____

   ____ + ____ = ____

Name ______________________ Date ___________

Hands On: Model Subtraction

CA Standards
KEY NS 2.1, KEY NS 2.5

Show the story with counters. Write the numbers.

1. Pablo has 5 balloons. 2 balloons blow away. How many balloons are left?

   _____ balloons

   _____ blow away

   _____ balloons left

2. Del has 2 bags of popcorn. He gives 1 bag to his friend. How many bags are left?

   _____ bags

   _____ given away

   _____ bag left

3. Kace has 4 carrots. She eats 2 carrots. How many carrots are left?

   _____ carrots

   _____ carrots eaten

   _____ carrots left

4. There are 3 eggs in the nest. 1 egg hatches. How many eggs are left?

   _____ eggs

   _____ egg hatches

   _____ eggs left

5. Beth has 5 green balloons and 4 red balloons. 3 green balloons pop. How many green balloons does Beth have left?

   _____ green balloons

   _____ green balloons pop

   _____ green balloons left

6. Ted has 8 big marbles and 6 small marbles. He loses 2 small marbles. How many small marbles are not lost?

   _____ small marbles

   _____ small marbles lost

   _____ small marbles not lost

Name ______________________ Date __________

Draw to Subtract

CA Standards
KEY NS 2.1, KEY NS 2.5

You can draw a picture to subtract.

There are 9 ladybugs.
6 ladybugs fly away.

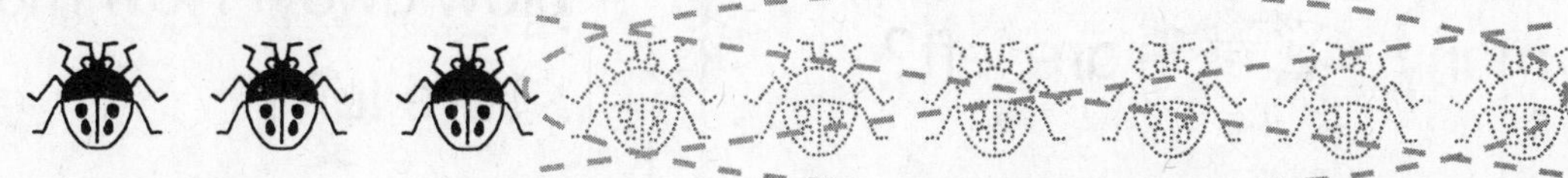

Solution: How many ladybugs are left? 3 ladybugs

Draw a picture to show the story.
Solve.

1. There are 7 ladybugs.
2 ladybugs fly away.

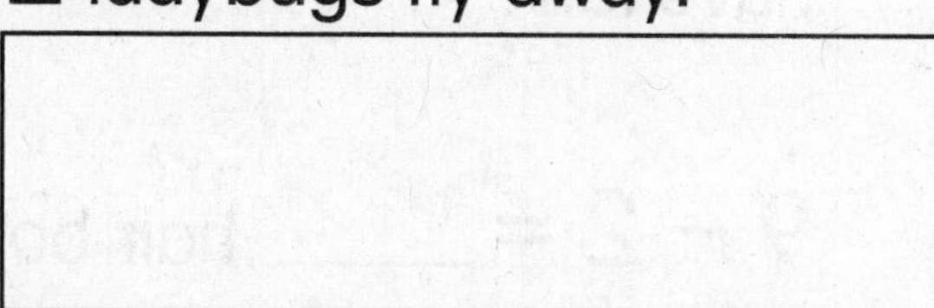

How many ladybugs are left?
_____ ladybugs

2. There are 6 ladybugs.
4 ladybugs fly away.

How many ladybugs are left?
_____ ladybugs

Spiral Review (Chapter 5, Lesson 2) **KEY** NS 2.1

Count on to add.

3. $\begin{array}{r} 6 \\ +2 \\ \hline \end{array}$

4. $\begin{array}{r} 5 \\ +1 \\ \hline \end{array}$

Name ______________________ Date __________

Draw to Subtract

CA Standards
KEY NS 2.1, KEY NS 2.5

Solve. Draw pictures if you wish.

1. Tad has 5 . Then 2 swim away. How many are left?

5 – 2 = _____ 

2. Tara has 7 . Then 4 blow away. How many are left?

7 – 4 = _____

3. Mimi has 8 apples. She gives 4 apples away. How many apples does Mimi have left?

8 – 4 = _____ apples

4. Kim has 9 hair bows. She gives 2 to a friend. How many hair bows does Kim have left?

9 – 2 = _____ hair bows

5. Bob has 10 red pencils and 7 green pencils. He loses 3 red pencils. How many red pencils does Bob have left?

_____ – _____ = _____ red pencils

6. Luis has 12 big shells and 11 small shells. He gives 5 small shells to Sal. How many small shells does Luis have left?

_____ – _____ = _____ small shells

Name ____________________ Date __________

Subtract to Find a Part

CA Standards
KEY NS 2.1, NS 2.0

There are 5 buttons in all. 3 buttons are in one part. How many are in the other part?

Solution: There are 2 buttons in the other part.

Whole	
5	
Part	Part
3	2

Use counters. Show the whole.
Move the counters to show one part.
Find the other part.

1.

Whole	
3	
Part	Part
2	___

2.

Whole	
6	
Part	Part
2	___

Spiral Review (Chapter 5, Lesson 3) **KEY NS 2.1, MR 1.2**

Use the number line. Find the sum.

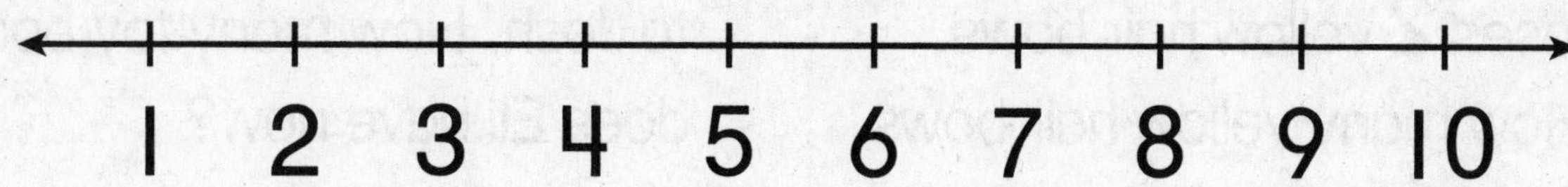

3. $\begin{array}{r} 6 \\ +2 \\ \hline \end{array}$

4. $\begin{array}{r} 7 \\ +3 \\ \hline \end{array}$

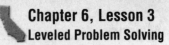

Subtract to Find a Part

CA Standards
KEY NS 2.1, NS 2.0

Show the story with counters.
Write the numbers.

1. Maria has 4 hats in all.

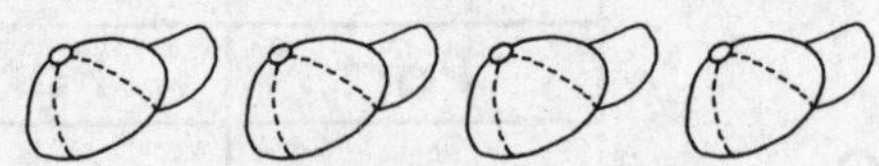

1 hat is yellow.
How many hats are red?

_____ hats in all _____

yellow _____ red

2. Ed has 5 toy trucks.

He broke 2 trucks.
How many trucks are not broken?

_____ trucks in all _____

broken _____ not broken

3. Emma has 3 game chips.
She lost 1 chip.
How many chips are not lost?

_____ chips in all _____

chip lost _____ chips not lost

4. Amed had 4 stickers.
He gave 3 stickers away.
How many stickers are left?

_____ stickers in all _____

given away _____ sticker left

5. Lora has 6 yellow hair bows and 5 green hair bows. She loses 2 yellow hair bows. How many yellow hair bows are not lost?

Circle the number that tells how many yellow hair bows Lora did not lose.

4 9 13

6. Eli has 7 toy cars and 9 toy boats. He gave 3 toy boats to Josh. How many toy boats does Eli have now?

Circle the number that tells how many toy boats Eli has now.

19 16 6

Subtraction Number Sentences

CA Standards
AF 1.2, KEY NS 2.1

You can use a minus sign and an equal sign to write about subtraction.

5 − 2 = 3

↑ minus sign ↑ equal sign

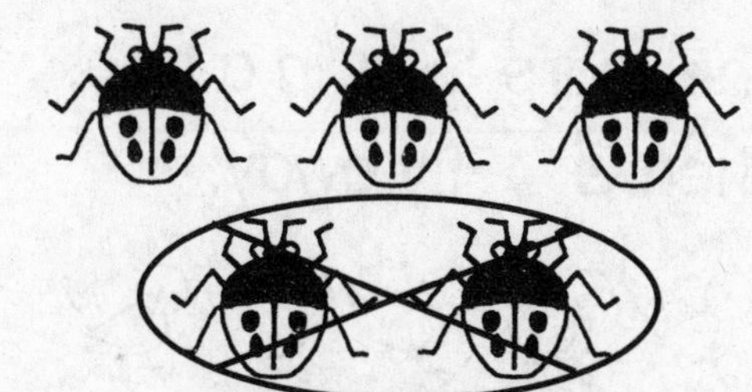

Solution: You can circle and cross out to show subtraction.

Circle and cross out to subtract.
Write how many are left.

1.

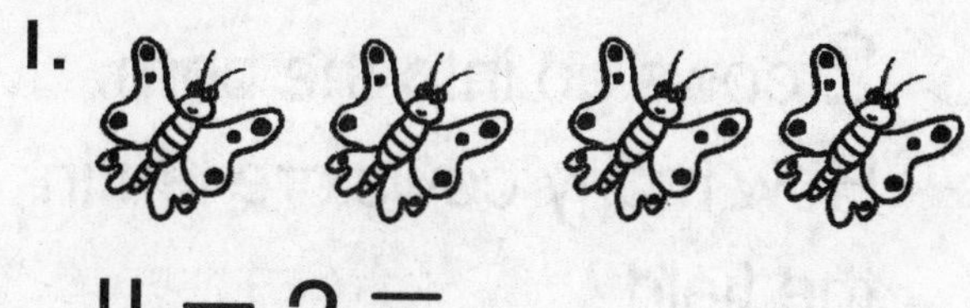

4 − 2 = ____

2.

2 − 2 = ____

3.

4 − 3 = ____

4.

3 − 2 = ____

Spiral Review (Chapter 5, Lesson 4) **KEY NS 2.1**

Write the sum.

5. 4 + 4

6. 3 + 3

Name ____________________ Date __________

Subtraction Number Sentences

CA Standards
AF 1.2, KEY NS 2.1

Write how many are left.

1. There are 5 in a tree.
Then 3 fly away.

How many are left?

5 − 3 = ______ left

2. 3 sit on a log.
2 hop away.
How many frogs are left?

3 − 2 = ______ left

3. 4 candles light the room.
1 candle burns out.
How many candles are left burning?

4 − 1 = ______ candles left

4. 6 cows are in the field.
2 cows go into the barn.
How many cows are left in the field?

6 − 2 = ______ cows left

5. There are 7 red ants and 3 black ants on a leaf.
Then 4 red ants crawl away.
How many ants are left?

______ − ______ = ______
ants left

6. There are 2 cats and 6 kittens in the basket.
2 kittens jump out.
How many kittens are left?

______ − ______ = ______
kittens left

Problem Solving: Subtraction Stories

CA Standards
KEY NS 2.5, KEY NS 2.1

You can use a picture to solve subtraction stories.
Which picture shows $6 - 2 = 4$?

You know that 6 is the whole, so look for the picture that has 6 as the whole. You know that 2 are taken away, so look for the picture where 2 are going away. You know that 4 are left, so look for the picture where 4 are left.
The picture on the left is the correct one.

Find the picture that matches the subtraction sentence. Circle your answer.

1. Which picture shows $5 - 1 = 4$?

2. Which picture shows $7 - 3 = 4$?

Spiral Review (Chapter 5, Lesson 5) **AF 1.1, AF 1.2**

Write a number sentence to solve.

3. There are 3 black cats and 2 brown cats. How many cats are there in all?
____ + ____ = ____

4. There are 5 pigs in the mud and 3 in the barn. How many pigs are there in all?
____ + ____ = ____

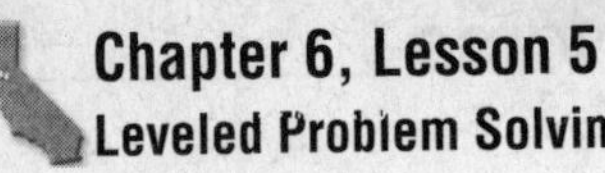

Name ______________________ Date __________

CA Standards
KEY NS 2.5, KEY NS 2.1

Problem Solving: Subtraction Stories

Solve. Draw pictures if you wish.

1. There are 4 muffins. The children eat 2 muffins. How many muffins are left?

   4 - 2 = _____ muffins

2. There are 5 glasses of water. 1 glass spills. How many glasses are left?

   5 - 1 = _____ glasses

3. 6 carrots grow in the garden. A rabbit eats 3 of the carrots. How many carrots are left?

   _____ - _____ = _____ carrots

4. The squirrel hides 5 nuts. It finds 3 of the nuts. How many nuts are still hiding?

   _____ - _____ = _____ nuts

5. There are 2 birds and 6 eggs in the nest. Then 1 bird flies away. How many birds are left?

   _____ ○ _____ ○ _____

6. There are 5 frogs and 8 ducks in the pond. Then 6 ducks swim away. How many ducks are left?

   _____ ○ _____ ○ _____

Hands On: Subtract from 7 and 8

CA Standards
AF 1.1, KEY NS 2.1

You can subtract from 8 or less.

Use 7 paper clips. Circle and cross out 2. Write the subtraction sentence.

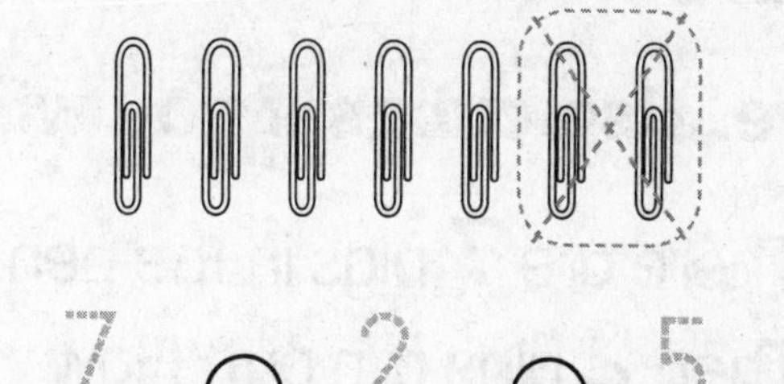

7 − 2 = 5

Use paper clips. Take away some.
Circle and cross out.
Write the subtraction sentence.

Use 7 paper clips.

1. ____ ◯ ____ ◯ ____

Use 8 paper clips.

2. 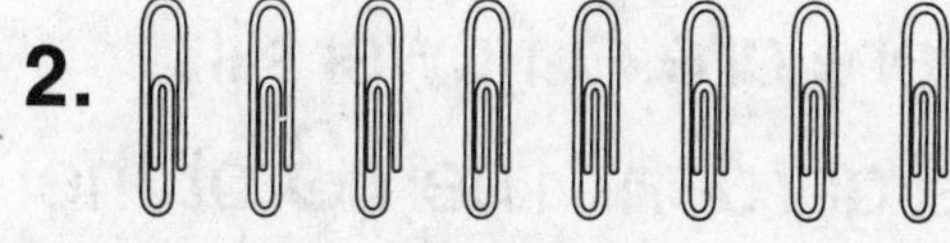 ____ ◯ ____ ◯ ____

3. 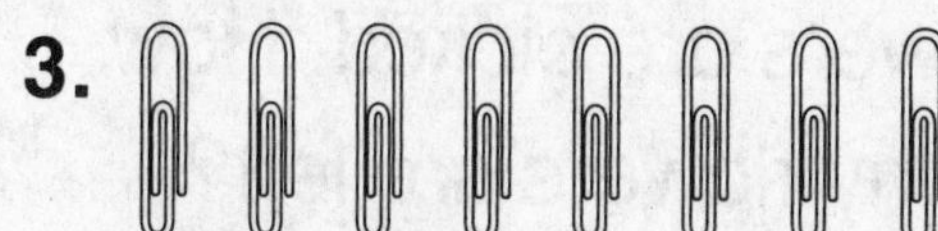 ____ ◯ ____ ◯ ____

Spiral Review (Chapter 6, Lesson 1) **KEY** NS 2.1, **KEY** NS 2.5, NS 2.0, MR 1.2

Use 10 pennies. Write the missing numbers.

4. Put 5 pennies heads up.
Put the rest tails up.
I have ____ pennies. ____ are heads up. The rest are tails up.
How many are tails up?
____

5. Put 7 pennies heads up.
Put the rest tails up.
I have ____ pennies. ____ are heads up. The rest are tails up.
How many are tails up?
____

Name ____________________ Date __________

Hands On: Subtract from 7 and 8

CA Standards
AF 1.1, KEY NS 2.1

Solve. Use cubes if you wish.

1. There are 7 pigs in the pen. Then 2 pigs run out. How many pigs are left in the pen?

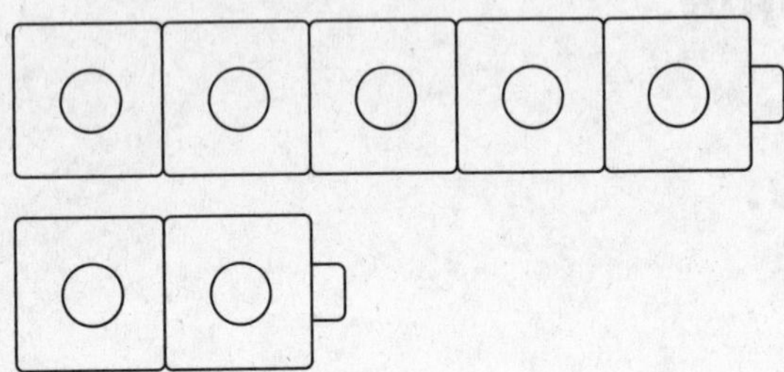

7 - 2 = __________ pigs

2. There are 8 plates on the counter. Mom puts 4 of the plates away. How many plates are left?

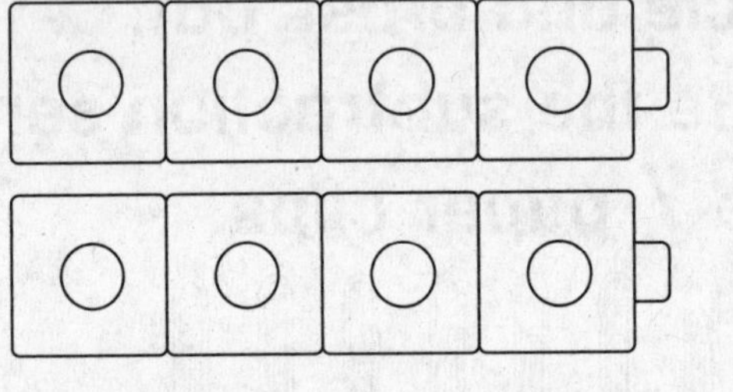

8 - 4 = __________ plates

3. There are 7 puppies in the store. 1 of the puppies finds a home. How many puppies are left?

7 - 1 = __________ puppies

4. There are 8 flowers in the garden. Then 3 of the flowers are picked. How many flowers are left?

8 - 3 = __________ flowers

5. There are 8 yellow markers and 7 red markers in the jar. Maria takes 2 yellow markers out of the jar. How many yellow markers are left?

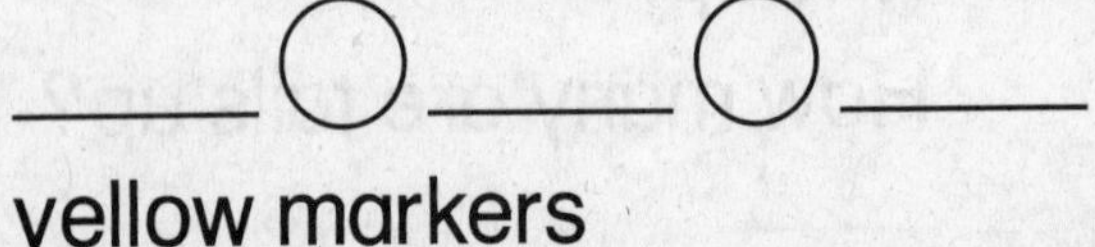

yellow markers

6. There are 5 blue stickers and 7 green stickers in the book. Anthony takes out 1 green sticker. How many green stickers are left?

____ ◯ ____ ◯ ____

green stickers

Name ______________________ Date __________

Hands On: Subtract from 9 and 10

CA Standards
KEY NS 2.1, NS 2.0

You can subtract from 10 or less.

Use 9 paper clips. Circle and cross out 3. Write the subtraction sentence.

9 − 3 = 6

Use 9 paper clips. Take away some.
Circle and cross out.
Write the subtraction sentence.

1. ___ ○ ___ ○ ___

2. ___ ○ ___ ○ ___

3. ___ ○ ___ ○ ___

Spiral Review (Chapter 6, Lesson 2) **KEY** NS 2.5, **KEY** NS 2.1

Draw a picture to show the story.
Solve.

4. There are 7 ducks. 2 ducks swim away.

How many ducks are left?

____

5. There are 8 birds. 3 birds fly away.

How many birds are left?

____

Hands On: Subtract from 9 and 10

CA Standards
KEY NS 2.1, NS 2.0

Solve. Use cubes if you wish.

1. There are 9 cows in the barn. Then 3 cows go out to the field. How many cows are left in the barn?

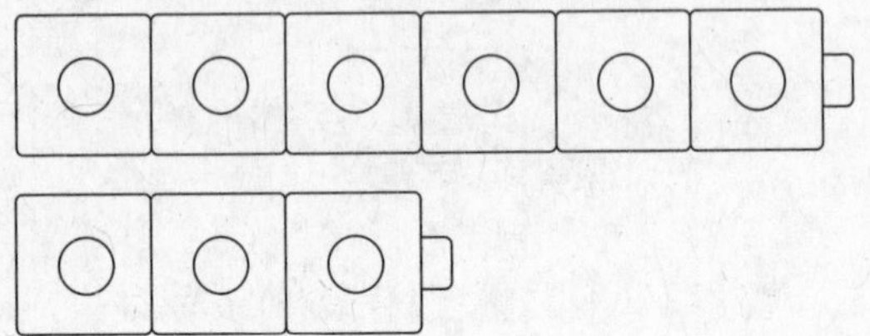

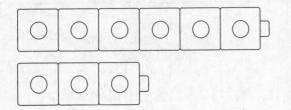

9 − 3 = __________ cows

2. There are 10 apples on the tree. Then 5 apples fall off the tree. How many apples are left?

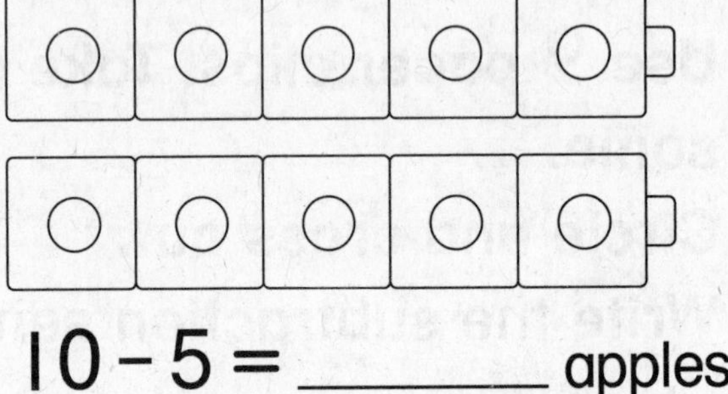

10 − 5 = ________ apples

3. There are 10 kittens in the basket. 3 of the kittens jump out. How many kittens are left?

10 − 3 = ________ kittens

4. There are 9 carrots in the garden. A rabbit eats 4 of the carrots. How many carrots are left?

9 − 4 = __________ carrots

5. There are 10 yellow crayons and 9 blue crayons in the box. Sal takes 2 blue crayons out of the box. How many blue crayons are left?

_____ ◯ _____ ◯ _____ blue crayons

6. There are 10 red stickers and 9 green stickers in the book. Amanda takes out 4 red stickers. How many red stickers are left?

_____ ◯ _____ ◯ _____ red stickers

Subtract in Vertical Form

CA Standards KEY NS 2.1, KEY NS 2.5

You can write the same subtraction fact in two ways.
The difference is the same.

Subtract across.

7 – 2 = 5 ← difference

Subtract down.

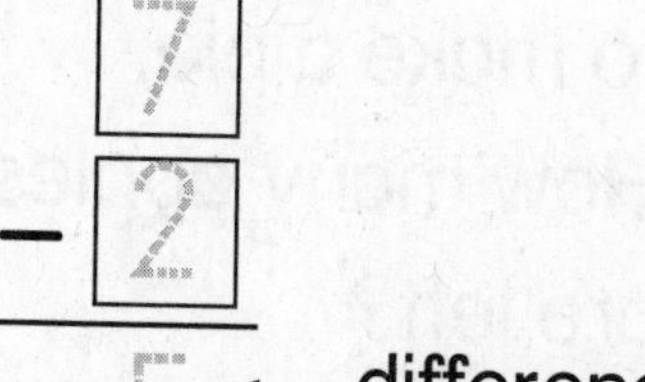

$$\begin{array}{r} 7 \\ -\ 2 \\ \hline 5 \end{array}$$ ← difference

Complete each subtraction fact. Write the difference.

1. 

$$\begin{array}{r} 6 \\ -\ 2 \\ \hline \end{array}$$

____ – ____ = ____

2. 

$$\begin{array}{r} 7 \\ -\ 4 \\ \hline \end{array}$$

____ – ____ = ____

3. 

$$\begin{array}{r} 3 \\ -\ 1 \\ \hline \end{array}$$

____ – ____ = ____

4. $$\begin{array}{r} 6 \\ -\ 6 \\ \hline \end{array}$$

____ – ____ = ____

Spiral Review (Chapter 6, Lesson 3) **KEY** NS 2.1, NS 2.0

Find the missing part. Use counters if you wish.

5.

Whole	
5	
Part	Part
2	

6.

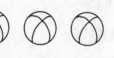

Whole	
4	
Part	Part
3	

Name ______________________ Date __________

Subtract in Vertical Form

CA Standards
KEY NS 2.1, KEY NS 2.5

Read to solve. Complete the subtraction fact.

1. Len has 7 apples. He uses 6 apples to make a pie. How many apples are left?

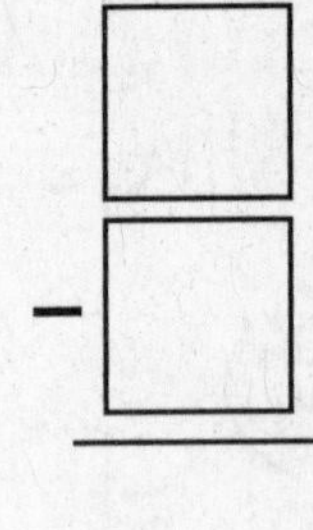

2. Belle makes 8 belts. She gives 3 belts to her brothers. How many belts are left?

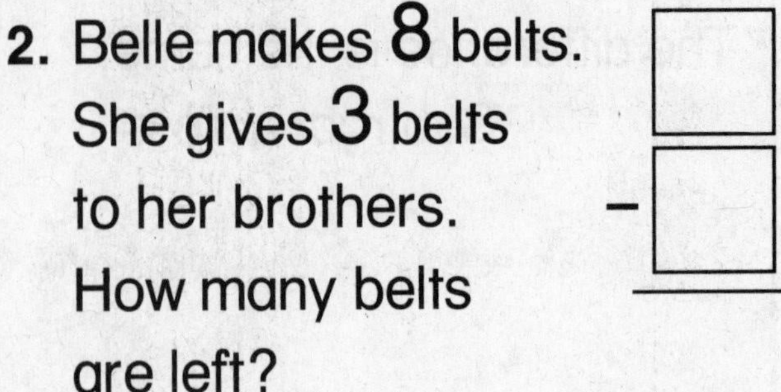

3. Chris has 8 trays to paint. He paints 5 trays. How many trays are left to paint?

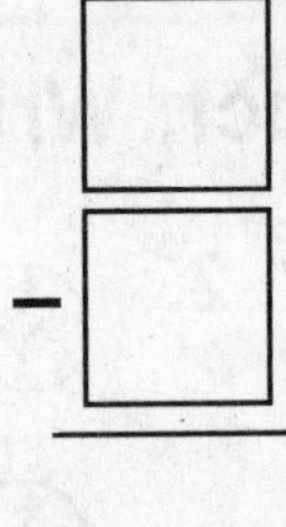

4. Hilary has 7 beads. She uses 4 beads to make a necklace. How many beads are left?

5. Enrique has 8 carrots and 7 potatoes. He uses 2 potatoes to make soup. How many potatoes are left?

6. Cassie has 7 green beads and 8 blue beads. She uses 5 blue beads to make a bracelet. How many blue beads are left?

Name ______________________ Date __________

Subtract All or None

CA Standard
KEY NS 2.1

When you subtract zero from a number, the difference is the number.

4 − 0 = 4

When you subtract a number from itself, the difference is zero.

4 − 4 = 0

Write the difference.

1. 3 − 3 = ____

2. 5 − 0 = ____

3. 2 − 0 = ____

4. 4 − 4 = ____

5. 6 − 6 = ____

6. 4 − 0 = ____

7. 1 − 0 = ____

8. 3 − 3 = ____

Spiral Review (Chapter 6, Lesson 4) **AF 1.2, KEY NS 2.1**

Circle and cross out to subtract. Write how many are left.

9.

5 − 3 = ____

10.

6 − 2 = ____

Name ______________________ Date __________

Subtract All or None

CA Standard
KEY NS 2.1

Read to solve. Write the difference.

1. Ricky has 5 apples.
He eats 0 apples.
How many apples are left?

5 – 0 = ________ apples

2. Ms. Lee has 4 stickers.
She gives all 4 stickers to the class. How many stickers are left?

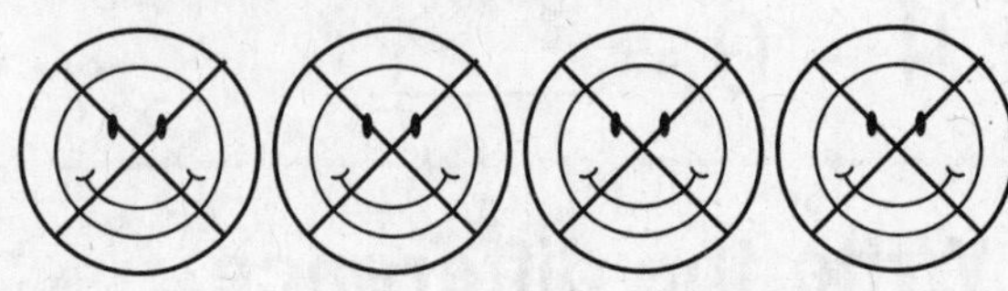

4 – 4 = ________ stickers

3. Ellie has 3 juice boxes.
She does not drink any of them. How many juice boxes are left?

3 – 0 = ______ juice boxes

4. Darryl decorates 6 eggs.
He gives 6 friends each one egg. How many eggs are left?

6 – 6 = ________ eggs

5. Jamal has 7 toy cars and 3 toy trucks. He gives 3 toy trucks away.
How many toy trucks does he have left?

_____ ◯ _____ ◯ _____
toy trucks

6. Rosita has 8 pink balloons and 6 red balloons. She does not give any pink balloons away. How many pink balloons are left?

_____ ◯ _____ ◯ _____
pink balloons

Problem Solving: Draw a Picture

CA Standards
KEY NS 2.5, MR 2.2

Use pictures to solve subtraction problems.

There are 5 birds.
3 birds fly away.
How many birds are left?

Solution:
There are __2__ birds left.

To model the problem, show 5 paper clips for birds. Now take away 3. Count how many are left.

Draw the problem. Write the answer.

1. David has 2 hot dogs. He eats 1 hot dog. How many hot dogs does he have left? ______ hot dog

2. Orlee has 6 dolls. She gives 3 dolls away. How many dolls does she have left? ______ dolls

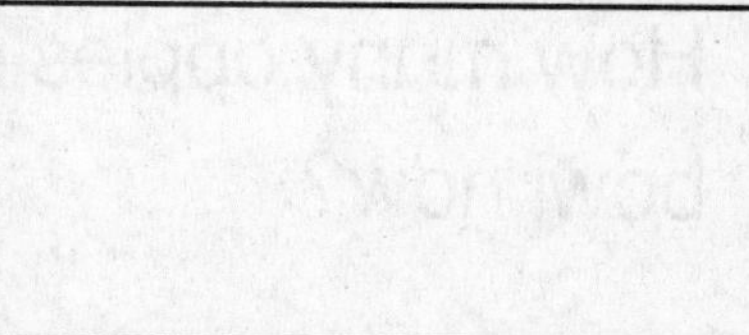

Spiral Review (Chapter 6, Lesson 5) **KEY** NS 2.5, **KEY** NS 2.1

Find the picture that matches the subtraction sentence. Circle your answer.

3. Which picture shows
$5 - 2 = 3$?

4. Which picture shows
$6 - 2 = 4$?

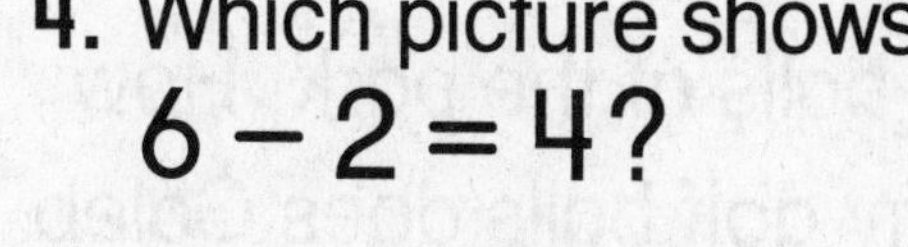

Name ____________________ Date __________

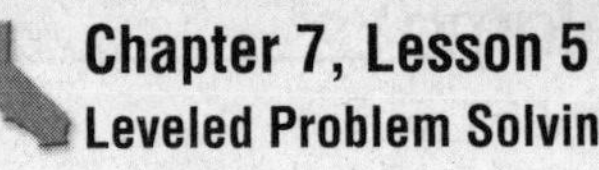

Problem Solving: Draw a Picture

CA Standards
KEY NS 2.5, MR 2.2

Read to solve. Write the difference.

1. There are 8 bees on a flower. Then 3 bees fly away. How many bees are left on the flower?

   8 − 3 = __________ bees

2. There are 6 birds in the tree. Then 2 birds fly away. How many birds are left in the tree?

   6 − 2 = __________ birds

3. There are 7 apples in the bowl. Sasha takes 4 apples. How many apples are in the bowl now?

   7 − 4 = __________ apples

4. Julian has 9 baseballs. He throws 3 baseballs over the fence. How many baseballs does he have left?

   9 − 3 = __________ baseballs

5. Caleb has 7 golf balls and 5 basketballs. He loses 5 golf balls at the park. How many golf balls does Caleb have left?

   ____ ◯ ____ ◯ ____
   golf balls

6. Jaquilla has 9 red books and 8 green books. She gives 4 green books to a friend. How many green books does Jaquilla have left?

   ____ ◯ ____ ◯ ____
   green books

Name ______________________ Date ____________

Hands On: Count Back to Subtract

CA Standards
KEY NS 2.5, KEY NS 2.1

You can count back to subtract.

8 − 2 = 6

7, 6

Count back to subtract.

1.

____, ____

6 − 2 = ____

2.

____, ____, ____

8 − 3 = ____

3.

____

6 − 1 = ____

4.

____, ____

10 − 2 = ____

Spiral Review (Chapter 7, Lesson 1) **AF 1.1 KEY NS 2.1**

Write the subtraction sentence.

5.

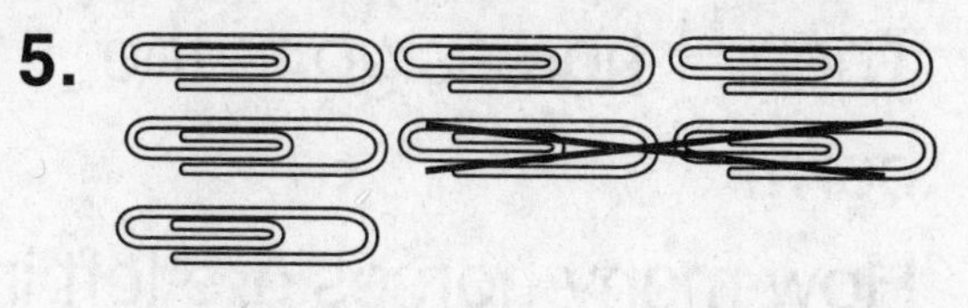

____ − ____ = ____

6.

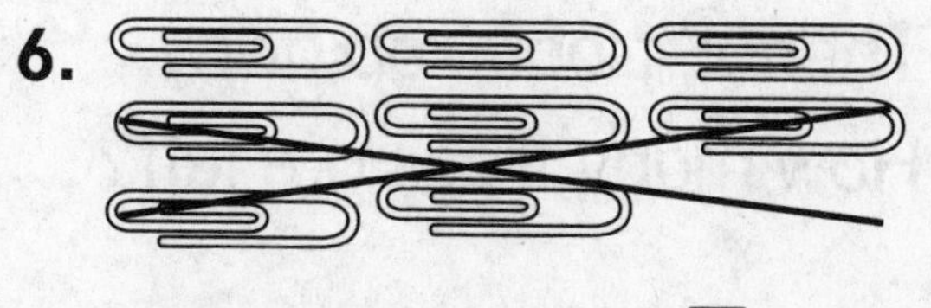

____ − ____ = ____

7. Mike has 7 pencils. He gives 3 to his friends. How many pencils does Mike have now?

____ − ____ = ____

CA Standards
KEY NS 2.5, KEY NS 2.1

Hands On: Count Back to Subtract

Count back to subtract.
Write the subtraction sentence.
Solve.

1. The squirrel finds 8 nuts. It eats 2 of the nuts. How many nuts does the squirrel have left?

   8 - 2 = ______ nuts

2. The dog has 6 bones. It hides 3 bones. How many bones are left?

   6 - 3 = ______ bones

3. There are 5 birds sitting in a tree. Then 3 birds fly away. How many birds are left?

   ____ ○ ____ ○ ____ birds

4. There are 8 bees in a hive. Then 2 bees fly away. How many bees are left?

   ____ ○ ____ ○ ____ bees

5. There are 6 ducks and 9 frogs swimming in the pond. Then 2 frogs hop away. How many frogs are left?

   ____ ○ ____ ○ ____ frogs

6. There are 10 horses and 7 cows in the field. Then 4 horses go to the barn. How many horses are left in the field?

   ____ ○ ____ ○ ____ horses

Use a Number Line to Subtract

CA Standard KEY NS 2.5

Find 7 − 2.

You can use a number line to subtract.

Start at 7. Count back 2.

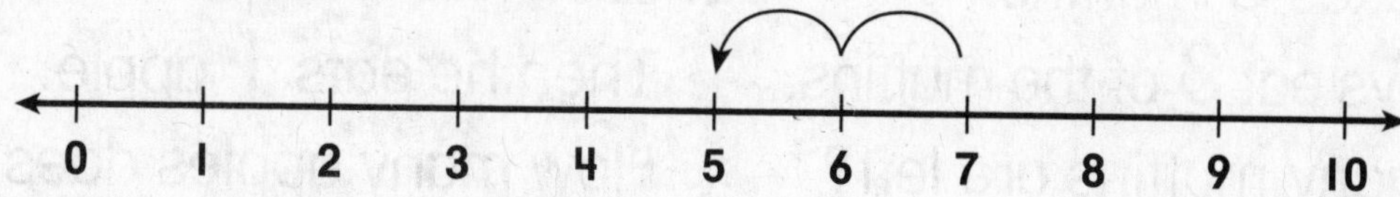

You end on 5. 7 − 2 = 5

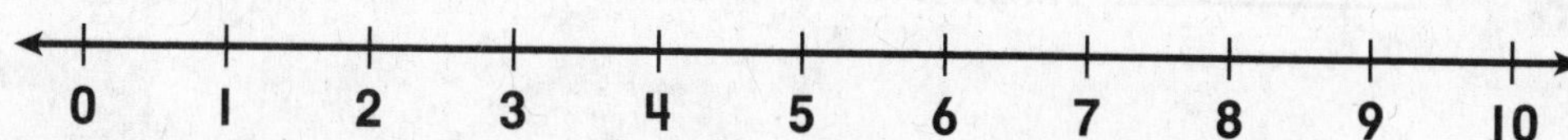

Use the number line to find the difference.

1. 6 − 3 = ______
2. 4 − 2 = ______
3. 7 − 1 = ______

4. 5 − 2 = ______
5. 8 − 2 = ______
6. 4 − 1 = ______
7. 9 − 3 = ______

Spiral Review (Chapter 7, Lesson 2) **KEY NS 2.1, NS 2.0**

Write the subtraction sentence.

8.

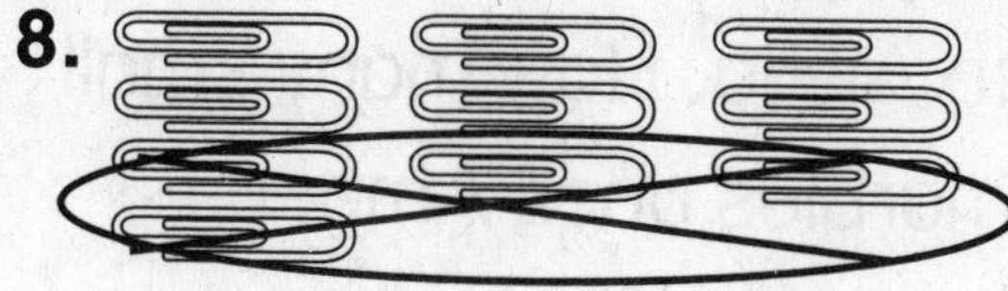

______ ⊖ ______ ⊜ ______

9.

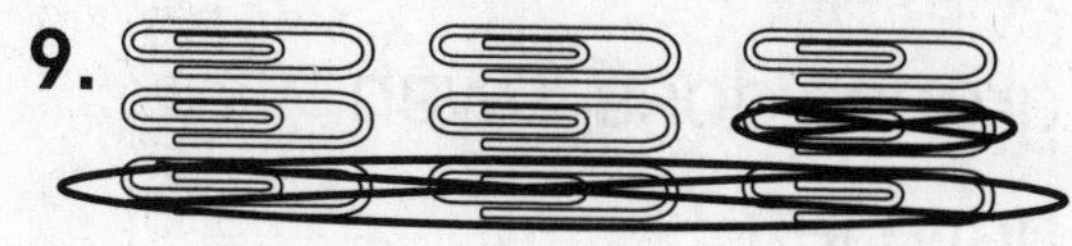

______ ⊖ ______ ⊜ ______

10. Austin has 10 erasers. He gives 7 of them to his friends. How many erasers does Austin have now?

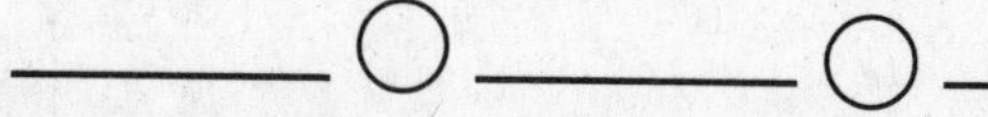

______ ○ ______ ○ ______ erasers

Use a Number Line to Subtract

CA Standard
KEY NS 2.5

Read and solve. Use the number line.

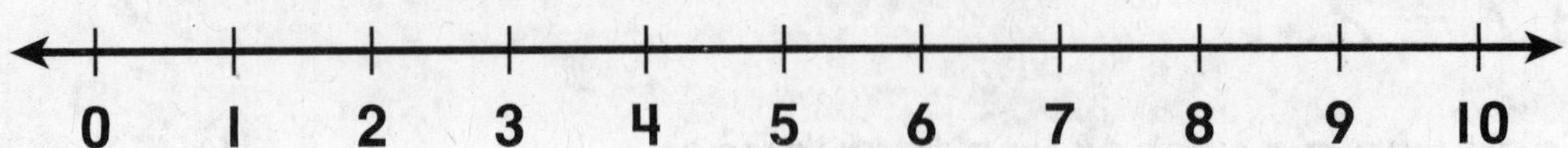

1. Dad bakes 6 muffins. The boys eat 3 of the muffins. How many muffins are left?

   6 − 3 = ________ muffins

2. Jack has 5 apples. Then he eats 1 apple. How many apples does Jake have left?

   5 − 1 = ________ apples

3. Ari saves 9 pennies. Then she spends 2 pennies. How many pennies does Ari have left?

   ________ pennies

4. Terri colors 10 pictures. She gives 3 pictures to friends. How many pictures does Terri have now?

   ________ pictures

5. Owen has 8 grapes and 6 cherries. Then he eats 4 grapes. How many grapes does Owen have left?

   ________ grapes

6. Amber has 9 big marbles and 10 small marbles. She gives 7 small marbles to Aisha. How many small marbles does Amber have now?

   ________ small marbles

Name ______________________ Date __________

Use Addition to Subtract

CA Standards
KEY NS 2.2, KEY NS 2.1

You can use a related addition fact to check your subtraction.

Subtract.

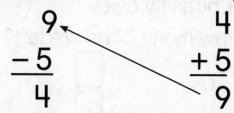

$$\begin{array}{r} 9 \\ -5 \\ \hline 4 \end{array}$$

Check by adding.

$$\begin{array}{r} 4 \\ +5 \\ \hline 9 \end{array}$$

Subtract. Check by adding.

1. $\begin{array}{r} 9 \\ -7 \\ \hline \end{array}$ $\begin{array}{r} \square \\ +\square \\ \hline \square \end{array}$

2. $\begin{array}{r} 6 \\ -3 \\ \hline \end{array}$ $\begin{array}{r} \square \\ +\square \\ \hline \square \end{array}$

3. $\begin{array}{r} 7 \\ -3 \\ \hline \end{array}$ $\begin{array}{r} \square \\ +\square \\ \hline \square \end{array}$

4. $\begin{array}{r} 8 \\ -4 \\ \hline \end{array}$ $\begin{array}{r} \square \\ +\square \\ \hline \square \end{array}$

Spiral Review (Chapter 7, Lesson 3) **KEY** NS 2.1

Write the difference.

5. 6 − 2 = ____

6. 8 − 3 = ____

7. Luis has 3 soccer balls. He gives 1 to a friend. How many soccer balls does he have now?

_____ − _____ = _____ $\begin{array}{r} \square \\ -\square \\ \hline \square \end{array}$

Name ____________________ Date __________

Use Addition to Subtract

CA Standards
KEY NS 2.2, KEY NS 2.1

Subtract. Check by adding.

1. 5 ducks are in the pond.
2 ducks swim away.
How many ducks are left?

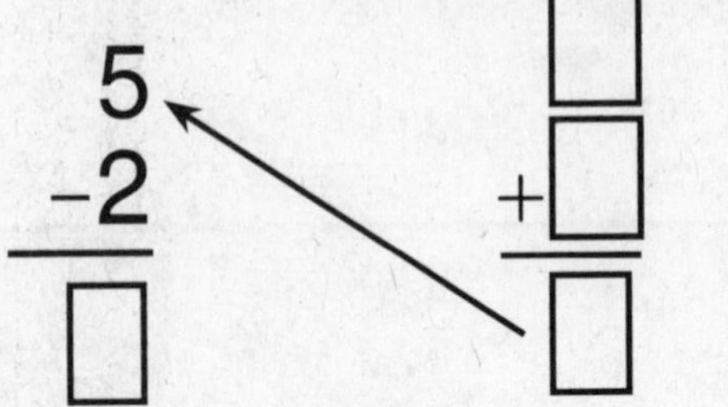

2. 6 birds are in the nest.
4 birds fly away.
How many birds are left?

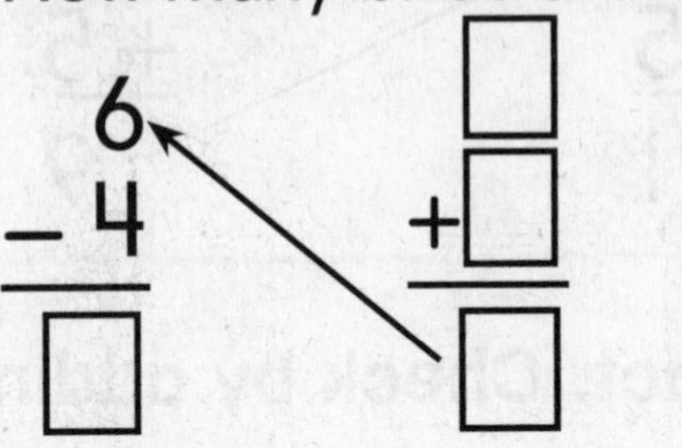

3. Marty has 8 books.
He takes 2 books back to the library. How many books does Marty have left?

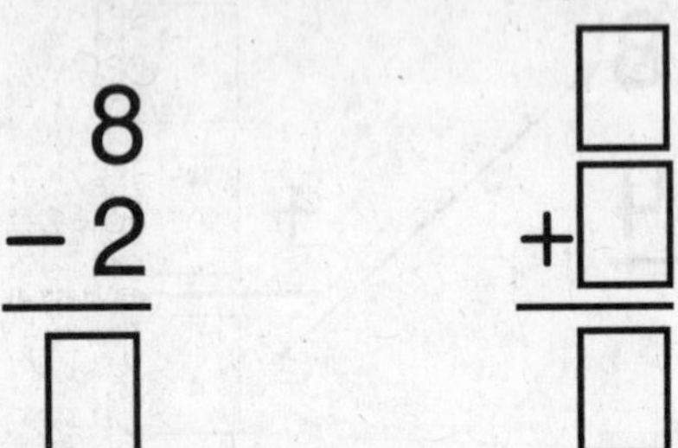

4. Anita writes 7 letters.
She puts 3 letters in the mailbox. How many letters does Anita have left?

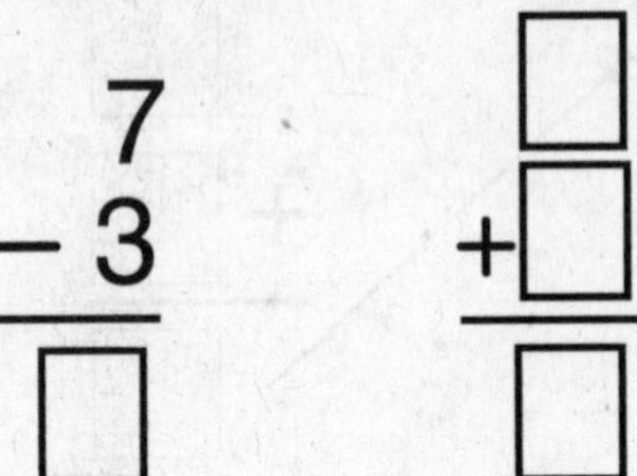

5. Henry has 6 green pens and 8 red pens. He loses 3 red pens. How many red pens does Henry have left?

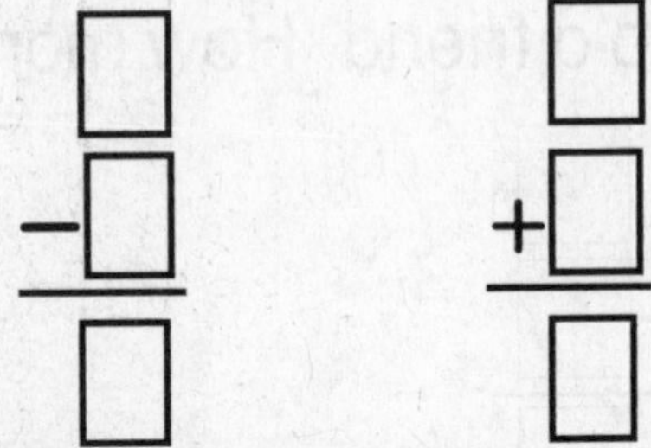

6. Rico has 9 apples and 10 oranges. He eats 2 apples. How many apples does Rico have now?

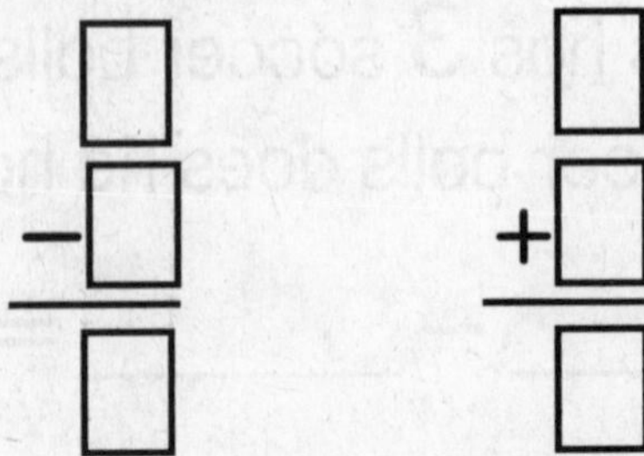

Subtract to Compare

CA Standards
KEY NS 2.5, KEY NS 2.1

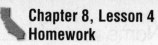

How many more than are there?

You can match sets.

You can subtract to compare sets of objects.

$7 - 5 = \underline{2}$

There are 2 more than .

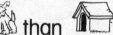

Match. Then subtract.

1. How many more than are there?

$7 - 4 =$ ____

2. How many fewer than are there?

$8 - 7 =$ ____

Spiral Review (Chapter 7, Lesson 4) **KEY NS 2.1**

Write the difference.

3. $5 - 5 =$ ____

4. $6 - 0 =$ ____

5. There are three birds in a birdhouse. All three of them leave. How many are left? Write the difference. $3 - 3 =$ ____

Name ______________________ Date __________

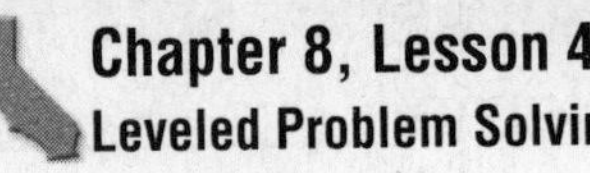

Subtract to Compare

CA Standards
KEY NS 2.5, KEY NS 2.1

Draw a picture.
Match. Then subtract.

1. Al has 3 bugs.
Tom has 2 bugs.
How many more bugs does Al have?

3 – 2 = _____

2. There are 6 cats.
There are 4 baskets.
How many fewer baskets than cats are there?

6 – 4 = _____

3. There are 7 children.
There are 5 glasses of milk.
How many fewer glasses of milk than children are there?

7 – 5 = _____

4. Barb has 8 apples.
Ray has 5 apples.
How many more apples does Barb have than Ray?

8 – 5 = _____

5. Tina has 5 cookies and 4 candies. Rosa has 4 cookies and 3 candies. How many fewer things to eat does Rosa have than Tina?

_____ – _____ = _____

6. Luke has 3 big rocks and 8 small rocks. Stu has 5 big rocks and 7 small rocks. How many more rocks does Stu have than Luke?

_____ – _____ = _____

Name ____________ Date ________

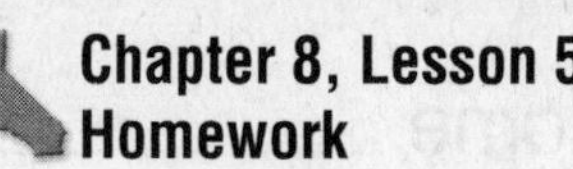

Problem Solving: Write a Number Sentence

CA Standards
AF 1.1, AF 1.2

You can use what you know in a story to write a subtraction sentence.

There are 6 kittens in the basket.

4 kittens jump out.

How many kittens are left?

What do you know?

- You know that the whole is 6.
- You know that the part to subtract is 4.

6 − 4 = 2

Write a number sentence to find the difference.

1. There are 7 cows in the field. 3 cows go to the barn. How many cows are left in the field?

2. There are 9 birds in the tree. Then 6 birds fly away. How many birds are left?

Spiral Review (Chapter 7, Lesson 5) **KEY** NS 2.5, MR 2.2

Write the answer.

3. Andy has 4 balloons. Then 2 balloons pop. How many balloons does he have left?

   ______ balloons

4. Tamika has 6 apples. She gives 2 apples to Mimi. How many apples does Tamika have now?

   ______ apples

5. Ramón has 5 candy bars. He gives 2 of them to his friends. How many candy bars are left? ________ candy bars

Name ____________________ Date __________

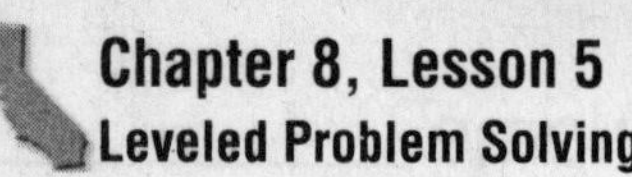

Problem Solving: Write a Number Sentence

CA Standards
AF 1.1, AF 1.2

Write a number sentence to find the difference.

1. Alita counts 4 pigs in a pen. Then 1 pig gets out. How many pigs are left in the pen?

   4 − 1 = _____ pigs

2. Miguel sees 6 spiders in a web. Then 2 spiders crawl away. How many spiders are left in the web?

   6 − 2 = _____ spiders

3. Dave sees 9 birds in the tree. Then 3 birds fly away. How many birds are left in the tree?

   _____ ◯ _____ ◯ _____ birds

4. Kim counts 8 ants on a log. Then 4 ants crawl away. How many ants are left on the log?

   _____ ◯ _____ ◯ _____ ants

5. Chu has 8 big shells and 10 small shells. 4 small shells wash away into the water. How many small shells does he have left?

   _____ ◯ _____ ◯ _____ small shells

6. Sally has 12 green balloons and 9 red balloons. Then 5 green balloons pop. How many green balloons does Sally have left?

   _____ ◯ _____ ◯ _____ green balloons

Hands On: Relate Addition and Subtraction

CA Standards
KEY NS 2.2, KEY NS 2.5

These facts are related facts.
They have the same parts and wholes.

How many cubes in all?
4 + 2 = 6

How many white?
6 − 4 = 2

Whole	
6	
Part	Part
▣ ▣ ▣ ▣	◻ ◻

Show the parts. Complete the related facts.

1. 4 and 1 ___ + ___ = ___ ___ − ___ = ___
2. 5 and 4 ___ + ___ = ___ ___ − ___ = ___
3. 6 and 2 ___ + ___ = ___ ___ − ___ = ___
4. 5 and 3 ___ + ___ = ___ ___ − ___ = ___
5. 3 and 3 ___ + ___ = ___ ___ − ___ = ___

Spiral Review (Chapter 8, Lesson 1) **KEY NS 2.5**

Count back to subtract. Use cubes if you wish.

6.

___, ___
7 − 2 = ___

7.

___, ___, ___
6 − 3 = ___

8. Mr. Thomas has 8 chickens. Then 3 chickens ran away. How many chickens does Mr. Thomas have now? 8 − 3 = ___

Name ____________________ Date __________

Hands On: Relate Addition and Subtraction

CA Standards
KEY NS 2.2, KEY NS 2.5

1. Jan sees 7 birds.
Then she sees 2 more birds.
How many birds does she see in all?
7 + 2 = _____
Write a related subtraction fact.
9 − 2 = _____

2. Joey finds 4 coins.
He loses 2 of the coins.
How many coins does Joey have left?
4 − 2 = _____
Write a related addition fact.
2 + 2 = _____

3. There are 4 eggs in the nest.
The mother bird lays 3 more eggs.
How many eggs are there in all?
_____ + _____ = _____
Write a related subtraction fact.
_____ − _____ = _____

4. There are 8 ladybugs on a leaf.
Then 6 ladybugs fly away.
How many ladybugs are left on the leaf?
_____ − _____ = _____
Write a related addition fact.
_____ + _____ = _____

5. Pam has 2 apples and 4 bananas.
She eats 2 bananas.
How many pieces of fruit does Pam have left?
_____ − _____ = _____
Write a related addition fact.
_____ + _____ = _____

6. Nick has 5 grapes and 3 oranges.
He gets 4 more grapes.
How many pieces of fruit does Nick have in all?
_____ + _____ = _____
Write a related subtraction fact.
_____ − _____ = _____

Name ______________________ Date __________

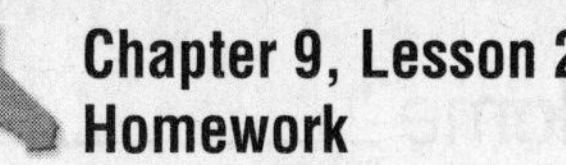

Hands On: Fact Families

CA Standards
KEY NS 2.2, KEY NS 2.5

Related facts make a fact family.

8 is the whole. 2 and 6 are the parts.

$2 + 6 = 8$ $8 - 6 = 2$

$6 + 2 = 8$ $8 - 2 = 6$

Whole	
8	
Part	Part
2	6

Complete the fact family.

1.

Whole	
9	
Part	Part
7	2

7 + ____ = ____ 9 − ____ = ____

2 + ____ = ____ 9 − ____ = ____

2.

Whole	
7	
Part	Part
3	4

____ + ____ = ____ ____ − ____ = ____

____ + ____ = ____ ____ − ____ = ____

3.

Whole	
6	
Part	Part
4	2

____ + ____ = ____ ____ − ____ = ____

____ + ____ = ____ ____ − ____ = ____

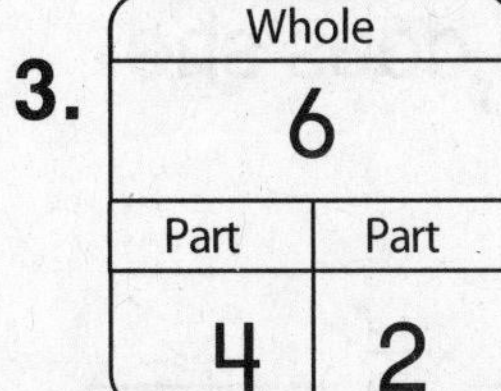

(Chapter 8, Lesson 2) **KEY NS 2.5**

Use the number line to find the difference.

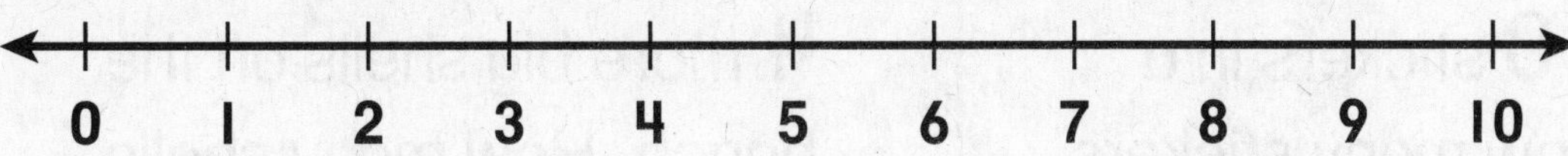

4. $9 - 3 =$ ____

5. $8 - 2 =$ ____

6. Enrico has 6 baseball cards. He gives 2 of them to his best friend. How many baseball cards does he have now?

$6 - 2 =$ ____

Name ______________ Date __________

Hands On: Fact Families

CA Standards
KEY NS 2.2, KEY NS 2.5

Read and solve.

1. Lupe picks 5 green apples. Then she picks 3 red apples. How many apples does Lupe have in all? Write a related fact.

_____ + _____ = _____

_____ − _____ = _____

2. Les makes 6 clay pots. Then he breaks 2 pots. How many clay pots does he have left? Write a related fact.

_____ − _____ = _____

_____ + _____ = _____

3. Bree has 7 fish. Then she gives 3 to a friend. How many fish does Bree have left?

_____ − _____ = _____

4. Drea sees 8 squirrels in the park. Then she sees 1 squirrel in her yard. How many squirrels does she see in all?

_____ + _____ = _____

5. Paul has 5 red stickers and 4 blue stickers. He puts 3 stickers in a book. How many stickers does Paul have left?

_____ − _____ = _____

6. Lori has 8 big shells and 4 small shells. She finds 4 more big shells on the beach. How many shells does Lori have now?

_____ + _____ = _____

Name ______________________ Date __________

Chapter 9, Lesson 3
Homework

Use Addition to Help You Subtract

CA Standards
KEY NS 2.2, MR 3.0

Some cows are in the barn. 3 more cows come to the barn. Now there are 8 cows in the barn. How many cows were in the barn to start with?

3 + __5__ = 8 8 − 3 = __5__

Solve. Complete the number sentences.

1. Some dogs are in the doghouse. 2 more dogs come. Now there are 9 dogs in the doghouse. How many dogs were in the doghouse to start?

   2 + ___ = 9 9 − 2 = ___

2. There are 6 ducks in the pond. Some ducks swim away. 3 ducks stay in the pond. How many ducks swam away?

   3 + ___ = 6 6 − 3 = ___

Spiral Review (Chapter 8, Lesson 3) **KEY** NS 2.1, **KEY** NS 2.2

Subtract. Check by adding.

3. $\begin{array}{r} 8 \\ -2 \\ \hline \end{array}$

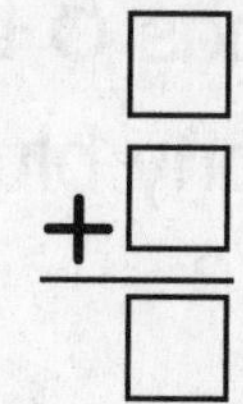

4. $\begin{array}{r} 7 \\ -3 \\ \hline \end{array}$

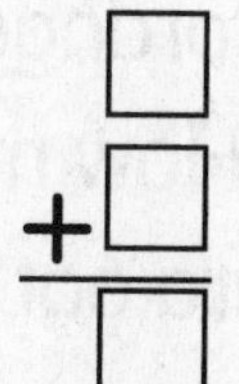

5. Mina has 9 strawberries. She ate 3 of them. How many strawberries are left? __________

Use Addition to Help You Subtract

CA Standards
KEY NS 2.2, MR 3.0

Solve.

1. There are 5 apples on the tree. Then 3 apples fall to the ground. How many apples are left on the tree?

   5 − 3 = _____ apples

2. There are 6 mice in the cage. Then 2 mice get out. How many mice are left in the cage?

   6 − 2 = _____ mice

3. There are 9 balls in the basket. Some balls fall out of the basket. There are 4 balls left in the basket. How many balls fell out?

   _____ − _____ = _____ balls

4. Some children are playing. 2 more children come. Now there are 8 children playing. How many children were there to start with?

   _____ − _____ = _____ children

5. There 8 apples and 11 oranges in the bowl. Sara eats some oranges. There are 9 oranges left in the bowl. How many oranges did Sara eat?

   _____ ◯ _____ ◯ _____ oranges

6. Grace has 10 blue balloons and 9 red balloons. Some blue balloons pop. Now Grace has 6 blue balloons. How many blue balloons popped?

   _____ ◯ _____ ◯ _____ blue balloons

Name ______________________ Date __________

Check Subtraction with Addition

CA Standards
KEY NS 2.2, KEY NS 2.1

You can use a related addition fact to check your subtraction.

Subtract. Check by adding.

$$\begin{array}{r} 8 \\ -5 \\ \hline 3 \end{array} \qquad \begin{array}{r} 3 \\ +5 \\ \hline 8 \end{array}$$

Subtract. Check by adding.

1. $\begin{array}{r} 9 \\ -3 \\ \hline \end{array}$ $\begin{array}{r} \square \\ +\square \\ \hline \square \end{array}$

2. $\begin{array}{r} 10 \\ -2 \\ \hline \end{array}$ $\begin{array}{r} \square \\ +\square \\ \hline \square \end{array}$

3. $\begin{array}{r} 7 \\ -4 \\ \hline \end{array}$ $\begin{array}{r} \square \\ +\square \\ \hline \square \end{array}$

Spiral Review (Chapter 8, Lesson 4) **KEY** NS 2.5, **KEY** NS 2.1

Look at the picture. Subtract.

4. How many more dogs than cats are there?

8 − 3 = ____

5. How many fewer caterpillars than birds are there?

7 − 4 = ____

6. There are 7 fish in a pond. Then 5 ducks come over to the pond. How many more fish than ducks are there?

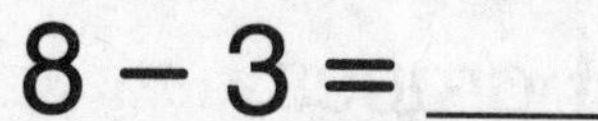

7 − 5 = ____

Check Subtraction with Addition

CA Standards KEY NS 2.2, KEY NS 2.1

Subtract. Check by adding.

1. 6 frogs are in a pond.
I frog hops away.
How many frogs are left in the pond?

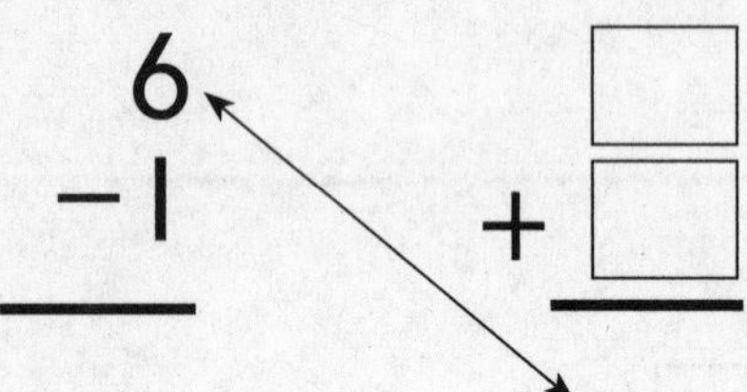

2. 7 bees are in a hive.
3 bees fly away.
How many bees are left in the hive?

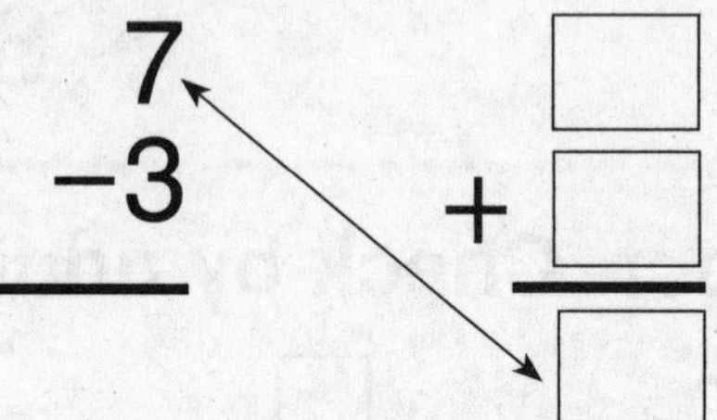

3. Rosita has 9 apples.
She gives 3 apples to Mary.
How many apples does Rosita have left?

9
−3
____ + □ □ ____ □

4. Cassie has 8 softballs. She throws 5 softballs over the fence.How many softballs does Cassie have left?

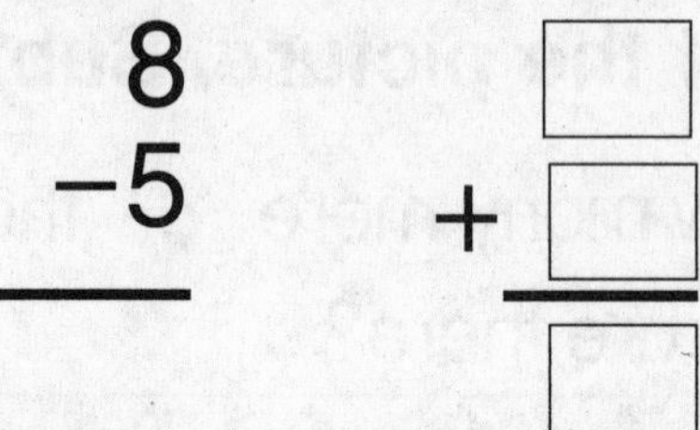

5. Zach has 6 green books and 10 blue books.
He takes 3 blue books to the library. How many blue books does Zach have left?

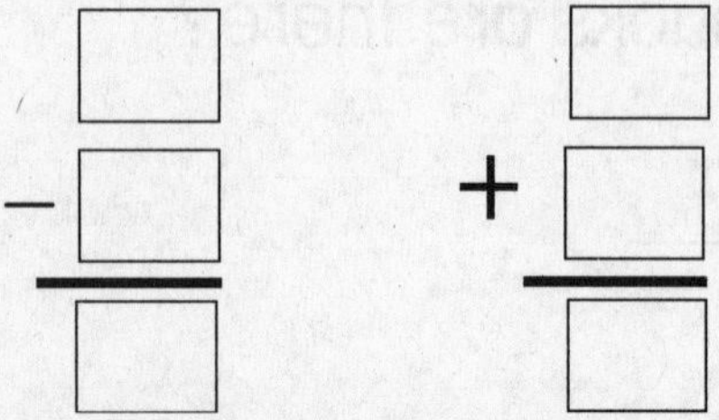

6. Enrique has 11 grapes and 12 cherries.
He eats 4 grapes.
How many grapes does Enrique have left?

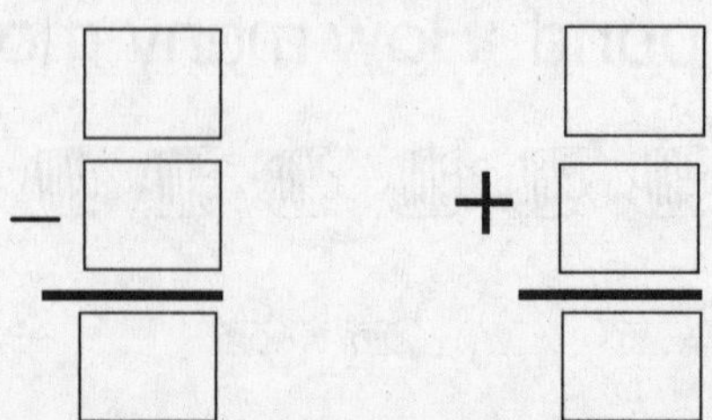

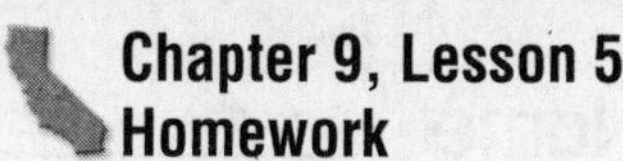

CA Standards
AF 1.1, MR 1.0

Problem Solving: Choose the Operation

You can add or subtract to solve a problem. Choose the operation to solve.

1. 6 children are at the park.
   2 children go home.
   How many children are left? _____ children

2. 5 children are playing soccer.
   3 more join them.
   How many children are playing now? _____ children

Spiral Review (Chapter 8, Lesson 5) **AF 1.1, AF 1.2**

Write a number sentence to find the difference.

3. There are 7 birds in a nest. 3 birds fly away. How many birds are left in the nest?

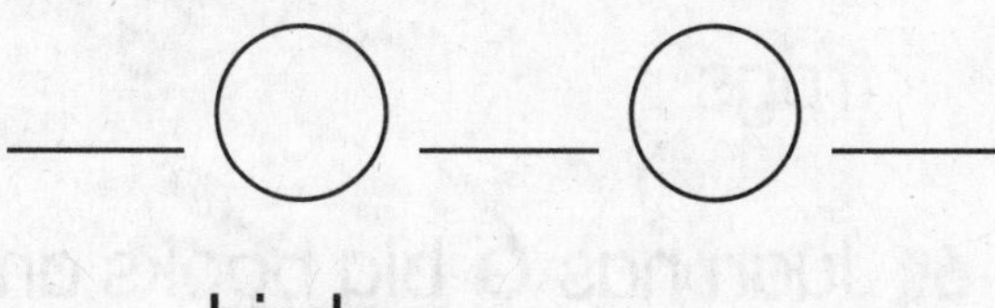

_____ birds

4. There are 8 flowers in the garden. Then 4 flowers are picked. How many flowers are left in the garden?

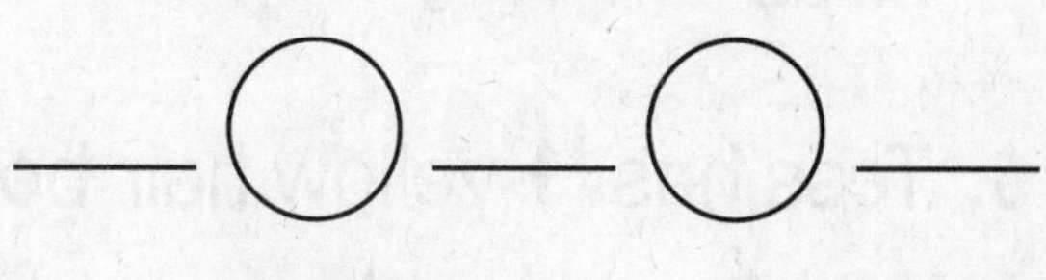

_____ flowers

5. There are 9 bees in a beehive. Then 4 of them leave. How many bees are left in the beehive?

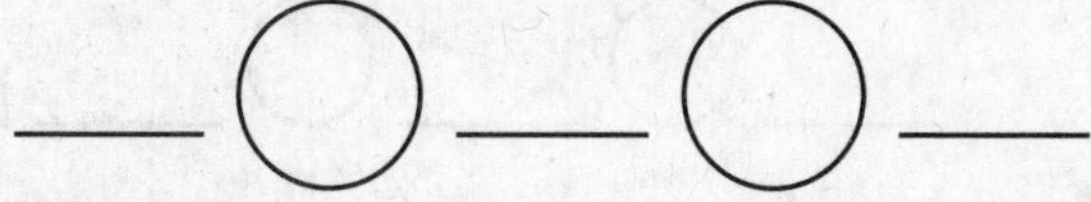

_____ bees

Name ____________________ Date __________

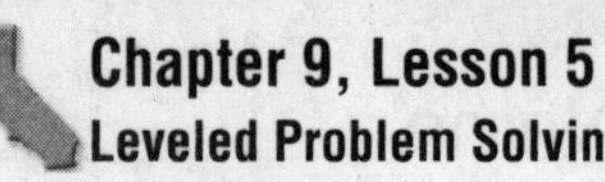

Problem Solving: Choose the Operation

CA Standards
AF 1.1, MR 1.0

Solve.

1. The rabbit has 5 cabbages. It eats 3 cabbages. How many cabbages does rabbit have left?

   5 ◯ 3 = ______ cabbages

2. The bird has 4 caterpillars. It gets 3 more caterpillars. How many caterpillars does bird have now?

   4 ◯ 3 = ______ caterpillars

3. There are 6 birds in the nest. Then 2 more birds fly to the nest. How many birds are in the nest now?

   ____ ◯ ____ ◯ ____ birds

4. There are 9 frogs in the pond. Then 7 frogs hop away. How many frogs are left in the pond?

   ____ ◯ ____ ◯ ____ frogs

5. Tess has 4 yellow hair bows and 6 red hair bows. She loses 3 red hair bows. How many red hair bows does Tess have left?

   ____ ◯ ____ ◯ ____ red hair bows

6. Juan has 6 big books and 8 small books. He gets 5 more big books at the library. How many big books does Juan have now?

   ____ ◯ ____ ◯ ____ big books

Hands On: Make a Tally Chart

CA Standard
SDAP 1.0, SDAP 1.2

Look at the tally chart. How many of each type of toy is there?

Each | stands for 1 toy.

Each 𝍸 stands for 5.

Solution: There are 3 dolls and 5 robots.

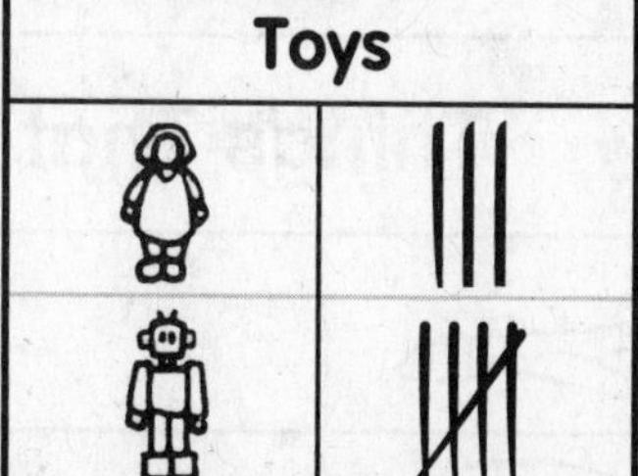

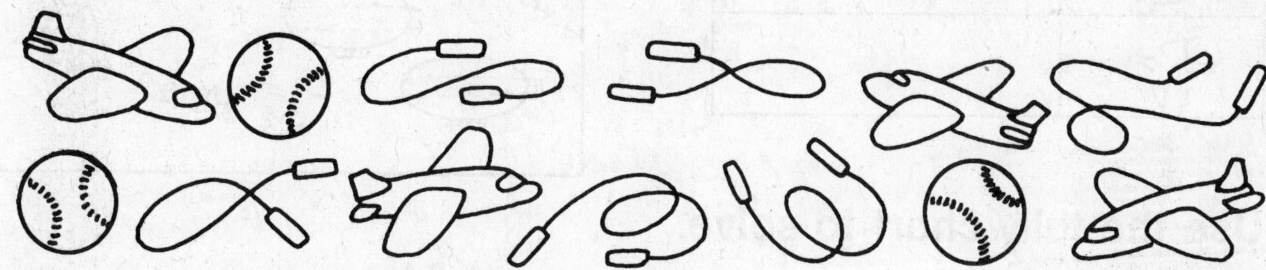

Use the picture. Cross out one item and write a tally mark in the chart. Repeat until you complete the tally chart.

Toys	
(jump rope)	1.
(ball)	2.
(airplane)	3.

Spiral Review (Chapter 9, Lesson 1) **KEY** NS 2.2, **KEY** NS 2.5

Complete the related facts.

1. 5 and 1

____ + ____ = ____

____ − ____ = ____

2. 5 and 3

____ + ____ = ____

____ − ____ = ____

Name ____________________ Date __________

Hands On: Make a Tally Chart

CA Standards
SDAP 1.0, SDAP 1.2

Use the picture.
Complete the tally chart.

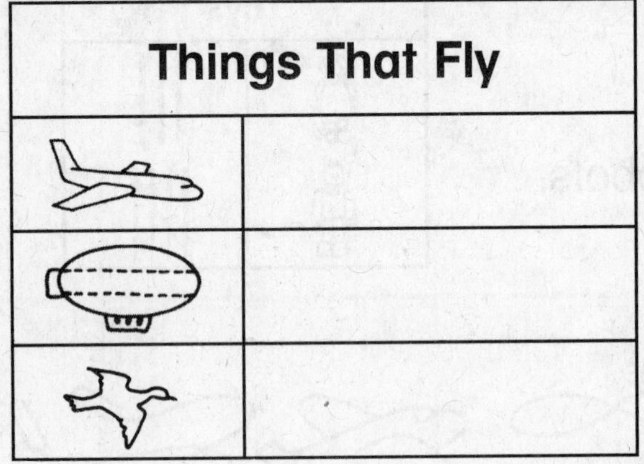

Use the tally chart to solve.

1. Timmy counts the ✈. How many does he count?

2. Flor counts the blimps. How many does she count?

_____ blimps

3. Deb counts the birds. How many does she count?

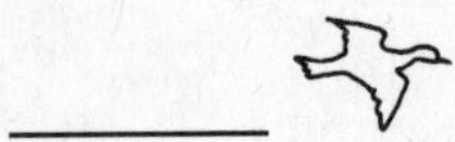

4. Sal counts ✈ and blimps. How many does he count in all?

_____

5. How many more ✈ and blimps are there than birds?

_____

6. How many more birds and blimps are there than ✈?

_____

Name ______________________ Date __________

Make and Read a Picture Graph

CA Standard
SDAP 1.0, SDAP 1.2

You can draw I for each animal in the picture.

Animals at the Zoo	
lion	(3 marks)
elephant	(5 marks)

Use the picture.
Make a picture graph.
Draw one for each animal.

More Animals at the Zoo		
1.	monkey	
2.	bear	(1 mark)
3.	zebra	

Spiral Review (Chapter 9, Lesson 2) **KEY** NS 2.2

Complete the fact family.

Whole	
5	
Part	Part
3	2

4. _____ + _____ = _____

5. _____ − _____ = _____

6. _____ + _____ = _____

7. _____ − _____ = _____

Name ____________________ Date __________

Make and Read a Picture Graph

CA Standards
SDAP 1.0, SDAP 1.2

Read the picture graph. Solve.
Each 🯅 stands for one child.

What Children Read

My Dog Buzz	🯅 🯅 🯅 🯅 🯅
Rocket to the Moon	🯅 🯅 🯅
Bedtime Joke Book	🯅 🯅 🯅 🯅 🯅 🯅

Key: Each 🯅 stands for 1 child

1. How many children read *My Dog Buzz*?

   __________ children

2. How many children read *Rocket to the Moon*?

   __________ children

3. Which book did most children read?

   ____

4. Which book did the fewest children read?

   ____

5. How many more children read *Rocket to the Moon and My Dog Buzz than Bedtime Joke Book*?

   ____

6. Five more children vote. Three of them read *Rocket to the Moon* and two of them read *My Dog Buzz.*

   Now which book did most children read?

   ____

Make a Bar Graph

CA Standard
SDAP 1.2

You can use a tally chart to make a bar graph.
Color one box for each tally.

Solution:

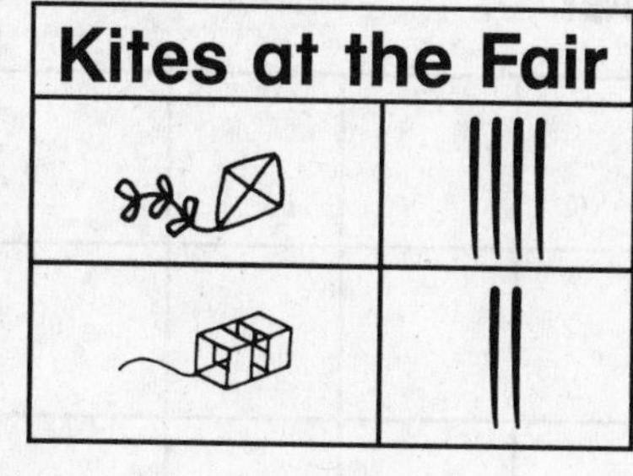

Kites at the Fair						
(kite)	■	■	■	■		
(box kite)	■	■				
	0 1	2	3	4	5	6

Use the tally chart to make a bar graph.
Color one box for each tally.

1.
2.
3.

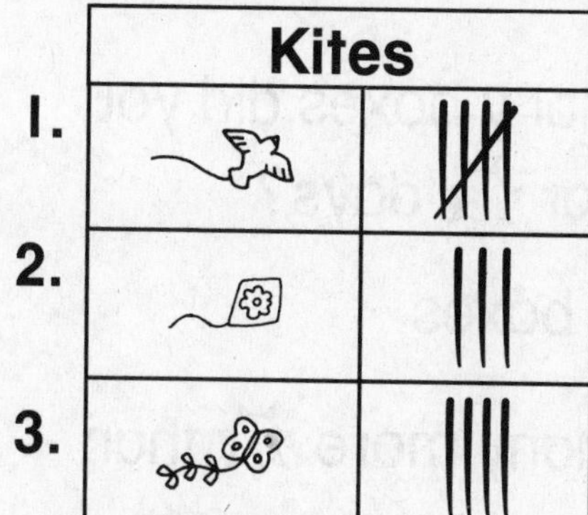

Kites at the Fair						
(bird kite)						
(flower kite)						
(butterfly kite)						
	0 1	2	3	4	5	6

Number of Kites

Spiral Review (Chapter 9, Lesson 3) **MR** 3.0, **KEY** NS 2.2

Write the number sentences and complete the table.

Whole	
8	
Part	Part
2	

4. $2 + \_\_\_\_ = 8$

5. $8 - 2 = \_\_\_\_$

Make a Bar Graph

CA Standard
SDAP 1.2

Use the tally chart to make a bar graph.
Color one box for each tally. Then solve.

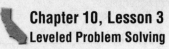

Weather	Day
	卌 I
	IIII
	卌 II

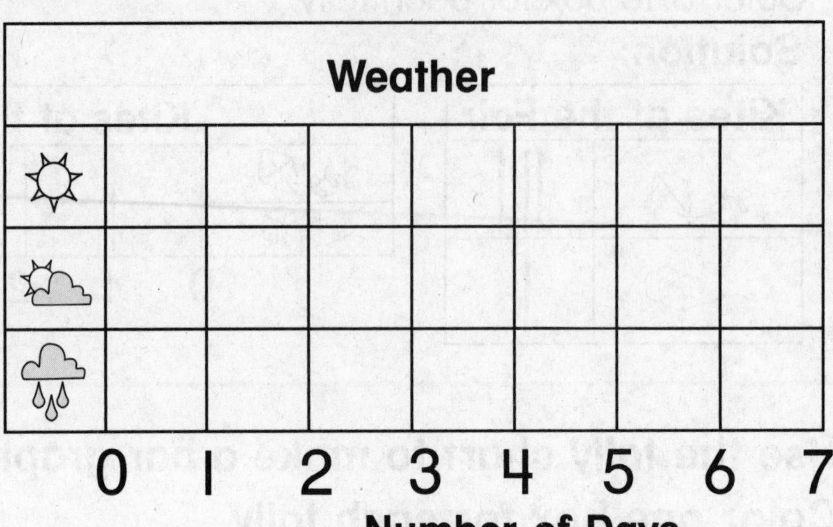

1. How many boxes did you color for days?

   ______ boxes

2. How many boxes did you color for days?

   ______ boxes

3. How many days are days?

   ______ days

4. How many more than days are there?

   ______ more days

5. How many fewer days are there than and days?

   ______ fewer days

6. How many more and days are there than days?

   ______ more days

Name _______________________ Date ____________

Read a Bar Graph

CA Standard
SDAP 1.2

Each box on the graph stands for one kind of dog.

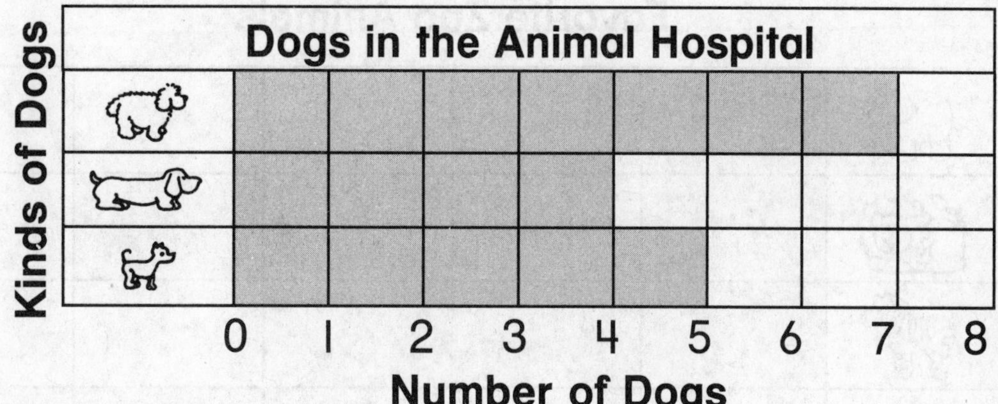

How many are in the animal hospital?

Solution: There are 7 .

1. How many are in the animal hospital?

____

2. How many more are in the animal hospital than ?

____

Spiral Review (Chapter 9, Lesson 4) **KEY** NS 2.1, **KEY** NS 2.2

Subtract. Check by adding.

3.

$$\begin{array}{r} 9 \\ -4 \\ \hline \end{array}$$

$+\square$ $\square$ $\square$

4.

$$\begin{array}{r} 10 \\ -3 \\ \hline \end{array}$$

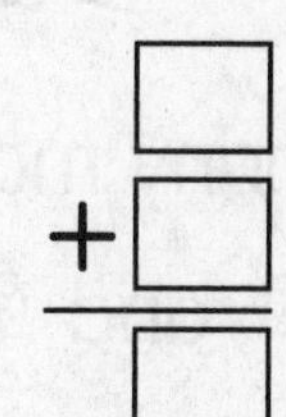

Name ____________________ Date __________

Read a Bar Graph

CA Standard
SDAP 1.2

Use the bar graph. Solve.

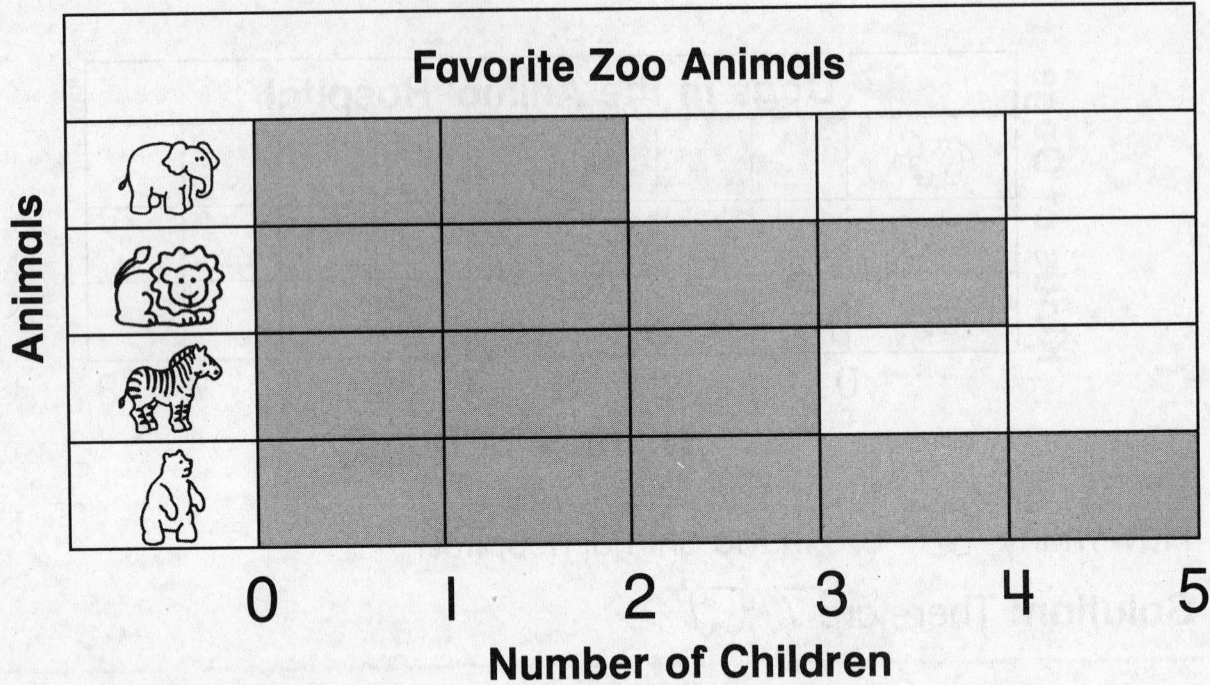

1. How many kinds of animals does the graph show?

   ______ kinds

2. How many children chose (lion)?

   ______ children

3. Circle the animal most children like.

4. How many more children like (bear) than (elephant)?

   ______ more children

5. How many more children like (lion) and (zebra) than (bear)?

   ______ more children

6. How many fewer children like (bear) than (elephant) and (lion)?

   ______ fewer child

Name ____________________ Date __________

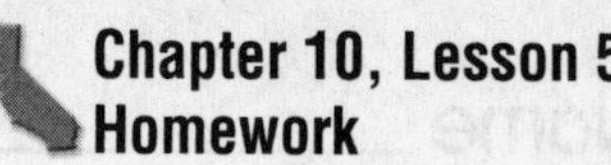

Problem Solving: Use Graphs

CA Standards
SDAP 1.2, MR 2.2

Use the graph. How many small cars are there?

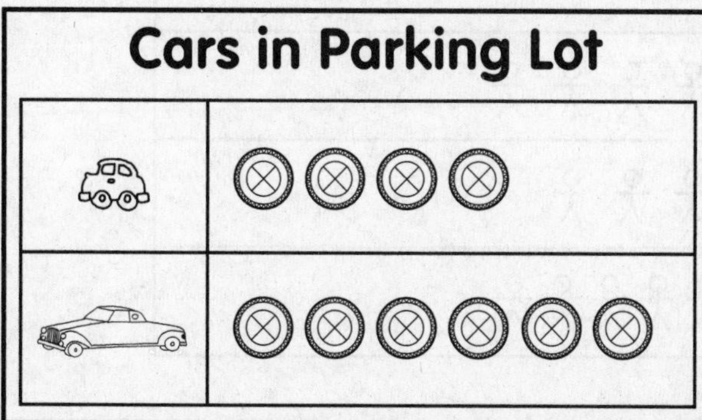

Solution: __4__ small cars.

Use the picture graph to solve each problem.

1. How many big cars are there? ______ big cars

2. 3 more small cars drive into the parking lot. Draw the wheels to show 3 more small cars on the graph. How many more small cars are there than big cars now?

   ______ more small car

Spiral Review (Chapter 9, Lesson 5) **AF** 1.1, **MR** 1.0, **NS** 2.0

Write a number sentence for each story.

3. There are 5 bees in a hive. Then 2 bees fly away. How many bees are left?

   ______ ◯ ______ ◯ ______

4. There are 6 birds in a nest. Then 3 birds fly away. How many birds are there now?

   ______ ◯ ______ ◯ ______

Name ______________________ Date __________

Problem Solving: Use Graphs

CA Standards
SDAP 1.2, MR 2.2

Talent Show	
Sing	🯅 🯅 🯅 🯅 🯅
Dance	🯅 🯅 🯅 🯅
Play instrument	🯅 🯅 🯅 🯅 🯅 🯅

Use the picture graph to solve.

1. How many children will dance?

   ________ children

2. How many children will sing?

   ________ children

3. How many children will sing or dance in all? Write the number sentence.

   ____ ◯ ____ ◯ ____ in all

4. How many more children will play an instrument than dance? Write the number sentence.

   ____ ◯ ____ ◯ ____ children

5. How many more children will dance or play an instrument than sing? Write the number sentence.

   ____ ◯ ____ ◯ ____ children

6. There are 4 more children who decide to sing. There are 3 more children who decide to dance. Now how many children will sing or dance in all? Write the number sentence.

   ____ ◯ ____ ◯ ____ in all

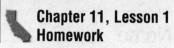

Hands On: Sort Objects

CA Standards
SDAP 1.1, SDAP 2.0

You can sort objects by color, size, or shape.

Tell how the objects are alike.
Write color, size, or shape.

1.  ____________

2.  ____________

3.  ____________

Spiral Review (Chapter 10, Lesson 1) **SDAP 1.2, SDAP 1.0**

Use the tally chart to solve.

4. How many 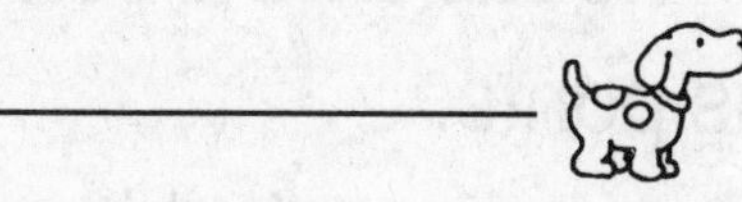 are there?

____

Animals	
dog	𝍸 I
cat	III

5. Which has the most?
Circle.

Hands On: Sort Objects

CA Standards
SDAP 1.1, SDAP 2.0

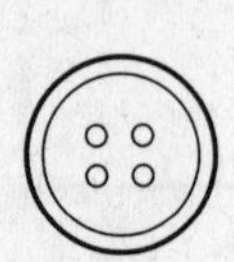
A

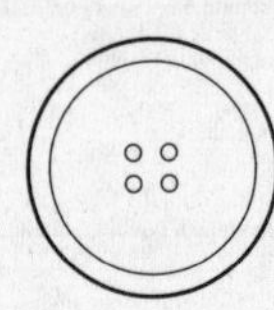
B

C

D

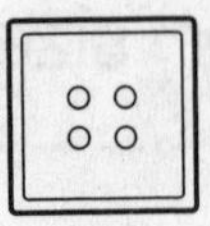
E

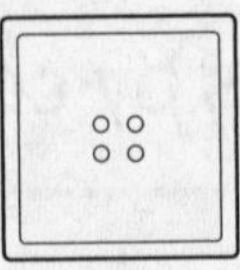
F

G

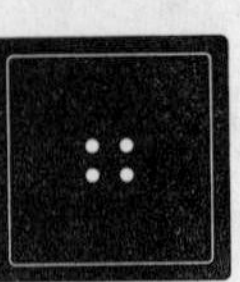
H

1. Chase counts all the black buttons.
How many buttons does he count?

____

2. Mary counts all the square buttons.
How many buttons does she count?

____

3. JaQuilla loses a button on her shirt.
She needs a small round button.
It should be white.
Which button can JaQuilla use?

____

4. Chad loses the button on his backpack.
It is large and black.
It has a square shape.
Which button should Chad use?

____

5. Chloe finds a jacket that needs a new button.
It should be large and black.
What are Chloe's choices for buttons?

____

6. Logan needs a new button for his pants.
He needs a small white button.
What are Logan's choices for buttons?

____

Name ______________________ Date __________

Color Patterns

CA Standards
SDAP 2.0, KEY SDAP 2.1

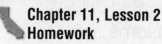

This pattern is gray, lined, gray, lined, gray.
The next color in the pattern is lined.

Solution: 

Circle the cube that comes next.

1. 

2. 

3.

Spiral Review (Chapter 10, Lesson 2) **SDAP 1.2. SDAP 1.0**

Make a picture graph. Use ☺ to stand for each animal.

4. There are 4 zebras in the zoo. There are two fewer giraffes than zebras.

5. How many giraffes are there?

____

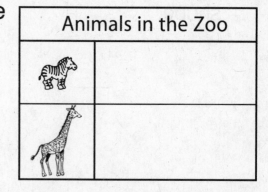

Animals in the Zoo	
zebra	
giraffe	

Name ______________________ Date __________

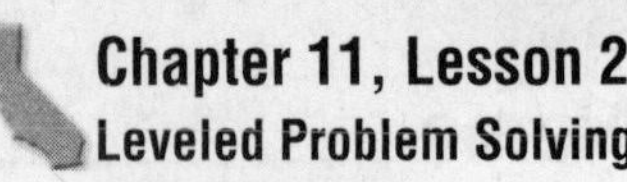

Color Patterns

CA Standards
SDAP 2.0, KEY SDAP 2.1

Solve.

1. Amy makes this pattern.

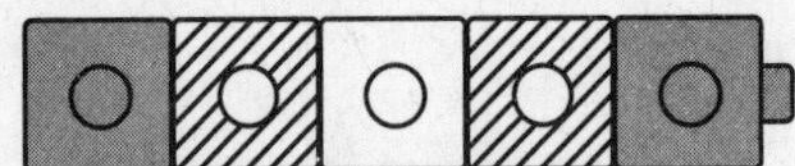

She did not color one cube.

Circle the correct color cube.

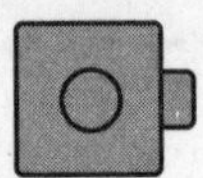 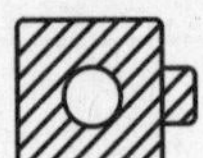

2. Gary makes this pattern.

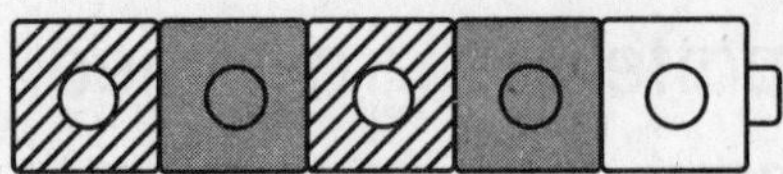

He did not color one cube.

Circle the correct color cube.

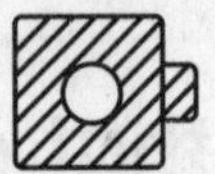 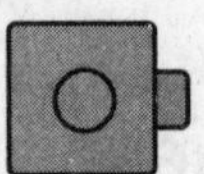

3. Brad makes this pattern.

He did not color one cube.

Color that cube.

4. Rosa makes this pattern.

She did not color one cube.

Color that cube.

5. Kate makes this pattern.

She left out one shape.

Draw and color the missing shape.

___

6. Aldo makes this pattern.

He left out one shape.

Draw and color the missing shape.

___

Name ______________ Date ________

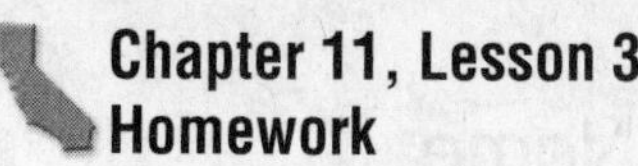

Shape and Size Patterns

CA Standards
SDAP 2.0, KEY SDAP 2.1, MR 1.0

You can make a pattern with shapes.

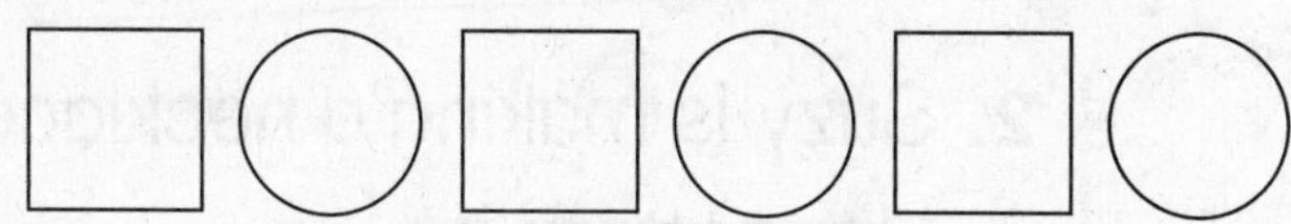

This is a square, circle, square, circle, square, circle pattern.

Circle the shape that comes next.

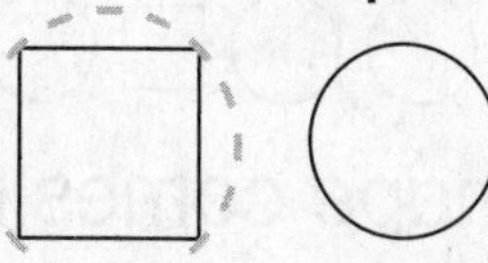

Circle the shape that comes next.

1. 

2. 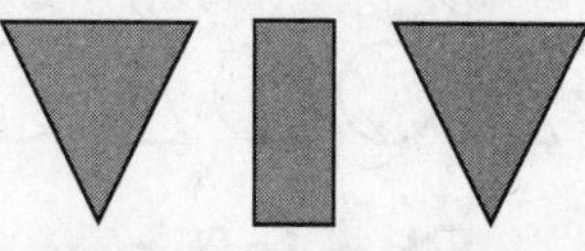 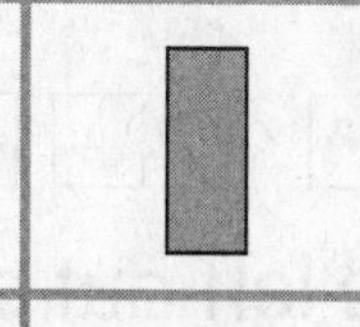

3. 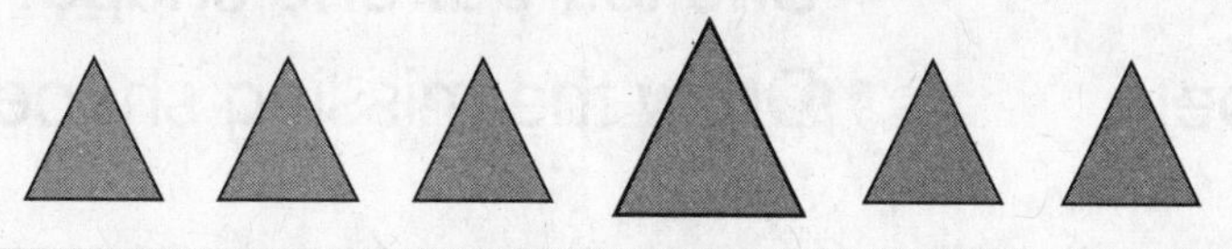 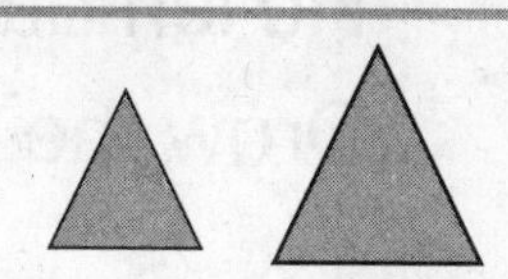

4. 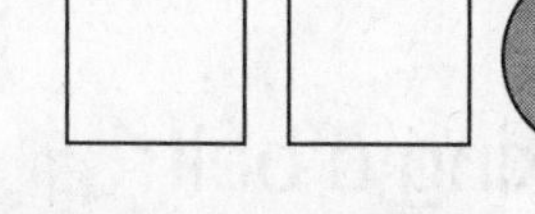 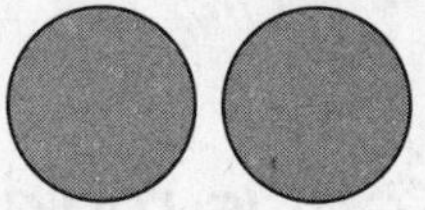 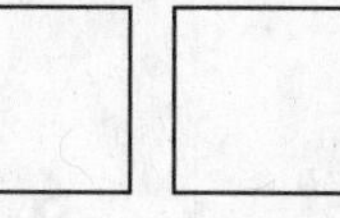 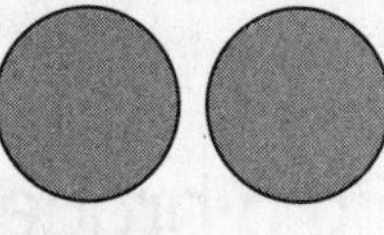 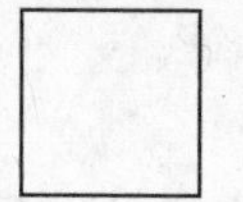 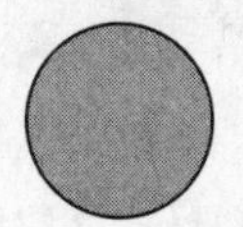

Spiral Review (Chapter 10, Lesson 3) **SDAP 1.2**

Use the tally chart to complete the bar graph for cats.

5.
6.

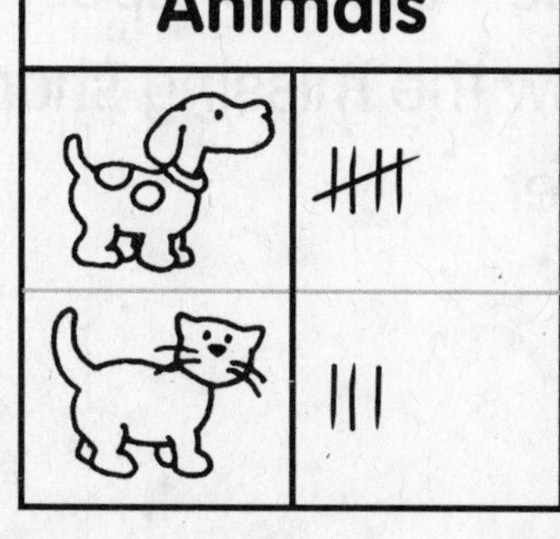

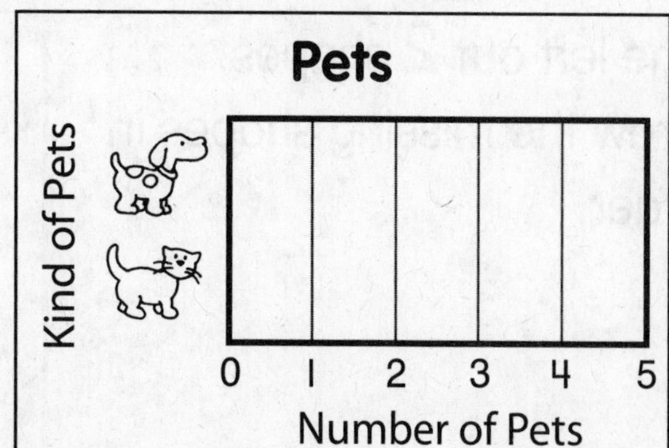

Name ____________________ Date __________

Shape and Size Patterns

CA Standards
SDAP 2.0, KEY SDAP 2.1

Solve.

1. Randy is making a belt.
His pattern is

What shape comes next?

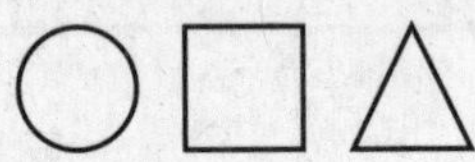

2. Suzy is making a necklace.
Her pattern is

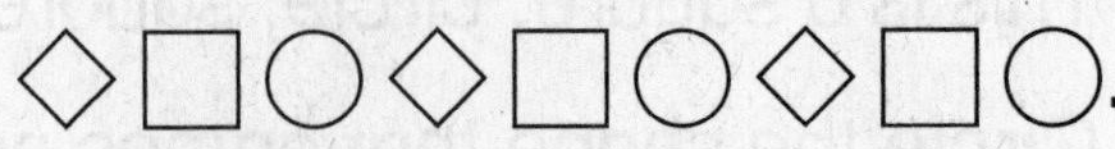

What shape comes next?

3. Pedro is making a quilt.
His pattern is

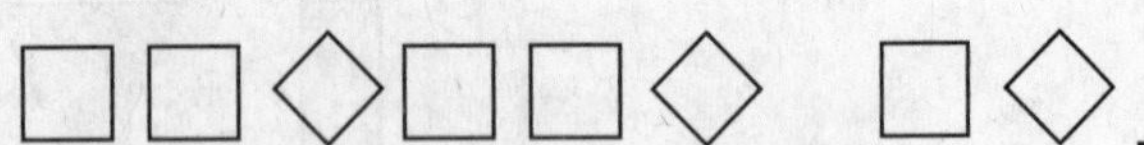

He left out one shape.
Draw the missing shape.

4. Kara is making a scarf.
Her pattern is

She left out one shape.
Draw the missing shape.

5. Trina is making a bracelet.
Her pattern is

She left out 2 shapes.
Draw the missing shapes in order.

6. Kent is making a belt.
His pattern is

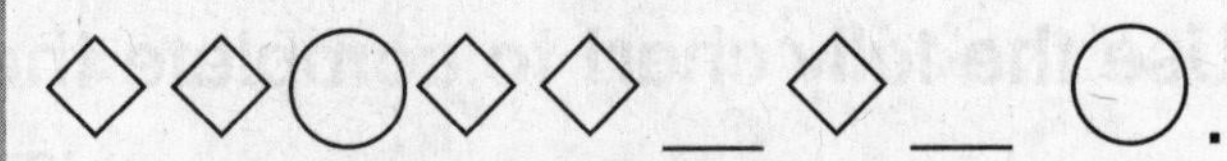

He left out 2 shapes.
Draw the missing shapes in order.

Hands On: Motion and Rhythmic Patterns

CA Standards
SDAP 2.0, KEY SDAP 2.1

What comes next in this pattern?

Act out the pattern. **Solution:**

Look at each motion or sound pattern.
Act out the pattern.
Circle what comes next.

1. 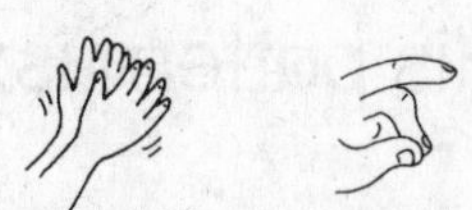

2. 

3. 

Spiral Review (Chapter 10, Lesson 4) **SDAP 1.2**

Use the bar graph to solve.

4. How many  are there?

____

5. How many more than are there?

_________ more

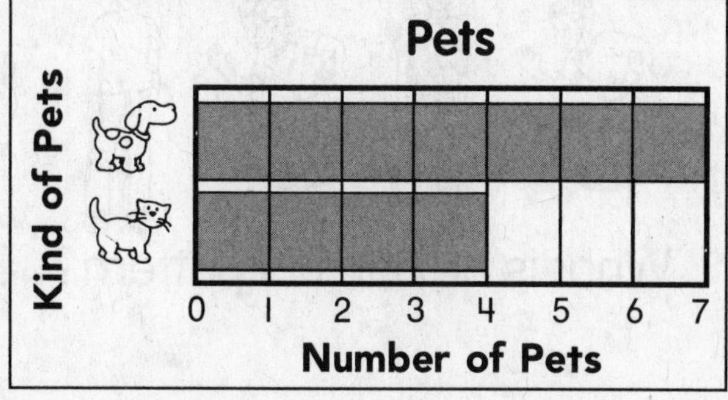

CA Standard
SDAP 2.0, KEY SDAP 2.1

Hands On: Motion and Rhythmic Patterns

Solve.

1. Alexis hears these sounds.

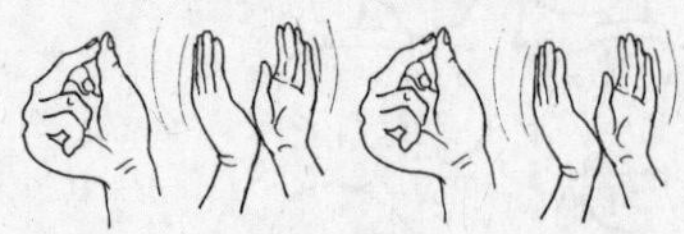

What sound will she hear next?

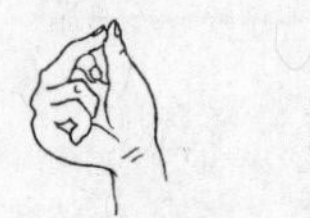

2. Miles does these motions.

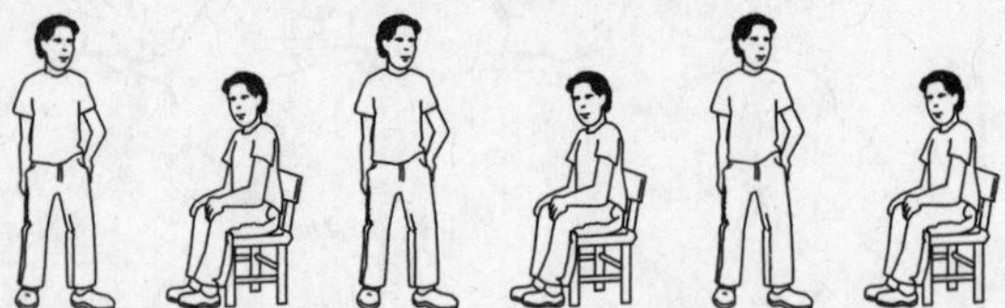

What should he do next?

3. Noah does these motions. His pattern is:

What should he do next?

____

4. Mia hears these sounds.

What sound will she hear next?

____

5. Mason makes this pattern.

What is next in his pattern?

____

6. Mia makes this pattern.

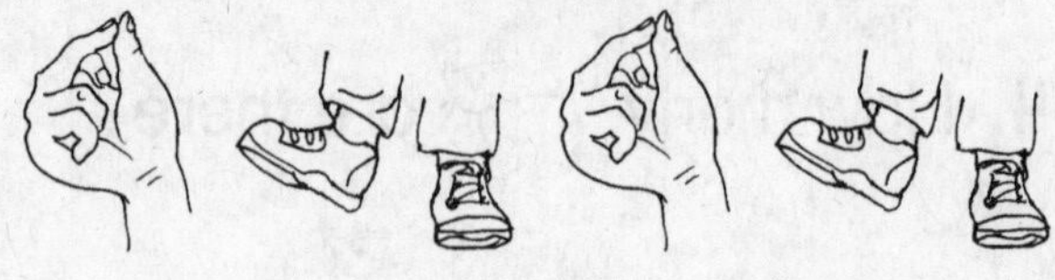

What is next in her pattern?

____

Name ______________________ Date __________

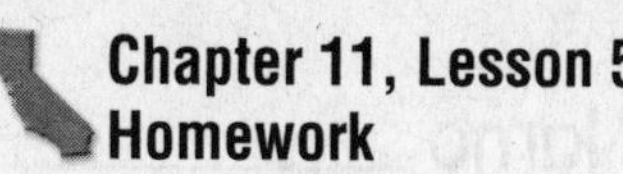

Problem Solving: Translate Patterns

CA Standards
KEY SDAP 2.1, MR 3.0

Show the pattern below in a different way.

Solution: [ ] [ ] [ ] [ ] [ ] [ ] [ ] [ ]

Find the pattern. Draw shapes to show it in another way.

1. 

2. 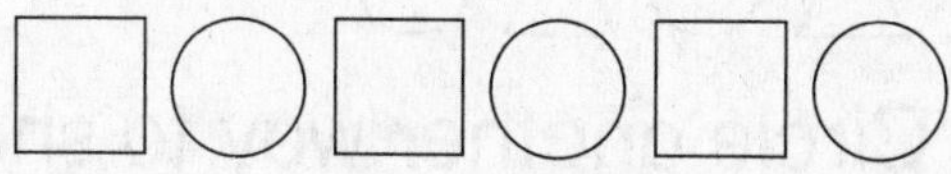

3. 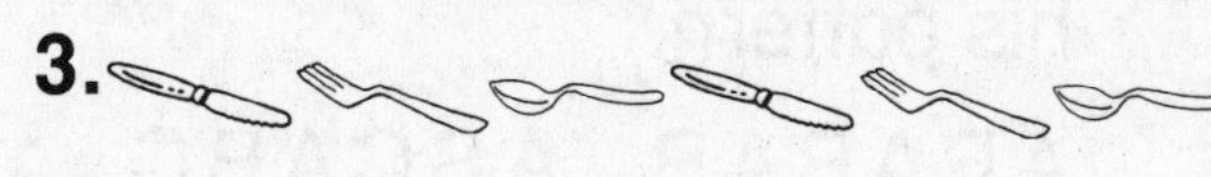

4. 

Spiral Review (Chapter 10, Lesson 5) **SDAP 1.2, MR 2.2**

Use the picture graph to solve.

5. How many [truck] are there?

__________ [truck]

6. How many more [car] than [truck] are there?

__________ more [car]

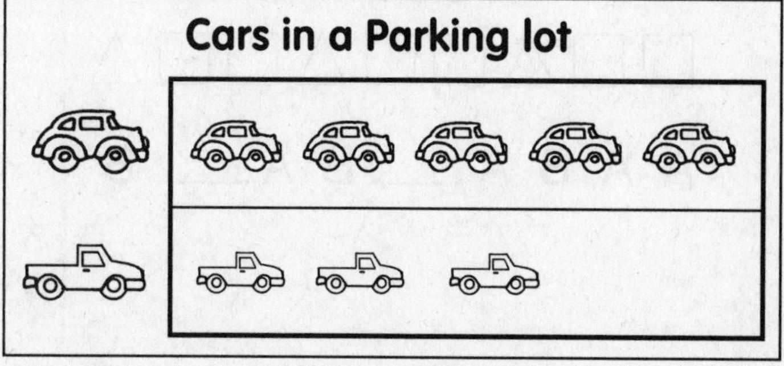

Problem Solving: Translate Patterns

CA Standards
KEY SDAP 2.1, MR 3.0

Solve.

1. Kurt makes this pattern.

What will come next in the pattern?

2. Sandy makes this pattern.

1, 3, 5, 1, 3, 5, 1, 3, 5, 1, 3, ____

Circle the number that comes next in her pattern.

1 3 5

3. Tara makes this pattern.

Circle another way to show her pattern.

ABAB AABA

4. Jamal makes this pattern.

Circle another way to show his pattern.

ABABAB ABCABC

5. Tom makes a shape pattern. Jena copies the pattern with letters. She can only use the letters A and B. She starts the pattern with A. Write the missing letters.

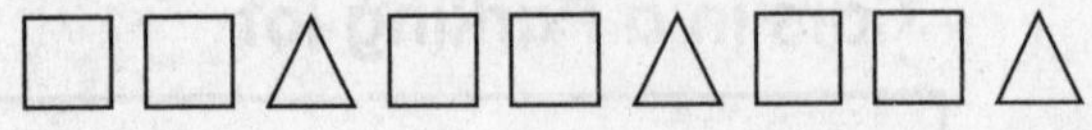

A A B A ____ B A ____ B

6. Abby makes a shape pattern. Tony copies the pattern with letters. He can only use the letters A and B. He starts the pattern with A. Write the missing letters.

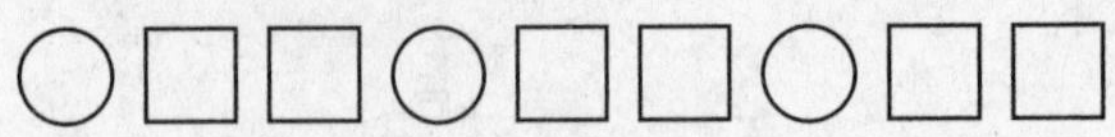

A ____ B A B B ____ B B

Name ____________________ Date __________

Hands On: Model Numbers to 100

CA Standards
KEY NS 1.1, KEY NS 2.4

You can count crayons by ones.

You can also make groups of ten.

10 ones equal 1 ten.

Solution: There are 20 crayons.

Write the number of tens shown. Then write the total number of paper clips.

1. 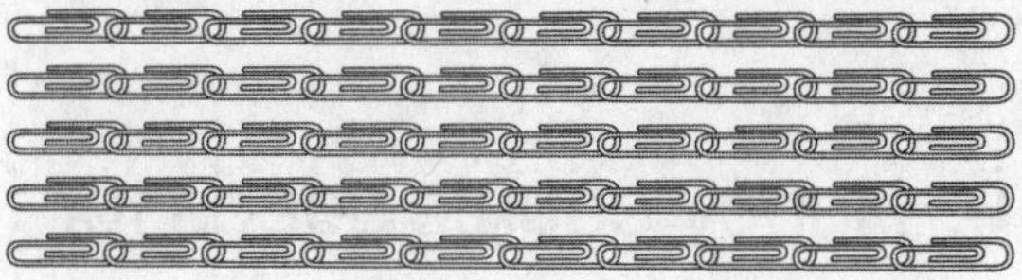 _______ tens

_______ fifty

2. 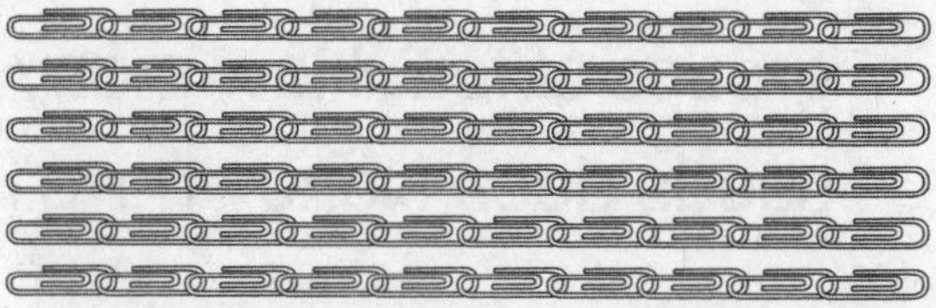 _______ tens

_______ sixty

3. 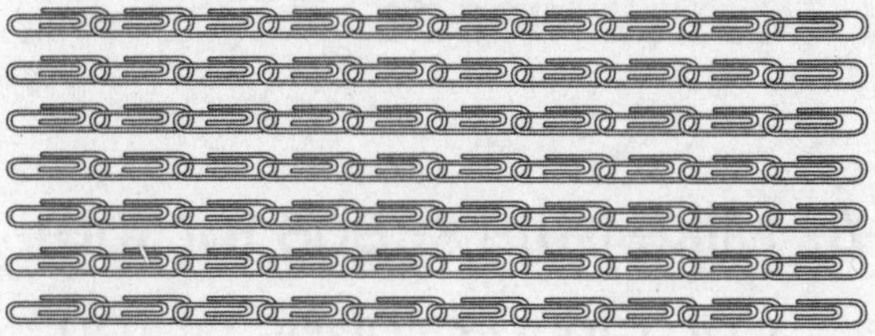 _______ tens

_______ seventy

Spiral Review (Chapter 11, Lesson 1) **SDAP 1.1, SDAP 2.0**

Tell how the objects are alike. Write color, size, or shape.

4.   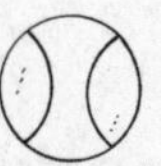

____

5.   

____

Hands On: Model Numbers to 100

CA Standards
KEY NS 1.1, KEY NS 2.4

Solve.

1. Sandy counts her shells from the beach. She puts them in 2 groups of ten. How many shells does Sandy have?

_____ shells

2. Raúl counts his rocks from his collection. He puts them in 3 groups of ten. How many rocks does Raúl have?

_____ rocks

3. Jack counts pennies from a jar. He puts them in 7 groups of ten. How many pennies does Jack have?

_____ pennies

4. Nancy counts seeds for the garden. She puts them in 6 groups of ten. How many seeds does Nancy have?

_____ seeds

5. Lara puts coins from a jar in groups of ten. She has 4 groups of pennies and 4 groups of dimes. How many coins does Lara have in all?

_____ coins

6. Mike puts seeds for the garden in groups of ten. He has 5 groups of carrot seeds and 4 groups of celery seeds. How many seeds does Mike have in all?

_____ seeds

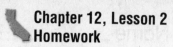

Hands On: One More, One Less

CA Standards
KEY NS 2.3, KEY NS 1.1

The number that is **1** **more** comes **after**. 79, 80

The number that is **1** **less** comes **before**. 79, 80

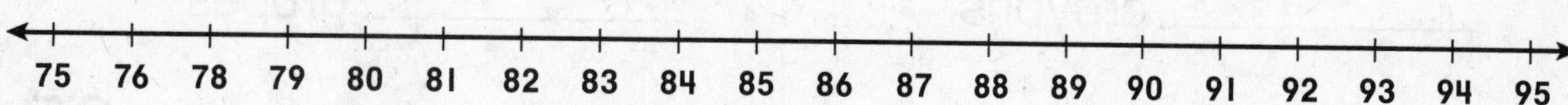

Write the number that is 1 more.

1. 92, _____
2. 77, _____
3. 80, _____

Write the number that is 1 less.

4. _____, 87
5. _____, 84
6. _____, 70

Spiral Review (Chapter 11, Lesson 2) **SDAP 2.0, KEY SDAP 2.1**

Circle what comes next in each pattern.

7. 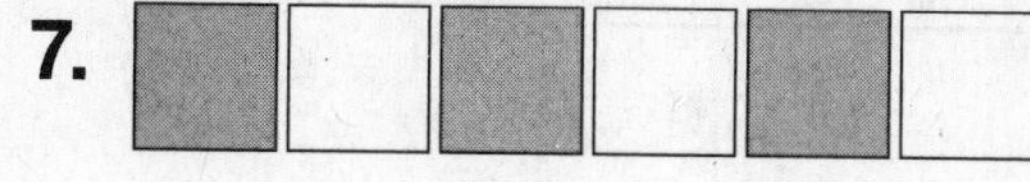

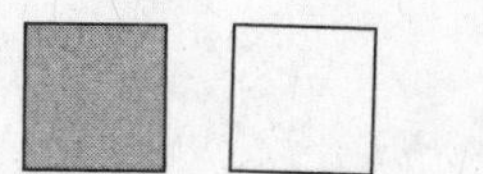

8. 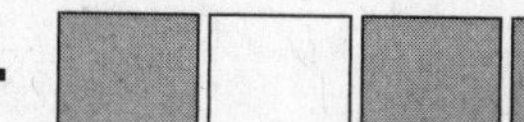 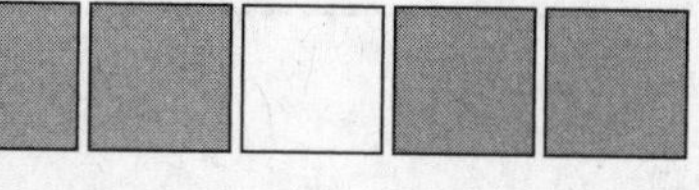

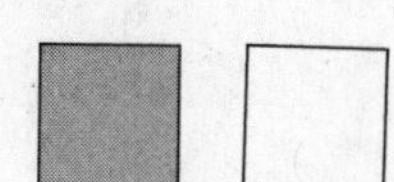

Name ____________________ Date __________

Hands On: One More, One Less

CA Standards
KEY NS 2.3, KEY NS 1.1

Solve.

1. Raúl has 1 more than 32 crayons. How many crayons does he have?

   __________ crayons

2. Sari has 1 less than 19 grapes. How many grapes does she have?

   __________ grapes

3. Audrey has 1 more than 27 markers. Millie has 1 less than 30 markers. Who has more markers?

   Audrey Millie

4. Gavin has 1 more than 35 marbles. Marceal has 1 less than 34 marbles. Who has more marbles?

   Gavin Marceal

5. Colin has 1 more than 19 toy cars. Sean has 1 less than 22 toy cars. Martin has 1 more toy car than Sean. Who has the most toy cars?

   ____

6. Tamika has 1 more than 44 shells. Holly has 1 less than 44 shells. Riley has 1 more shell than Holly. Who has the most shells?

   ____

Name ______________________ Date ___________

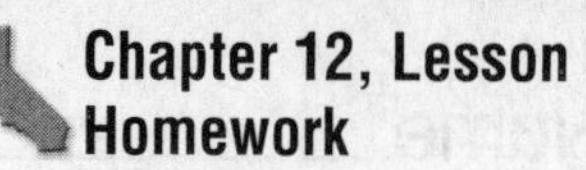

Ten More, Ten Less

CA Standards
KEY NS 2.3, KEY NS 1.1

To find 10 more,
add 1 to the tens place.

Solution: 51, 61

To find 10 less,
subtract 1 from the tens place.

Solution: 68, 78

Write the number that is 10 more.

1. 72, ____
2. 61, ____
3. 53, ____
4. 87, ____
5. 52, ____
6. 67, ____

Write the number that is 10 less.

7. ____, 87
8. ____, 79
9. ____, 64
10. ____, 92
11. ____, 66
12. ____, 72

Spiral Review (Chapter 11, Lesson 3) **SDAP 2.0, KEY SDAP 2.1**

Find the pattern. Circle the shape that comes next.

13. △○○△○○△

14. □□□□□□□□□

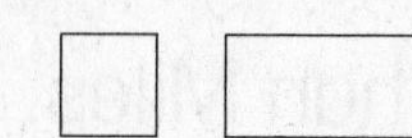

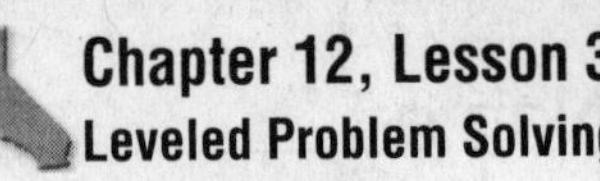

Ten More, Ten Less

CA Standards
KEY NS 2.3, KEY NS 1.1

Solve.

1. How many crayons does Mona have?

________ crayons

2. How many shells does Caleb have?

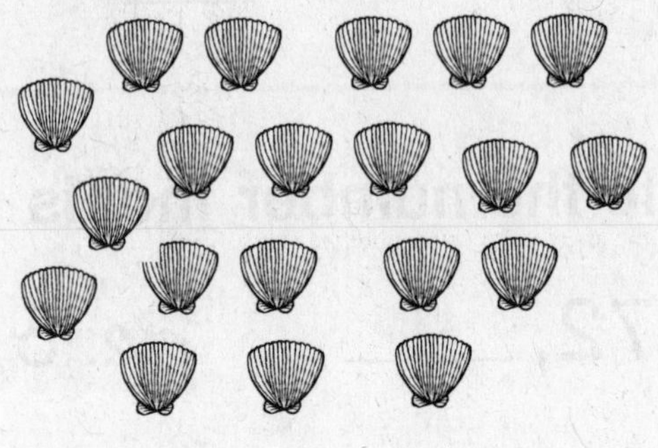

________ shells

3. Ella has 62 pencils. Pedro has 10 more pencils than Ella. How many pencils does Pedro have?

________ pencils

4. Sami has 76 rocks. Vinny has 10 less rocks than Sami. How many rocks does Vinny have?

________ rocks

5. Miles has 25 stamps. Sally has 10 less stamps than Miles. How many stamps do they have in all?

________ stamps

6. Sue Jong has 24 balls. Mike has 10 more balls than Sue Jong. How many balls do they have in all?

________ balls

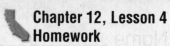

Read and Write Numbers to 100

CA Standards
KEY NS 1.1, NS 1.4

You can show a number as tens and ones.

Tens	Ones
4	3

Solution: 4 tens and 3 ones

40 + 3 = 43

Write each number.

1.

Tens	Ones
8	2

_____ tens and _____ ones

_____ + _____ = _____

2.

Tens	Ones
5	9

_____ tens and _____ ones

_____ + _____ = _____

3.

Tens	Ones
7	5

_____ tens and _____ ones

_____ + _____ = _____

4.

Tens	Ones
9	9

_____ tens and _____ ones

_____ + _____ = _____

Spiral Review (Chapter 11, Lesson 4) **KEY** SDAP 2.1, SDAP 2.0

Look at each motion or sound pattern.
Act out the pattern. Circle what comes next.

5. 

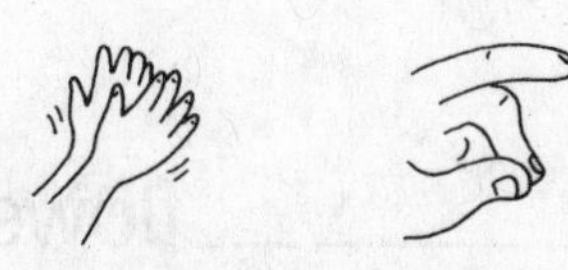

6. 

Read and Write Numbers to 100

CA Standards
KEY NS 1.1, NS 1.4

Solve.

1. Abby reads 2 books. Each book has 10 pages. How many pages does she read?

   10 pages 20 pages

2. Sal has 3 boxes. Each box holds 10 marbles. How many marbles does Sal have?

   30 marbles 70 marbles

3. Ricardo has 10 boxes. Each box holds 10 model cars. Ricardo buys 2 more model cars. How many model cars does Ricardo have in all?

   ____________ cars

4. Mattie packs 7 boxes for the clothing drive. There are 10 shirts in each box. Mattie adds 7 more shirts. How many shirts does Mattie pack in all?

   ____________ shirts

5. Mr. Wu loads 5 boxes of pears and 3 boxes of apples into his van. Each box holds 10 pieces of fruit. He has 6 more pears. How many pieces of fruit does Mr. Wu load in all?

   ____________ pieces of fruit

6. Ms. Ritz arranges 3 vases of roses and 3 vases of tulips. There are 10 flowers in each vase. She adds 8 more roses. How many flowers does Ms. Ritz arrange in all?

   ____________ flowers

Name ______________________ Date __________

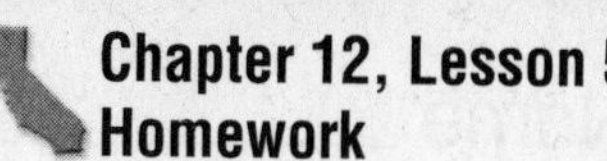

Problem Solving: Reasonable Answers

CA Standards
NS 3.1, MR 2.0

About how many books will fit in Ellie's backpack?

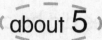

about 50 (about 5)

5 books is the answer. It makes more sense.

Estimate. Circle the answer that makes sense.

1. About how many hours did Linda spend at the library today?

   about 2 hours
   about 20 hours

2. About how many muffins can Sheila eat at one meal?

   about 16 muffins
   about 2 muffins

3. About how many coins can Nicki hold in one hand?

   about 100 coins
   about 10 coins

4. About how many kittens can fit in a small basket?

   about 4 kittens
   about 24 kittens

Spiral Review (Chapter 11, Lesson 5) **KEY SDAP 2.1, SDAP 2.0, MR 3.0**

Find the pattern. Draw shapes to show it in another way.

5. 

6.

Problem Solving: Reasonable Answers

CA Standards
NS 3.1, MR 2.0

Estimate. Circle the answer that makes sense.

1. Ted holds some pencils in his hand. About how many pencils can he hold?

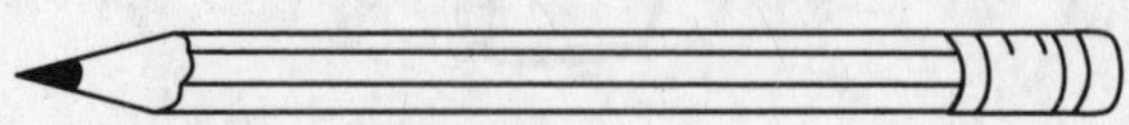

about 10 about 55

2. Charlie counted the pages in a book. About how many pages did he count?

about 2 about 24

3. What is the greatest number of cubes Sue Jung can put in the bag?

about 3 about 30

4. Rob gives each of his classmates a book. About how many books does Rob give out?

about 20 about 60

5. Juan has a jar filled with 75 coins. He has another jar that is more than twice as big. About how many coins can Juan fit in the bigger jar?

about 90 about 200

6. The class is going on a trip. The children will ride in buses. About how many children can fit in 3 buses?

about 30 about 90

Name ____________________ Date __________

Count by Tens

CA Standards
KEY NS 2.4, KEY NS 2.3

What number comes next if you skip count by 10s?

Find 60 on the chart.
Skip count by 10s.

60, 70, 80

1	2	3	4	5	6	7	8	9	10
11	12	13	14	15	16	17	18	19	20
21	22	23	24	25	26	27	28	29	30
31	32	33	34	35	36	37	38	39	40
41	42	43	44	45	46	47	48	49	50
51	52	53	54	55	56	57	58	59	60
61	62	63	64	65	66	67	68	69	70
71	72	73	74	75	76	77	78	79	80
81	82	83	84	85	86	87	88	89	90
91	92	93	94	95	96	97	98	99	100

Solution: The number 80 comes next.

Write the missing numbers. Skip count by 10s.

1. 10, ____, 30, ____
2. 60, ____, 80, ____
3. 40, ____, ____, 70
4. 70, ____, 90, ____
5. 20, 30, ____, ____
6. 30, ____, ____, 60
7. 70, ____, ____, 100
8. 50, ____, 70, ____

Spiral Review (Chapter 12, Lesson 3) **KEY NS 2.3, KEY NS 1.1**

9. Write the number that is 10 more.

   68, ____

10. Write the number that is 10 less

   72, ____

Name ______________________ Date ____________

Count by Tens

CA Standards
KEY NS 2.4, KEY NS 2.3

Read the problem.
Then count by 10s to solve.

1. There are 10 chairs in a row. How many chairs are in 2 rows?

______ chairs

2. Chase has 4 boxes of crayons. Each box has 10 crayons. How many crayons does Chase have?

______ crayons

3. Tracy puts 10 flowers in each vase. She fills 5 vases. How many flowers did she use?

______ flowers

4. Harris has 7 sheets of stickers. Each sheet has 10 stickers How many stickers does Harris have?

______ stickers

5. Eric puts photos in an album. He puts 10 photos on each page. He fills 12 pages. How many photos did he use?

______ photos

6. Jan is counting markers. Each box has 10 markers. There are 4 boxes of red markers. There are 2 more boxes of blue markers than red markers. How many markers are there in all?

______ markers

Name ______________________ Date __________

Number Patterns

CA Standards
KEY NS 2.3

You can use the words *more than* and *less than* to tell about number patterns.

25 is 1 more than 24.

24 is 10 less than 34.

1	2	3	4	5	6	7	8	9	10
11	12	13	14	15	16	17	18	19	20
21	22	23	24	25	26	27	28	29	30
31	32	33	34	35	36	37	38	39	40
41	42	43	44	45	46	47	48	49	50
51	52	53	54	55	56	57	58	59	60
61	62	63	64	65	66	67	68	69	70
71	72	73	74	75	76	77	78	79	80
81	82	83	84	85	86	87	88	89	90
91	92	93	94	95	96	97	98	99	100

1. Write the number that is 1 more.

   28, ______

2. Write the number that is 1 less.

   ______, 19

3. Write the number that is 10 more.

   15, ______

4. Write the number that is 10 less.

   ______, 22

Spiral Review (Chapter 12, Lesson 4) **NS 3.1, MR 2.0**

Write each number.

Tens	Ones
7	2

Tens	Ones
6	5

5. ______ tens and ______ ones

   ______ + ______ = ______

6. ______ tens and ______ ones

   ______ + ______ = ______

Number Patterns

CA Standard
KEY NS 2.3

Compare.

1. Ann picks 17 apples. Chad picks 1 more apple than Ann. How many apples does Chad pick?

   ________________ apples

2. Dan counts 20 cubes. Kim counts 10 more cubes. How many cubes does Kim count?

   ____________ cubes

3. Zach counts 20 pencils. Mark counts a number of pencils that is 1 less than 20. How many pencils does Mark count?

   ________________ pencils

4. 31 children want to see the lions. 10 more children want to see the elephants. How many children want to see the elephants?

   ________________ children

5. There are 32 children on the green bus and 22 children on the red bus. How many more children are on the green bus?

   ______ more children

6. The number on Hoon's house is 47. The number on Dan's house is 10 more. The number on Liz's house is 1 more than the number on Dan's house. What is the number on Dan's house? What is the number on Liz's house?

   ____

Name ______________________ Date __________

Problem Solving: Find a Pattern

CA Standards
KEY NS 2.4, MR 2.0

Dino does 2 pages of homework on Monday.
He does 2 more pages each day through Friday.
How many pages of homework does Dino do in one week?

Find the pattern. Start with 2 on Monday.
Skip count by 2s until you reach Friday.

Monday	Tuesday	Wednesday	Thursday	Friday
2	4	6	8	10

Solution: Dino does 10 pages of homework in one week.

1. Jess sends 10 e-mails each day.
   How many e-mails does she send in 5 days?

Day 1	Day 2	Day 3	Day 4	Day 5

______ e-mails

Spiral Review (Chapter 12, Lesson 5) **NS 3.1, MR 2.0**

Estimate. Circle the answer that makes more sense.

2. About how many hours did Tommy spend on his homework last night?

   about 2 hours
   about 20 hours

3. About how many pancakes can Sally eat for breakfast?

   about 30 pancakes
   about 3 pancakes

Name ____________________ Date __________

Problem Solving: Find a Pattern

CA Standards
KEY NS 2.4, MR 2.0

Read the problem.
Then find the pattern to solve.

1. One bird has 2 wings.
How many wings do 4 birds have?

1 bird	2 birds	3 birds	4 birds

_____ wings

2. One crab has 10 legs.
How many legs do 3 crabs have?

1 crab	2 crabs	3 crabs

_____ legs

3. Mario gets 2 dinosaur models each week.
How many dinosaur models does he have after 5 weeks?

Week 1	Week 2	Week 3	Week 4	Week 5

_____ dinosaur models

4. Kim puts 5 books in each box.
How many books does she need to fill 4 boxes?

1 box	2 boxes	3 boxes	4 boxes

_____ books

5. Pencils cost 10¢.
Kyle wants to buy 8 pencils.
How much money does he need?

_____ ¢

6. Bob runs 2 miles each day.
How many miles does he run in two weeks?

_____ miles

Name ____________________ Date __________

Hands On: Compare Numbers

CA Standards
KEY NS 1.2, MR 1.2

You can compare numbers using greater than and less than.

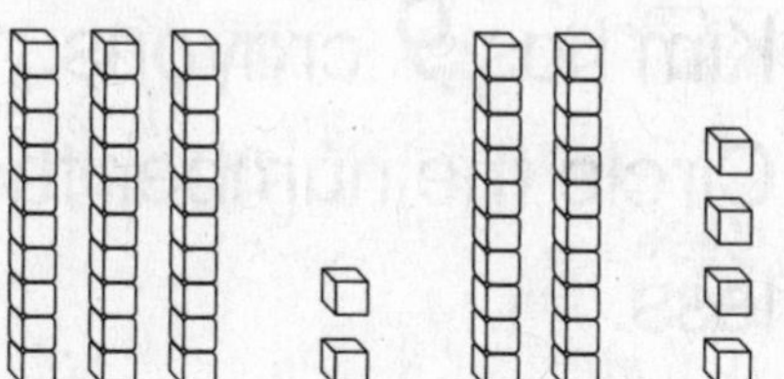

32 is **greater than** 24.

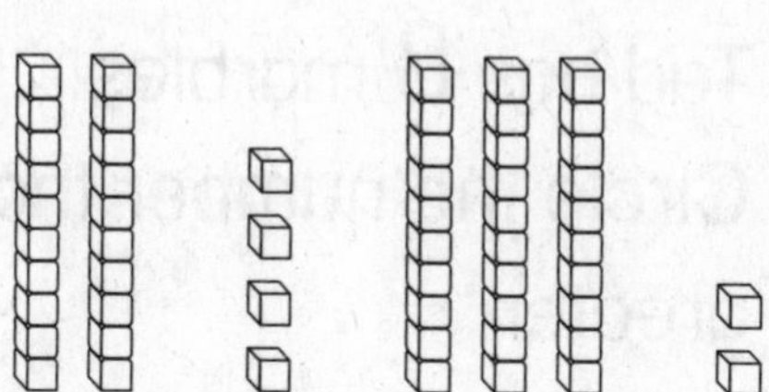

24 is **less than** 32.

Model the numbers. Draw quick pictures. Circle the number that is greater.

1. 26 37

2. 88 78

Circle the number that is less.

3. 74 47

4. 99 66

Spiral Review (Chapter 13, Lesson 1) **KEY** NS 2.4

Write the missing numbers. Skip count by 2s.

5. 20, _____, 24, _____

6. 74, _____, _____, 80

Name ____________________ Date __________

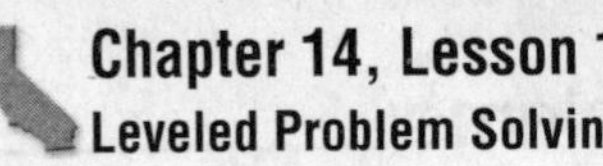

Hands On: Compare Numbers

CA Standards
KEY NS 1.2, MR 1.2

Solve.

1. Bryce has 19 marbles.
Tad has 8 marbles.
Circle the number that is greater.

19 8

2. MaryBeth has 16 crayons.
Kim has 9 crayons.
Circle the number that is less.

16 9

3. Sally's class reads 57 books this year.
Raúl's class reads 62 books this year.
Circle *is greater than* or *is less than.*

57 is greater than / is less than 62

4. Paul scores 89 on the math test.
Reed scores 92 on the math test.
Circle *is greater than* or *is less than.*

89 is greater than / is less than 92

5. Mike scores 28 points in the game.
Leon scores 32 points.
Write a sentence using the words **is less than.**

____

6. Kyra collects 86 cans for the food drive.
Ida collects 81 cans.
Write a sentence using the words **is greater than.**

____

Name ____________________ Date __________

Use Symbols to Compare Numbers

CA Standards
KEY NS 1.1, KEY NS 1.2

> means is greater than.

20 > 10

< means is less than.

5 < 10

= means is equal to.

5 = 5

Compare the numbers. Circle >, <, or =.

1. 

2. 

>
<
=

3. 

4. 

>
<
=

Spiral Review (Chapter 13, Lesson 2) **KEY** NS 2.4

Write the missing numbers. Skip count by 5s.

5. 20, ______, 30, ______

6. 75, ______, ______, 90

Use Symbols to Compare Numbers

CA Standards
KEY NS 1.2, KEY NS 1.1

Solve. Write >, <, or =.

1. Diane's team scores 12 runs in the game. Debbie's team scores 14 runs.

12 ◯ 14

2. Chen's house is 15 blocks from school. Matt's house is 9 blocks from school.

15 ◯ 9

3. Pete has 42 model cars. His brother has 40 model cars.

42 ◯ 40

4. Candy has 35 stuffed animals. Her sister has 35 stuffed animals.

35 ◯ 35

5. Enrique rides 26 blocks on his bike. Kevin rides 19 blocks on his bike.

__◯__ or __◯__

6. Marla has 37 stamps in her collection. Tina has 43 stamps in her collection.

__◯__ or __◯__

Use Estimation to Compare Numbers

CA Standards
NS 3.1, KEY NS 1.2

When you do not need to know the exact number, you can estimate.

Circle one group of ten. Estimate about how many are in each group. Count to check.

1. 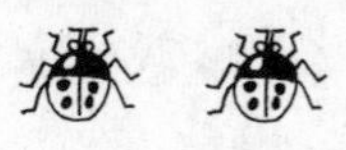

Estimate ______

Count ______

2. Estimate ______

Count ______

3. Estimate ______

Count ______

Spiral Review (Chapter 13, Lesson 3) **KEY** NS 2.4

Write the missing numbers. Skip count by 10s.

4. 20, ______, ______, 50

5. 60, ______, 80, ______

Use Estimation to Compare Numbers

CA Standards
NS 3.1, KEY NS 1.2

Solve. Circle a group of 10 to help you.

1. The children see turtles on their class trip. About how many turtles do they see?

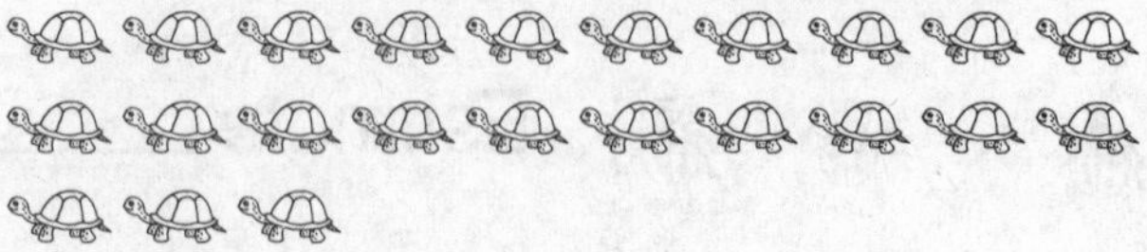

20 30

2. The children see ants marching on the ground. About how many ants do they see?

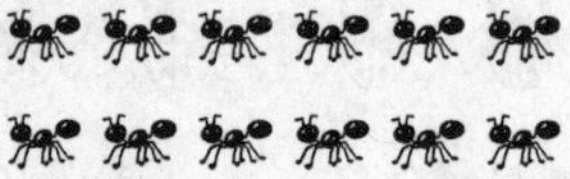

50 10

3. The children also see birds. About how many birds do they see?

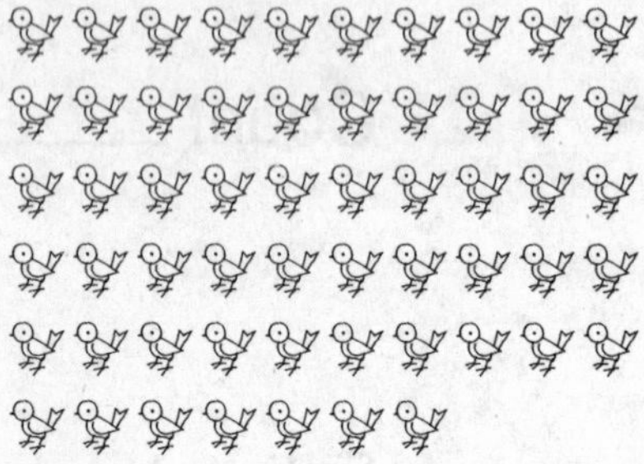

50 60

4. Next, the children see monkeys. About how many monkeys do they see?

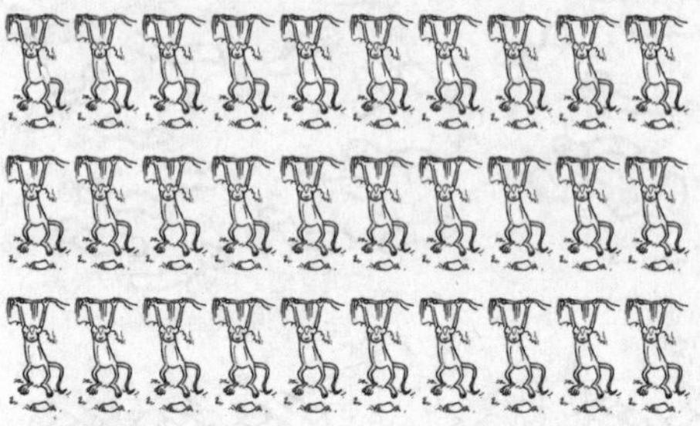

30 20

5. Finally, the children see flowers. About how many flowers do they see?

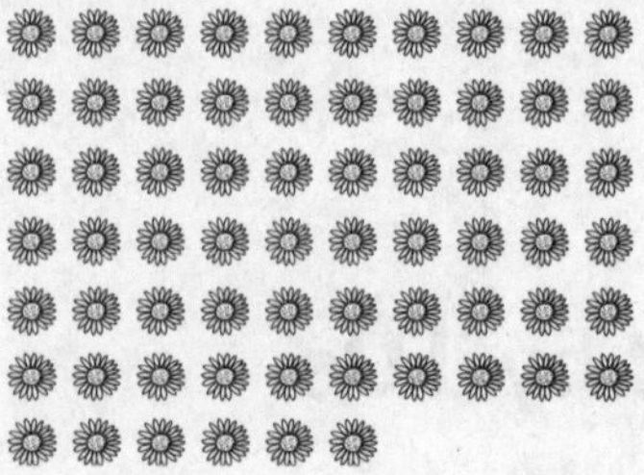

__________ flowers

6. It is time for the children to get on the bus. About how many children get on the bus?

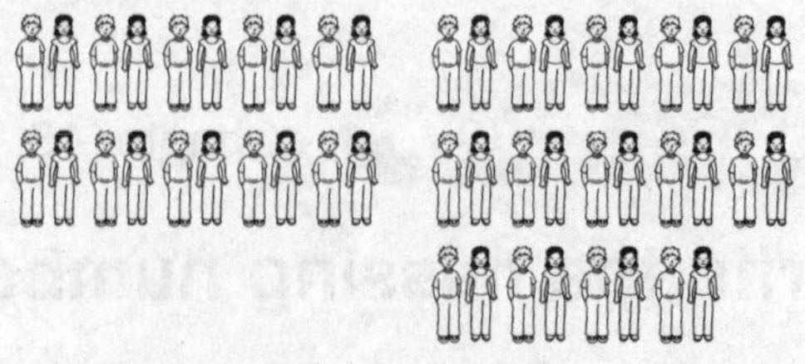

__________ children

Order Numbers

CA Standards
KEY NS 1.2, KEY NS 1.1

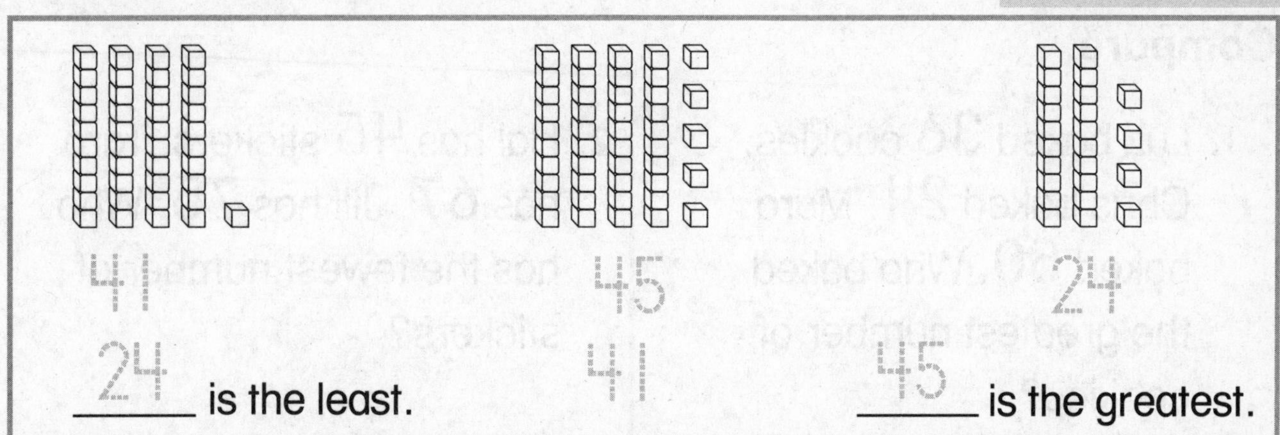

24 is the least. 41 45 is the greatest.

Look at the models.
Write the numbers from least to greatest.

1. 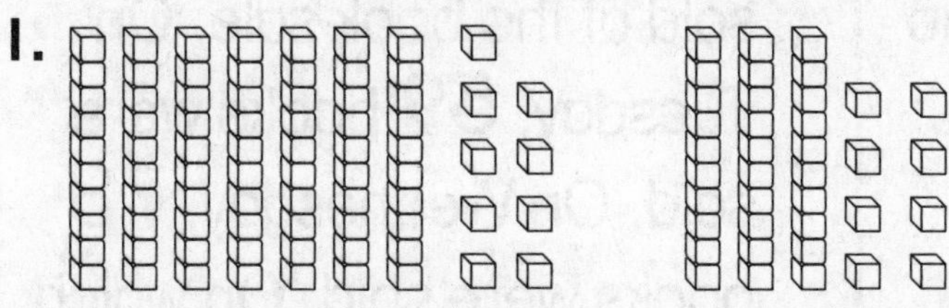 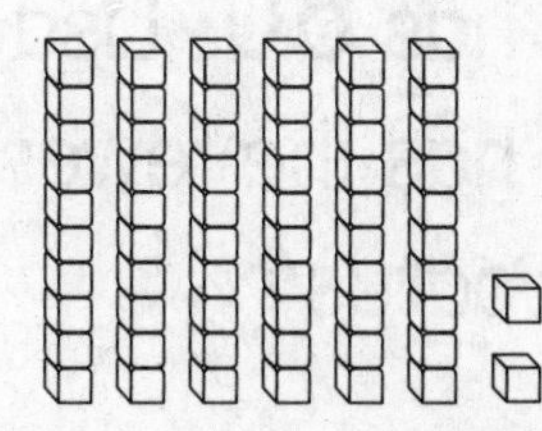

_____ least _____ _____ greatest

2. 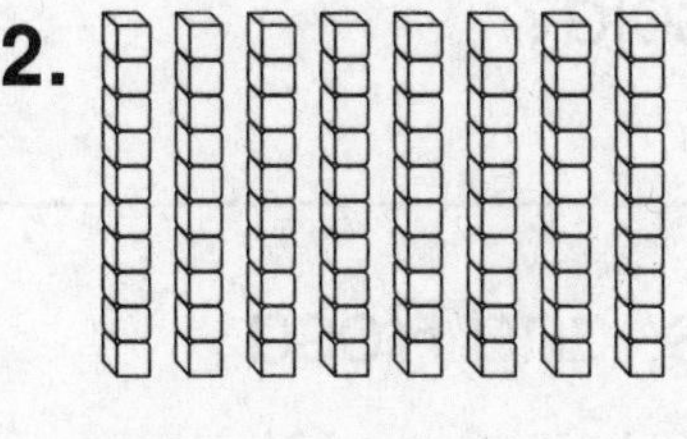 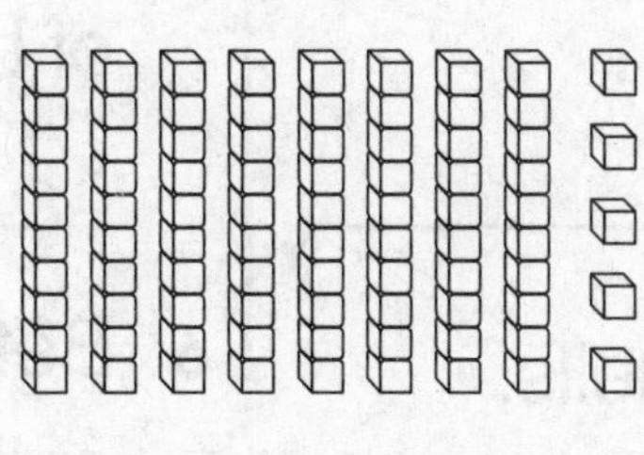 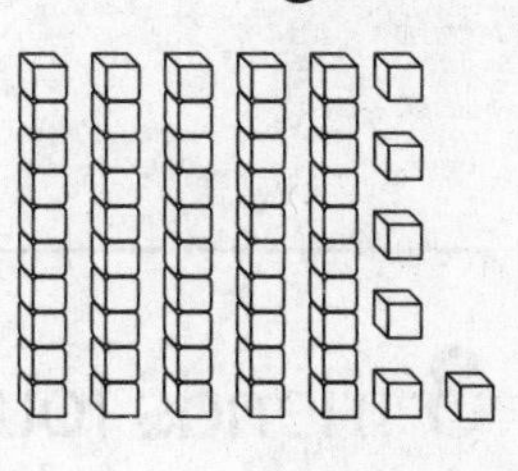

_____ least _____ _____ greatest

Spiral Review (Chapter 13, Lesson 4) **KEY NS 2.3**

Write the number.

3. Write the number that is 1 more.

67, _____

4. Write the number that is 1 less.

_____, 52

Order Numbers

CA Standards
KEY NS 1.2, KEY NS 1.1

Compare.

1. Luz baked 36 cookies. Chris baked 24. Mara baked 50. Who baked the greatest number of cookies?

____

2. Hal has 45 stickers. Taro has 67. Jill has 75. Who has the fewest number of stickers?

____

3. Jake has 72 cards. Tom has 60. Lisa has 84. Who has the fewest number of cards?

____

4. On Monday, 82 books were sold at the book sale. On Tuesday, 59 books were sold. On Wednesday, 78 books were sold. On which day was the greatest number of books sold?

____

5. 3 friends found shells. Todd found 54. Matt found 72. Jun found the fewest shells. How many shells could Jun have found?

____

6. Beth, Otis, and Rosa collected stamps. Otis collected the greatest number of stamps. Beth collected 70. Rosa collected 85. How many stamps could Otis have collected?

____

Problem Solving: Create and Solve

CA Standards
KEY NS 1.2, NS 3.1

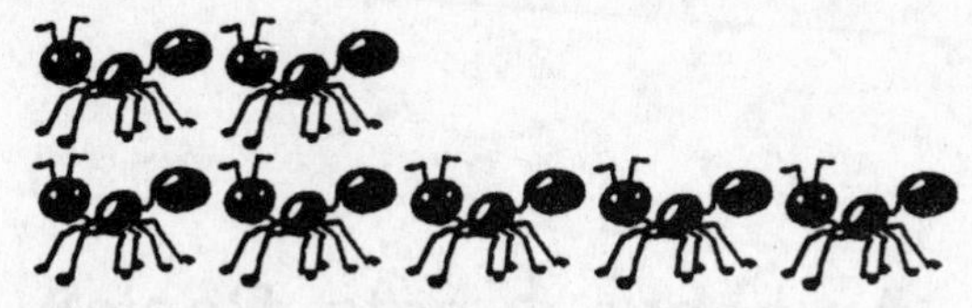

There are 7 ants. There are 15 bees.

7 < 15. There are fewer ants than bees.

Compare the groups.
Write the number sentence to compare.

1.

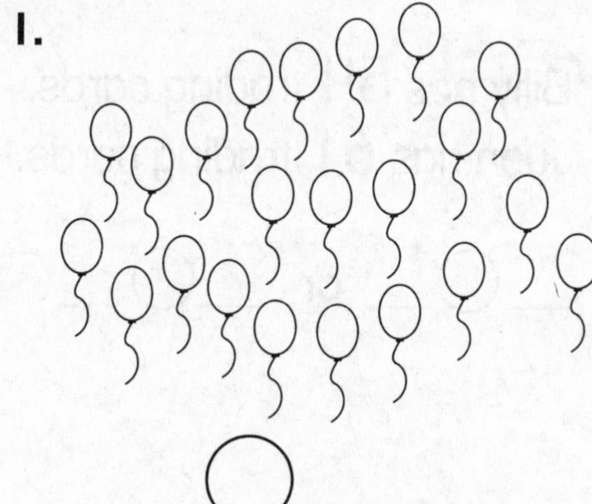

_____ ◯ _____

There is a greater number of  .

Spiral Review (Chapter 13, Lesson 5) **KEY** NS 2.4, NS 2.0

Find the pattern. Solve.

2. Jay reads 2 books each day. How many books does he read in 5 days?

_____ books

3. Meredith writes 2 letters each day. How many letters does she write in 6 days?

_____ letters

Problem Solving: Create and Solve

CA Standards
KEY NS 1.2, NS 3.1

Solve.

1. Maria has 4 baseballs. Tommy has 3 baseballs. Who has **more** baseballs?

   Maria Tommy

2. Andy has 6 hats. Becky has 8 hats. Who has **fewer** hats?

   Andy Becky

3. Emma has 32 stickers. Vicki has 23 stickers.

   ___ ○ ___ or ___ ○ ___

4. Billy has 54 trading cards. Juan has 61 trading cards.

   ___ ○ ___ or ___ ○ ___

5. Zack has 8 big marbles and 5 small marbles. Terri has 3 big marbles and 7 small marbles. Write a number sentence to show who has the greater number of marbles.

   ___ ○ ___ or ___ ○ ___

6. Sami has 6 red crayons and 5 blue crayons. Chu has 8 red crayons and 4 blue crayons. Write a number sentence to show who has the greater number of crayons.

   ___ ○ ___ or ___ ○ ___

Name ______________________ Date __________

Hands On: Count On to Add

CA Standards
KEY NS 2.5, MR 1.2

You can count on to add.
Start with the greater number. Write the sum.

8 + 3 = 11

Count on to add. Start with the greater number. Write each sum.

1. 3 + 4 = ____
2. 5 + 1 = ____
3. 8 + 2 = ____

4.	5.	6.	7.	8.
1	9	2	1	2
+ 6	+ 2	+ 8	+ 8	+ 7

Spiral Review (Chapter 14, Lesson 1) **KEY NS 1.2**

9. Circle the number that is greater.

28 36

10. Circle the number that is less.

19 27

Hands On: Count On to Add

CA Standards KEY NS 2.5, MR 1.2

Read to solve.

Count on to add.

1. There are 6 birds in the nest. Then 2 birds join them. How many birds are there in all?

6 + 2 = _____ birds

2. There are 4 kittens in the basket. Then 3 more kittens jump in the basket. How many kittens are there now?

4 + 3 = _____ kittens

3. There are 8 cows in the barn. Then 2 more cows join them. How many cows are in the barn now?

_____ cows

4. Callie finds 9 coins. Then she finds 3 more coins. How many coins does Callie have now?

_____ coins

5. Colin has 8 blue fish, 5 red fish, and 3 goldfish in the tank. He adds 3 more blue fish to the tank. How many blue fish are in the tank now?

_____ blue fish

6. Addy has 8 green balloons, 7 yellow balloons, and 6 red balloons. She finds 3 more yellow balloons. How many yellow balloons does Addy have now?

_____ yellow balloons

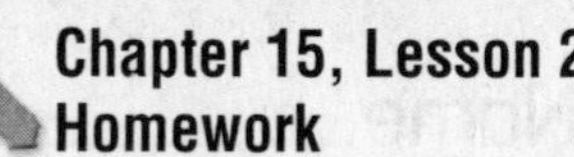

Sums to 11

CA Standards
KEY NS 2.1, MR 3.0

Knowing one addition fact can help you find another fact.

$5 + 3 = 8$ You know that $5 + 3$

$3 + 5 = 8$ has the same sum as $3 + 5$.

Write each sum.

1.	$\begin{array}{r} 8 \\ +3 \\ \hline \end{array}$	$\begin{array}{r} 3 \\ +8 \\ \hline \end{array}$	**2.**	$\begin{array}{r} 6 \\ +4 \\ \hline \end{array}$	$\begin{array}{r} 4 \\ +6 \\ \hline \end{array}$	**3.**	$\begin{array}{r} 9 \\ +2 \\ \hline \end{array}$ $\begin{array}{r} 2 \\ +9 \\ \hline \end{array}$
4.	$\begin{array}{r} 5 \\ +2 \\ \hline \end{array}$	$\begin{array}{r} 2 \\ +5 \\ \hline \end{array}$	**5.**	$\begin{array}{r} 7 \\ +2 \\ \hline \end{array}$	$\begin{array}{r} 2 \\ +7 \\ \hline \end{array}$	**6.**	$\begin{array}{r} 6 \\ +2 \\ \hline \end{array}$ $\begin{array}{r} 2 \\ +6 \\ \hline \end{array}$

7. $11 + 0 =$ ____ **8.** $3 + 3 =$ ____ **9.** $6 + 5 =$ ____

Spiral Review (Chapter 14, Lesson 2) **KEY NS 1 2**

Compare the numbers. Circle >, <, or =.

10.

11.

Name ______________________ Date __________

Sums to 11

CA Standards
KEY NS 2.1, MR 3.0

Solve.

1. There are 3 frogs in the pond.
Then 2 more frogs jump in the pond.
How many frogs are there in all?

$3 + 2 =$ _____ frogs

2. Karen has 4 goldfish.
Marta gives her 3 more goldfish.
How many goldfish does Karen have now?

$4 + 3 =$ _____ goldfish

3. Pablo has 6 trading cards.
Caleb gives him 4 more trading cards.
How many trading cards does Pablo have in all?

_____ trading cards

4. There are 6 birds in the nest.
Then 5 more birds fly to the nest.
How many birds are in the nest now?

_____ birds

5. Jada has 8 blue stickers and 7 red stickers.
She finds 4 more red stickers.
How many red stickers does she have now?

_____ red stickers

6. Logan has 3 green markers and 6 yellow markers.
He gets 8 more green markers. How many green markers does Logan have in all?

_____ green markers

Name ______________________ Date __________

Sums to 12

CA Standards
KEY NS 2.1, MR 3.0

Knowing one addition fact can help you find another fact.

$6 + 3 = \underline{9}$ You know that $6 + 3$

$3 + 6 = \underline{9}$ has the same sum as $3 + 6$.

Write each sum.

1. $\begin{array}{r} 9 \\ +3 \\ \hline \end{array}$ $\begin{array}{r} 3 \\ +9 \\ \hline \end{array}$

2. $\begin{array}{r} 7 \\ +4 \\ \hline \end{array}$ $\begin{array}{r} 4 \\ +7 \\ \hline \end{array}$

3. $\begin{array}{r} 8 \\ +1 \\ \hline \end{array}$ $\begin{array}{r} 1 \\ +8 \\ \hline \end{array}$

4. $\begin{array}{r} 9 \\ +2 \\ \hline \end{array}$ $\begin{array}{r} 2 \\ +9 \\ \hline \end{array}$

5. $\begin{array}{r} 7 \\ +3 \\ \hline \end{array}$ $\begin{array}{r} 3 \\ +7 \\ \hline \end{array}$

6. $\begin{array}{r} 7 \\ +2 \\ \hline \end{array}$ $\begin{array}{r} 2 \\ +7 \\ \hline \end{array}$

7. $6 + 6 =$ ____

8. $4 + 4 =$ ____

9. $5 + 5 =$ ____

Spiral Review (Chapter 14, Lesson 3) **NS 3.1**

Circle one group of ten.
Estimate about how many are in each group.
Count to check.

10. 

Estimate ____

Count ____

11. 

Estimate ____

Count ____

Name ____________________ Date __________

Sums to 12

CA Standards
KEY NS 2.1, MR 3.0

Solve.

1. There are 5 bees in a hive. Then 4 more bees fly to the hive. How many bees are there in all?

   $5 + 4 =$ _____ bees

2. There 4 apples in the bowl. Mom puts 3 more apples in the bowl. How many apples are in the bowl now?

   $4 + 3 =$ _____ apples

3. Jamal counts 6 birds in the tree. Larry counts 4 birds. How many birds do they count in all?

   _____ birds

4. Anita sees 5 ducks swimming in the pond. Leah sees 3 ducks on the grass. How many ducks do they see in all?

   _____ ducks

5. Jerry gets 8 red balloons and 7 green balloons at the fair. Sara gives him 4 more red balloons. How many red balloons does Jerry have in all?

   _____ red balloons

6. Jungi collects 6 blue stickers and 7 green stickers. He finds 5 more green stickers. How many green stickers does he have in all?

   _____ green stickers

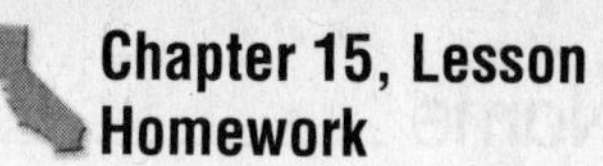

Add Three Numbers

CA Standard
NS 2.7

You can add three numbers in any order.

(5) (3) + 4	8 + 4 = 12	5 (3) + (4)	5 + 7 = 12	(5) 3 + (4)	9 + 3 = 12

Write the sum. Circle the 2 numbers you added first.

1. 3 + 6 + 2
2. 6 + 1 + 3
3. 1 + 7 + 1
4. 8 + 2 + 1
5. 1 + 6 + 2
6. 5 + 2 + 4
7. 3 + 2 + 7
8. 4 + 6 + 1
9. 5 + 3 + 3
10. 3 + 5 + 1
11. 3 + 1 + 2
12. 3 + 4 + 1

Spiral Review (Chapter 14, Lesson 2) **KEY** NS 1.2, NS 1.1

Write the numbers. Compare.
Circle >, <, or =.

13.

Tens	Ones
2	4

< > =

Tens	Ones
3	2

______ ______

14.

Tens	Ones
4	1

< > =

Tens	Ones
4	1

______ ______

Add Three Numbers

CA Standard
NS 2.7

Solve.

1. Kerri has 2 big marbles. She has 3 small marbles. Then she finds 2 more big marbles. How many marbles does she have in all?

   2 + 3 + 2 = ____ marbles

2. Mike has 6 apples. He finds 3 more apples. Then Joe gives him 1 more apple. How many apples does he have in all?

   6 + 3 + 1 = ____ apples

3. Anton walks 4 blocks to the store. He walks 4 blocks to Craig's house. He walks 2 blocks home. How many blocks does Anton walk?

   ____ + ____ + ____

   = ____ blocks

4. Mary finds 7 pennies in her purse. She finds 3 pennies in her pocket. She finds 1 penny on the sidewalk. How many pennies does Mary find?

   ____ + ____ + ____

   = ____ pennies

5. John plants 6 corn plants. He plants 3 tomato plants. He plants 4 bean plants. How many plants does he plant in all?

   ____ plants

6. Flor has 6 grapes. She has 3 oranges. She has 5 apples. How many pieces of fruit does Flor have?

   ____ pieces of fruit

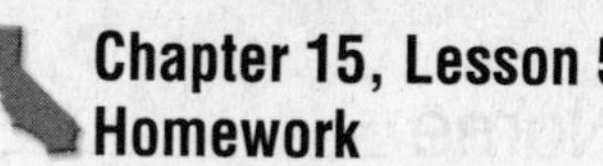

Missing Addends

CA Standards
KEY NS 2.1, NS 2.0

Find the missing addend.

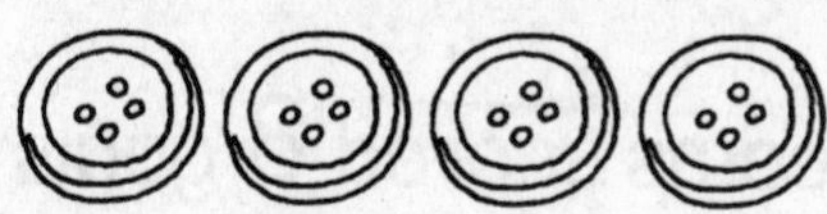

4 + 3 = 7

Use small objects. Write the missing addend.

1.  

6 + ____ = 12

2. 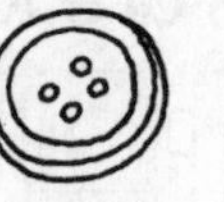   

7 + ____ = 9

3. ____ + 5 = 12

4. 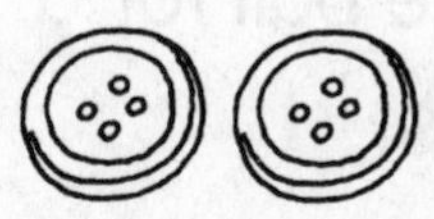  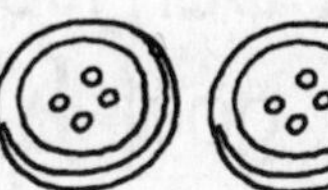

____ + 5 = 11

Spiral Review (Chapter 14, Lesson 5) **KEY NS 1.2**

Write the number sentence to compare.

5.   

____ ◯ ____

There is a greater number of  .

Missing Addends

CA Standards
KEY NS 2.1, NS 2.0

Solve.
Use ▢ if you wish.

1. There are 12 players on the soccer team.
8 players are at practice on time.
How many players are late?

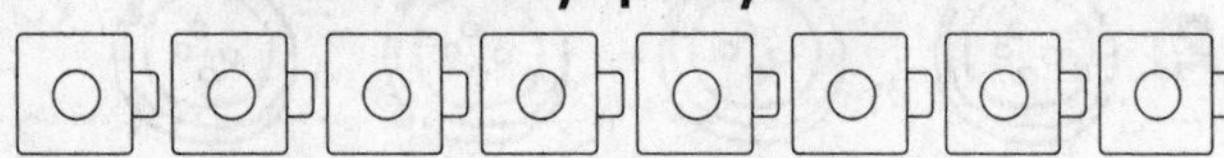

8 + ____ = 12

____ players

2. Two teams scored 8 goals in all.
One team scored 5 goals.
How many goals did the other team score?

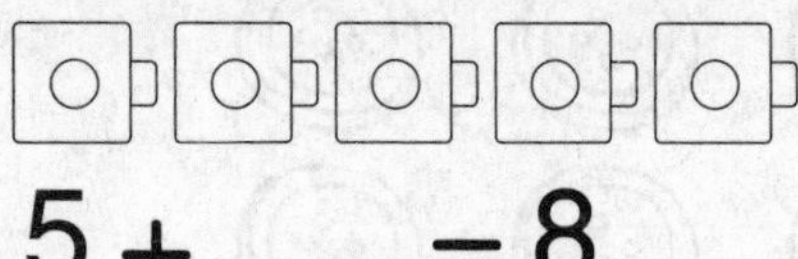

5 + ____ = 8

____ goals

3. Dan kicked the ball for a goal 11 times.
He missed 6 times.
How many goals did he make?

____ + 6 = 11

____ goals

4. 12 players had juice or water at halftime.
3 players had juice.
How many players had water?

____ + 3 = 12

____ players

5. There are 12 soccer balls.
7 are black and white.
The rest are yellow and white. How many soccer balls are yellow and white?

____ soccer balls

6. There are 18 people watching the soccer game.
9 people are wearing hats.
How many people are not wearing hats?

____ people

Name ______________________ Date __________

Problem Solving: Write a Number Sentence

CA Standards
AF 1.1, MR 2.2

You can make a table to solve problems.
Complete the table and solve.

1.

Kind of Sandwich	Number
Cheese	
Peanut butter	
Turkey	

2. How many turkey sandwiches are there?

_____ turkey sandwiches

3. How many peanut butter sandwiches and cheese sandwiches are there?

_____ in all

4. How many more cheese sandwiches than turkey are there?

_____ more

5. Jerry eats 2 peanut butter sandwiches for lunch. How many peanut butter sandwiches are there now?

_____ peanut butter sandwiches

Spiral Review (Chapter 14, Lesson 2) **KEY NS 1.2**

Compare the numbers. Write >, <, or =.

6. 63 ◯ 72

7. 70 ◯ 59

Name ________________ Date __________

Problem Solving: Write a Number Sentence

CA Standards
AF 1.1, MR 2.2

Solve.

1. There are 11 children. 7 children are boys. How many are girls?

   11 − 7 = ____ girls

2. Ben finds 8 big shells. He finds 3 small shells. How many shells does he have in all?

   8 + 3 = ____ shells

3. John has 11 math problems to do for homework. He finishes 6 problems before dinner. How many more problems does John have left?

   ____ ◯ ____ ◯ ____

   ____ problems

4. Cindy must read 12 pages in her book. She reads 5 pages. How many more pages does she have to read?

   ____ ◯ ____ ◯ ____

   ____ pages

5. Tamika solved 6 math problems. She has 9 new spelling words to learn. Tamika learns 8 of them. How many more words does she have to learn?

   ____ word

6. Hamid drew 5 pictures on Monday. On Tuesday he drew 6 pictures. He gave 4 pictures to his grandmother. How many pictures does Hamid have left?

   ____ pictures

Hands On: Count Back to Subtract

CA Standards
KEY NS 2.5, KEY NS 2.1

Count back on a number line to subtract.

Find 9 − 3.

Start from 9. Count back 3.

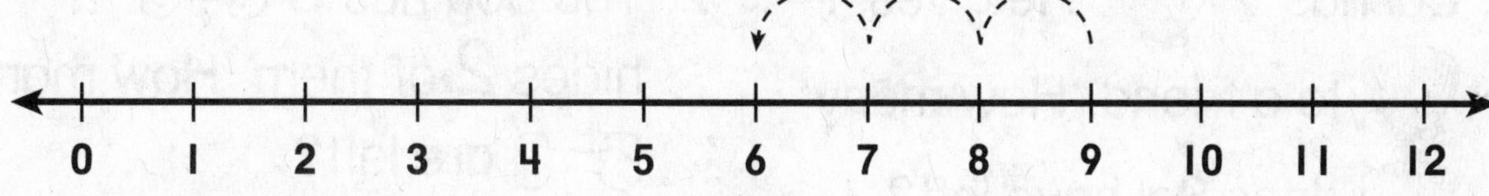

9 − 3 = 6

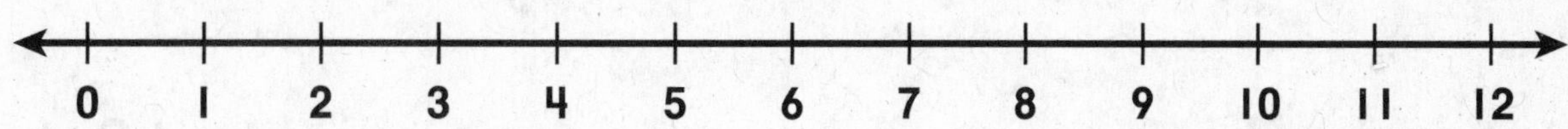

Count back to subtract.

1. 8 − 3 = ____
2. 10 − 2 = ____
3. 12 − 2 = ____
4. 11 − 1 = ____
5. 6 − 3 = ____
6. 11 − 3 = ____
7. 7 − 2 = ____
8. 10 − 1 = ____

Spiral Review (Chapter 15, Lesson 1) **KEY** NS 2.5, MR 1.2

Count on to add. Start with the greater number. Write each sum.

9. 3 + 5 = ____
10. 2 + 7 = ____

Name ______________________ Date __________

Hands On: Count Back to Subtract

CA Standards
KEY NS 2.5, KEY NS 2.1

Solve.

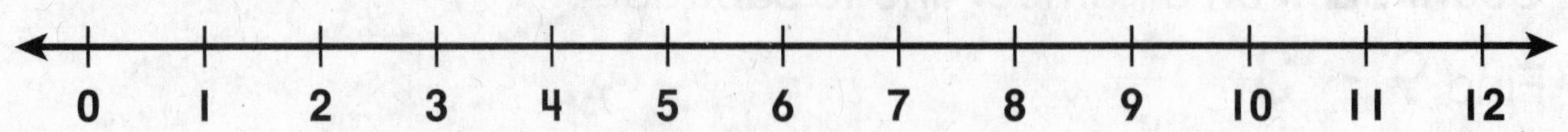

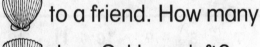

1. Sal has 9 shells. He gives 1 shell to a friend. How many shells does Sal have left?

2. The dog has 8 bones. It hides 2 of them. How many bones are left?

8 − 2 = ____

3. There are 11 clowns at the circus. 3 clowns ride bicycles. The others ride in a little car. How many clowns ride in the car?

____ clowns

4. The lion tamer has 10 lions and tigers. There are only 2 tigers. How many lions are there?

____ lions

5. There are 12 ducks and 11 frogs swimming in the pond. Then 3 frogs hop away. How many frogs are left?

___ ◯ ___ ◯ ___ frogs

6. There are 10 boys and 12 girls in the park. Then 3 boys go home. How many boys are left in the park?

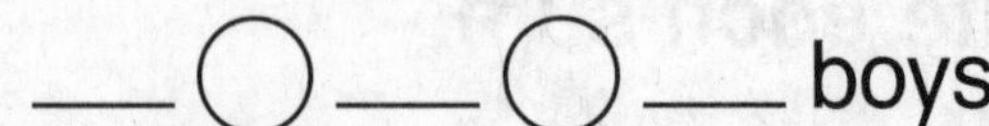

Name ______________________ Date __________

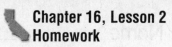

Subtract from 11 and Less

CA Standard
KEY NS 2.1, MR 3.0

Knowing one subtraction fact can help you find another fact.

$11 - 3 = \underline{8}$

$11 - 8 = \underline{3}$

Write each difference.

1. $\begin{array}{r} 11 \\ -2 \\ \hline \end{array}$ $\begin{array}{r} 11 \\ -9 \\ \hline \end{array}$

2. $\begin{array}{r} 8 \\ -3 \\ \hline \end{array}$ $\begin{array}{r} 8 \\ -5 \\ \hline \end{array}$

3. $\begin{array}{r} 9 \\ -2 \\ \hline \end{array}$ $\begin{array}{r} 9 \\ -7 \\ \hline \end{array}$

4. $\begin{array}{r} 10 \\ -6 \\ \hline \end{array}$ $\begin{array}{r} 10 \\ -4 \\ \hline \end{array}$

5. $\begin{array}{r} 11 \\ -4 \\ \hline \end{array}$ $\begin{array}{r} 11 \\ -7 \\ \hline \end{array}$

6. $\begin{array}{r} 10 \\ -2 \\ \hline \end{array}$ $\begin{array}{r} 10 \\ -8 \\ \hline \end{array}$

7. $11 - 0 =$ ____

8. $9 - 3 =$ ____

9. $10 - 5 =$ ____

Spiral Review (Chapter 15, Lesson 2) **KEY** NS 2.1, MR 3.0

Write each sum.

10. $\begin{array}{r} 6 \\ +4 \\ \hline \end{array}$ $\begin{array}{r} 4 \\ +6 \\ \hline \end{array}$

11. $\begin{array}{r} 9 \\ +2 \\ \hline \end{array}$ $\begin{array}{r} 2 \\ +9 \\ \hline \end{array}$

Name ______________________ Date __________

Subtract from 11 and Less

CA Standards
KEY NS 2.1, MR 3.0

Solve.

1. There are 7 apples on the tree. Sally picks 2 apples. How many apples are left on the tree?

   7 − 2 = _____ apples

2. There are 8 fish in the pond. Mickey catches 1 fish. How many fish are left in the pond?

   8 − 1 = _____ fish

3. JaQuilla has 9 buttons on her coat. Then 3 buttons fall off. How many buttons are left on her coat?

   _____ buttons

4. Ernesto has 11 coins. He gives 5 coins to Griffin. How many coins does Ernesto have left?

   _____ coins

5. Joseph has 10 red stickers and 11 blue stickers. He gives 4 blue stickers to Randi. How many blue stickers does Joseph have left?

   _____ blue stickers

6. Vicki has 11 cherries and 14 grapes. She shares 8 cherries with Allison. How many cherries does Vicki have left?

   _____ cherries

Subtract from 12 and Less

CA Standard
KEY NS 2.1, MR 3.0

Knowing one subtraction fact can help you find another fact.

12 − 3 = 9

12 − 9 = 3

Write each difference.

1. 12 − 2 = ___ 12 − 10 = ___
2. 9 − 3 = ___ 9 − 6 = ___
3. 10 − 3 = ___ 10 − 7 = ___
4. 11 − 2 = ___ 11 − 9 = ___
5. 12 − 1 = ___ 12 − 11 = ___
6. 11 − 7 = ___ 11 − 4 = ___
7. 12 − 0 = ___
8. 10 − 4 = ___
9. 12 − 6 = ___

Spiral Review (Chapter 15, Lesson 3) **KEY NS 2.1, MR 3.0**

Write each sum.

10. 7 + 4 = ___ 4 + 7 = ___
11. 9 + 3 = ___ 3 + 9 = ___

Name ______________________ Date ____________

Subtract from 12 and Less

CA Standards
KEY NS 2.1, MR 3.0

Solve.

1. There are 6 kittens in the basket. Then 2 kittens jump out. How many kittens are left in the basket?

   6 − 2 = _____ kittens

2. There are 9 bees in the hive. Then 4 bees fly away. How many bees are in the hive now?

   9 − 4 = _____ bees

3. Barbara has 12 stamps. She uses 2 stamps to mail letters. How many stamps does she have left?

   _____ stamps

4. Ray has 11 toy cars. He gives 3 toy cars to Keith. How many toy cars does Ray have left?

   _____ toy cars

5. Marcos has 12 oranges and 10 apples. He eats 3 oranges. How many oranges does he have left?

   _____ oranges

6. Kiera has 11 red hair bows and 12 blue hair bows. She loses 5 blue hair bows. How many blue hair bows does Kiera have now?

   _____ blue hair bows

Relate Addition and Subtraction

CA Standards
KEY NS 2.2, KEY NS 2.1

An addition fact and a subtraction fact that have the same numbers are related facts.

$$6 + 5 = \underline{11}$$
$$11 - 5 = \underline{6}$$

Use related facts to add and subtract.

1. $4 + 6 =$ ___ $10 - 6 =$ ___

2. $8 + 3 =$ ___ $11 - 3 =$ ___

3. $7 + 5 =$ ___ $12 - 5 =$ ___

4. $1 + 8 =$ ___ $9 - 8 =$ ___

5. $7 + 3 =$ ___ $10 - 3 =$ ___

6. $3 + 9 =$ ___ $12 - 9 =$ ___

Spiral Review (Chapter 15, Lesson 4) **NS 2.7**

Write the sum. Circle the two numbers you added first.

7. $4 + 2 + 6 =$ ___

8. $5 + 1 + 5 =$ ___

Relate Addition and Subtraction

CA Standards
KEY NS 2.2, KEY NS 2.1

Solve.

1. Jenny has 6 rings. She gets 2 more for a present. How many rings does Jenny have in all?

   6 + 2 = _____ rings

2. Sari has 8 rings. She gives 2 rings to her sister. How many rings does Sari have left?

   8 − 2 = _____ rings

3. Mario has 9 potatoes. He gets 3 more from his garden. How many potatoes does he have in all?

   ___ + ___ = ___ potatoes

4. Mindy has 12 tomatoes. She uses 9 tomatoes in a salad. How many tomatoes are left?

   ___ − ___ = ___ tomatoes

5. There are 12 carrot plants and 10 pepper plants. A rabbit eats 7 carrot plants. How many carrot plants are left?

   ___ − ___ = ___ carrot plants

6. There are 7 red roses and 8 white roses in a vase. Kristi adds 5 red roses to the vase. How many red roses are there in all?

   ___ + ___ = ___ red roses

Problem Solving: Use a Table

CA Standards
MR 1.1, KEY NS 2.1

You can make a table to help you solve problems.
There is a basket of fruit on the table.
The table shows the number of each kind of fruit.

Fruit	Number
Bananas	12
Apples	
Oranges	

Solve.

Complete the table.

1. There are 3 fewer apples in the basket than bananas. How many apples are in the basket?

   _____ apples

2. There are 2 more oranges in the basket than apples. How many oranges are in the basket?

   _____ oranges

Spiral Review (Chapter 15, Lesson 5) **KEY** NS 2.1, NS 2.0

Write the missing addend.

3. _____ + 7 = 11

4. 9 + _____ = 12

Problem Solving: Use a Table

CA Standards
KEY NS 2.1, MR 1.1

Solve.

1. There are 6 birds in the nest. There are 3 fewer eggs than birds. How many eggs are in the nest?

   $6 - 3 =$ _____ eggs

2. There are 8 cows in the barn. There are 2 more horses than cows. How many horses are in the barn?

   $8 + 2 =$ _____ horses

3. Jess has 9 library books. Sara has 3 more books than Jess. How many books does Sara have?

   _____ books

4. Bjorn has 11 toy cars. Jackson has 2 fewer toy cars than Bjorn. How many toy cars does Jackson have?

   _____ toy cars

5. Miriam has 5 yellow stickers and 4 green stickers. Grace has 2 more stickers than Miriam. How many stickers does Grace have?

   _____ stickers

6. Joey has 6 blue balloons and 5 red balloons. Julian has 3 fewer balloons than Joey. How many balloons does Julian have?

   _____ balloons

Name ____________________ Date __________

Hands On: Add Doubles

CA Standards
KEY NS 2.1, MR 1.2

A doubles fact has 2 addends that are the same.
Here are 2 examples of doubles facts.

5 + 5 = 10

3 + 3 = 6

Write each sum. Circle the doubles facts.

1. 4 + 4 = ____
2. 5 + 4 = ____
3. 6 + 6 = ____
4. 3 + 7 = ____
5. 6 + 2 = ____
6. 9 + 2 = ____
7. 5 + 5 = ____
8. 8 + 8 = ____
9. 8 + 1 = ____
10. 3 + 3 = ____
11. 8 + 4 = ____
12. 7 + 7 = ____

Spiral Review (Chapter 16, Lesson 1) **KEY** NS 2.5, **KEY** NS 2.1

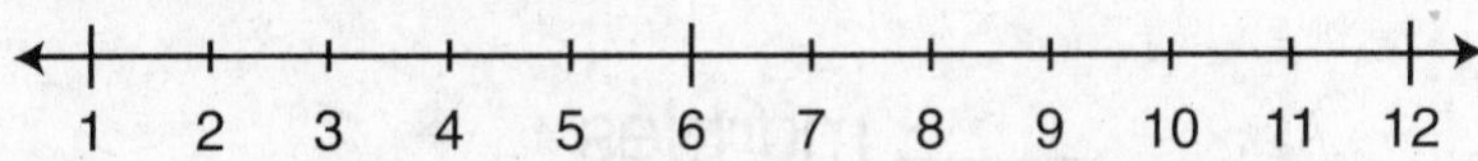

Use the number line. Subtract.

13. 12 − 4 = ____
14. 11 − 2 = ____

Hands On: Add Doubles

CA Standards
KEY NS 2.1, MR 1.2

Solve.

1. Kim has 2 bananas. She has 2 oranges. How many pieces of fruit does Kim have in all?

   2 + 2 = ____ pieces of fruit

2. Luka has 5 red . He has 5 green . How many does he have in all?

   5 + 5 = ____

3. There are 7 apples on the tree. There are 7 apples on the ground. How many apples are there in all?

   ____ apples

4. There are 6 flowers in a garden. There are 6 flowers in a vase. How many flowers are there in all?

   ____ flowers

5. Tara has 18 coins. She puts them into 2 equal groups. How many coins are in each group?

   ____ coins

6. Luis has 16 marbles. He puts them into 2 equal groups. How many marbles are in each group?

   ____ marbles

Name ______________________ Date ____________

Doubles Plus One

CA Standards
KEY NS 2.1, MR 3.0

A doubles fact has two addends that are the same.

5 + 5 = 10

Use the doubles plus one strategy to find other sums.

5 + 6 = 11

Find the sum.

1. 7 + 7 = ____ 7 + 8 = ____ 8 + 7 = ____
2. 8 + 8 = ____ 8 + 9 = ____ 9 + 8 = ____
3. 5 + 4 = ____
4. 4 + 3 = ____
5. 6 + 6 = ____
6. 7 + 6 = ____
7. 9 + 9 = ____

Spiral Review (Chapter 16, Lesson 2) **KEY** NS 2.1, MR 3.0

Write each difference.

8. 9 − 3 = ____ 9 − 6 = ____
9. 7 − 2 = ____ 7 − 5 = ____

Doubles Plus One

CA Standards
KEY NS 2.1, MR 3.0

Solve.

1. Ken finds 3 shells. Barb finds 4 shells. How many shells do they find in all?

   3 + 4 = ____ shells

2. Max has 5 coins. Emmy has 6 coins. How many coins do they have in all?

   5 + 6 = ____ coins

3. Diego has 8 carrots. Abigail has 9 carrots. How many carrots do they have in all?

   ____ carrots

4. Mike has 8 apples. Judy has 7 apples. How many apples do they have in all?

   ____ apples

5. Ming has 13 rocks. He puts them into 2 equal groups with some left over. How many rocks are in each group?

   ____ rocks

   How many rocks are left?

   ____ rock

6. Amanda has 19 grapes. She puts them into 2 equal groups with some left over. How many grapes are in each group?

   ____ grapes

   How many grapes are left?

   ____ grape

Hands On: Add with 10

CA Standards
KEY NS 2.1, NS 1.4

Use ten frames to add a number to 10.

Find 10 + 6.

Show 10.

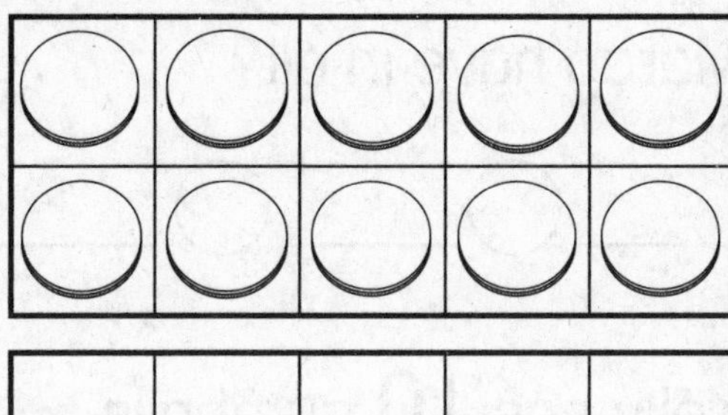

Show 6 more.

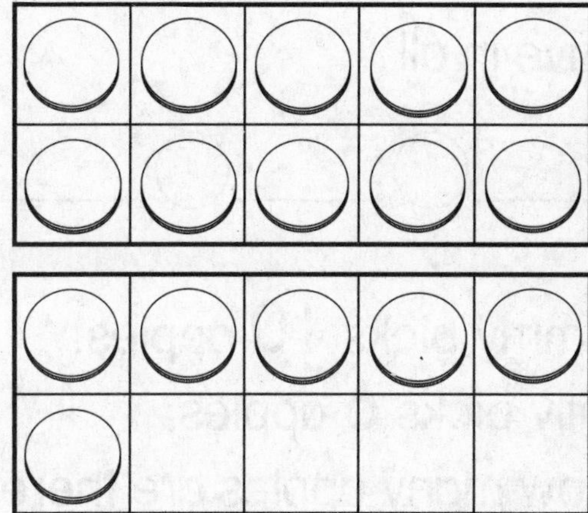

10 + 6 = 16

1. Show 10. Show 2 more.

2. Show 10. Show 8 more.

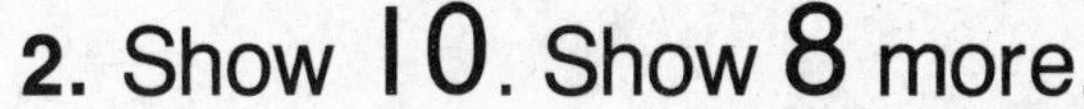

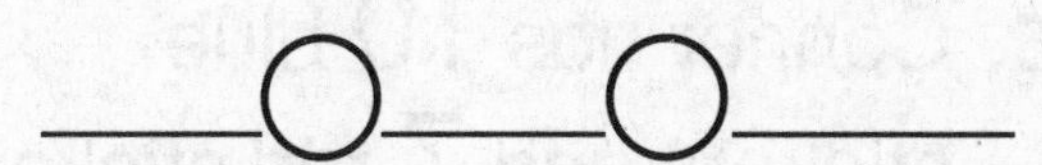

3. Show 10. Show 1 more.

4. Show 10. Show 3 more.

Spiral Review (Chapter 16, Lesson 3) **KEY** NS 2.1, MR 3.0

Write each difference.

5. $\begin{array}{r} 12 \\ -\ 3 \\ \hline \end{array}$ $\begin{array}{r} 12 \\ -\ 9 \\ \hline \end{array}$

6. $\begin{array}{r} 9 \\ -\ 2 \\ \hline \end{array}$ $\begin{array}{r} 9 \\ -\ 7 \\ \hline \end{array}$

Hands On: Add with 10

CA Standards
KEY NS 2.1, NS 1.4

Solve.

1. Tess has 10 coins.
Anita gives her 3 more.
How many coins does Tess have in all?

____ ◯ ____ ◯ ____

2. Marco has 10 toy cars.
He gets 5 more.
How many toy cars does Marco have in all?

____ ◯ ____ ◯ ____

3. Jimmy picks 10 apples.
Billy picks 6 apples.
How many apples are there in all?

____ ◯ ____ ◯ ____

4. Kelly has 10 gumballs.
Lukas gives her 7 more.
How many gumballs does Kelly have in all?

____ ◯ ____ ◯ ____

5. Conner has 10 blue stickers and 7 red stickers.
Amelia gives him 4 more blue stickers.
How many blue stickers does Conner have in all?

____ ◯ ____ ◯ ____

6. Tucker has 9 small marbles and 10 big marbles.
Tyra gives him 9 more big marbles. How many big marbles does Tucker have in all?

____ ◯ ____ ◯ ____

Name ______________________ Date __________

Hands On: Make a Ten to Add

CA Standards
KEY NS 2.1, MR 1.2

Make a 10 to help you add 7, 8, or 9.

Find 7 + 4.

Show 7 + 4.

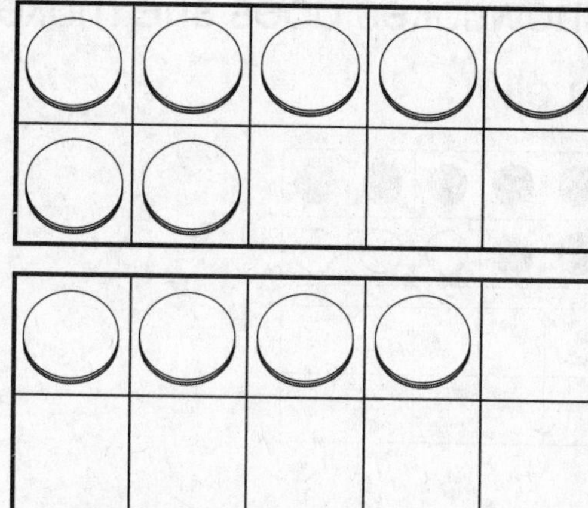

Make a 10.

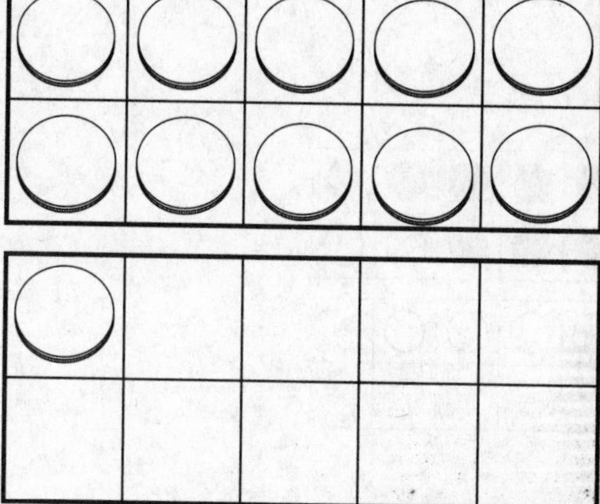

7 + 4 = __11__

1. Show 9 and 5 more.

   9 + 5 = ______

2. Show 9 and 4 more.

   9 + 4 = ______

3. Show 8 and 6 more.

   8 + 6 = ______

4. Show 8 and 7 more.

   8 + 7 = ______

Spiral Review (Chapter 16, Lesson 4) **KEY** NS 2.2, **KEY** NS 2.1

Use related facts to add and subtract.

5. $\begin{array}{r} 7 \\ +\ 5 \\ \hline \end{array}$ $\begin{array}{r} 12 \\ -\ 5 \\ \hline \end{array}$

6. $\begin{array}{r} 9 \\ +\ 3 \\ \hline \end{array}$ $\begin{array}{r} 12 \\ -\ 3 \\ \hline \end{array}$

Hands On: Make a Ten to Add

CA Standards
KEY NS 2.1, MR 1.2

Make a 10 to help you solve addition problems.

1. Lim Sing draws 8 cards. She draws 6 more cards. How many cards does she draw in all?

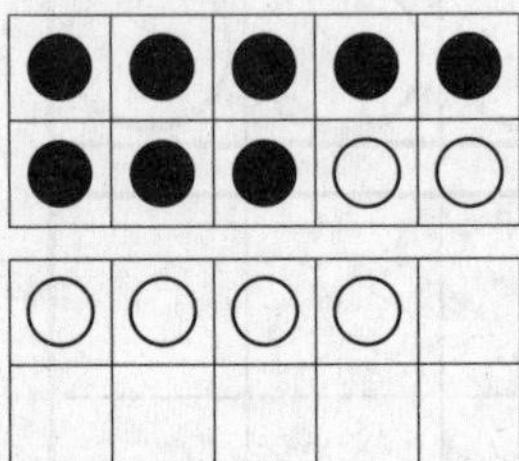

8 + 6 = _____ cards

2. Ruth makes 7 paper snowflakes. She makes 4 more. How many paper snowflakes does she make in all?

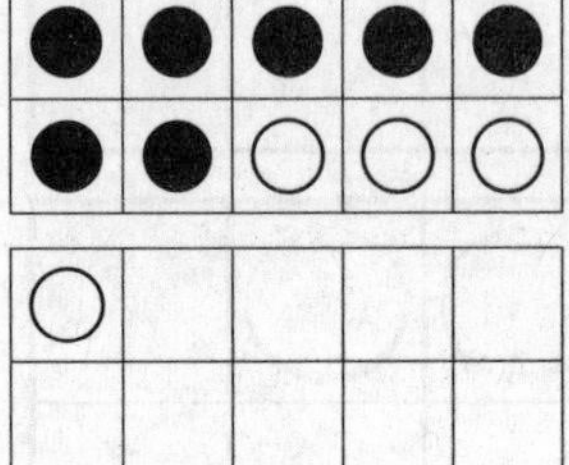

7 + 4 = _____ snowflakes

3. Paul brings 9 bags of popcorn to the party. Greg brings 6 bags of popcorn. How many bags of popcorn are there in all?

_____ bags of popcorn

4. The clown has 7 flowers in a hat. She has 8 flowers in her pocket. How many flowers does the clown have in all?

_____ flowers.

5. Grace has 9 baseball cards and 7 soccer cards. She gets 5 more baseball cards. How many baseball cards does she have in all?

_____ baseball cards

6. Omar has 8 green pencils and 7 blue pencils. He gets 5 more blue pencils. How many blue pencils does he have in all?

_____ blue pencils

Name ________________ Date __________

Add Three Numbers

CA Standards
KEY NS 2.1, NS 2.7

You can add three numbers in any order.

(5)		5		(5)	
(3)	[8]	(3)	+ 5	+ 3	[9]
+ 4	+ 4	+ (4)	[7]	+ (4)	+ 3
	12		12		12

The sum is the same each way.

Circle the 2 numbers you added first. Write the sum.

1. 4 + 6 + 5
2. 5 + 1 + 4
3. 3 + 7 + 3
4. 8 + 4 + 5
5. 5 + 6 + 3
6. 5 + 4 + 4
7. 3 + 6 + 7
8. 4 + 5 + 4

Spiral Review (Chapter 16, Lesson 5) **KEY** NS 2.1, MR 1.1

Solve.

9. Kara has 9 apples. Maria has 3 more apples than Kara. How many apples does Maria have?

_____ apples

10. Ian has 11 stickers. Justin has 3 fewer stickers than Ian. How many stickers does Justin have?

_____ stickers

Add Three Numbers

CA Standards
KEY NS 2.1, NS 2.7

Solve.

1. Millie has 2 coins. Amelia has 3 coins. Tasha has 2 coins. How many coins do they have in all?

   2 + 3 + 2 = _____ coins

2. There are 3 birds in the tree. Then 3 more birds fly to the tree. Then 2 more birds join them. How many birds are in the tree in all?

   3 + 3 + 2 = _____ birds

3. Jamal reads 4 books on Monday. He reads 6 books on Tuesday. He reads 4 books on Wednesday. How many books does Jamal read in all?

   _____ books

4. Dawn counts 8 ants on a log. She counts 6 ants on a leaf. She counts 4 ants on the ground. How many ants does Dawn count in all?

   _____ ants

5. Paula has 5 apples, 4 oranges, 6 bananas, and 10 grapes. How many pieces of fruit does Paula have in all?

   _____ pieces of fruit

6. Juan sees 8 cats, 4 dogs, 8 hamsters, and 2 rabbits at the pet store. How many animals does Juan see in all?

   _____ animals

Name ____________________ Date __________

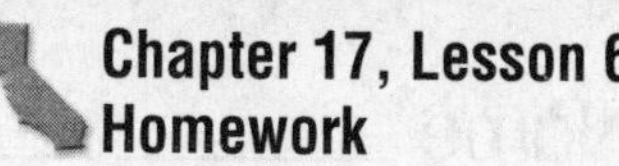

Problem Solving: Create and Solve

CA Standards
KEY NS 2.1, AF 1.3

You can write problems and use the strategies you have learned to solve them.

1. Write an addition sentence for the doubles fact shown in the picture.

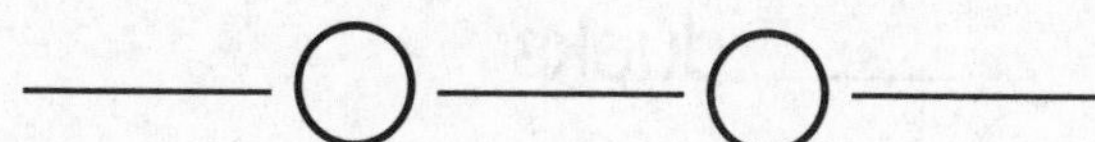

2. Write an addition sentence for another doubles fact.

____ ◯ ____ ◯ ____

Spiral Review (Chapter 16, Lesson 5) **KEY** NS 2.1, MR 1.1

Solve.

3. Tonya has 8 books. Missy has 3 more books than Tonya. How many books does Missy have?

____ books

4. Mark has 12 trading cards. Joel has 3 fewer trading cards than Mark. How many trading cards does Joel have?

____ trading cards

Problem Solving: Create and Solve

CA Standards
KEY NS 2.1, AF 1.3

Solve.

1. There are 4 birds in the nest. There are 5 birds flying in the air. How many birds are there in all?

   4 + 5 = ____ birds

2. There are 6 cows in the barn. There are 6 cows in the field. How many cows are there in all?

   6 + 6 = ____ cows

3. The dog has 7 bones. He digs up 7 more bones. How many bones does the dog have in all?

   ____ bones

4. There are 7 ducks swimming in the pond. Then 8 more ducks come to swim. How many ducks are in the pond now?

   ____ ducks

5. Emily has 16 coins. She puts them into 2 equal groups. How many coins are in each group?

   ____ coins

   How many coins are left?

   ____ coins

6. Bryce has 15 blocks. He puts them into 2 equal groups. How many blocks are in each group?

   ____ blocks

   How many blocks are left?

   ____ block

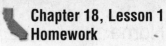

Hands On: Use Doubles to Subtract

CA Standards
KEY NS 2.2, KEY NS 2.1

Find 16 – 8. Use a doubles fact to help you subtract.

8 + 8 = 16

so, 16 – 8 = 8

Add. Then subtract.

1. 5 + 5 = ______
   10 – 5 = ______

2. 6 + 6 = ______
   12 – 6 = ______

3. 10 + 10 = ______
   20 – 10 = ______

4. 9 + 9 = ______
   18 – 9 = ______

5. $\begin{array}{r} 8 \\ +8 \\ \hline \end{array}$ $\begin{array}{r} 16 \\ -\ 8 \\ \hline \end{array}$

6. $\begin{array}{r} 4 \\ +4 \\ \hline \end{array}$ $\begin{array}{r} 8 \\ -4 \\ \hline \end{array}$

Spiral Review (Chapter 17, Lesson 1) **KEY** NS 2.1

Write each sum. Circle the doubles facts.

7. $\begin{array}{r} 5 \\ +5 \\ \hline \end{array}$

8. $\begin{array}{r} 4 \\ +5 \\ \hline \end{array}$

Hands On: Use Doubles to Subtract

CA Standards
KEY NS 2.2, KEY NS 2.1

Solve.

1. There are 4 birds in a tree. Then 4 more birds join them. How many birds are in the tree now?

   4 + 4 = _____ birds

2. There are 8 birds in the tree. Then 4 birds fly away. How many birds are left in the tree?

   8 − 4 = _____ birds

3. There are 7 children in the park. 7 more children come to the park. How many children are in the park in all?

   ___ + ___ = ___ children

   Then 7 children go home. How many children are in the park now?

   ___ − ___ = ___ children

4. There are 8 cows in the barn. Then 8 more cows join them. How many cows are in the barn now?

   ___ + ___ = ___ cows

   Then 8 cows leave the barn. How many cows are left in the barn?

   ___ − ___ = ___ cows

5. Tom is 5 years old. In how many years will he be 10 years old?

   _____ years

6. Gail is 18 years old. How many years ago was she 9?

   _____ years

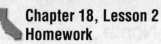

Name ______________________ Date __________

Subtract From 13 and 14

CA Standards
KEY NS 2.2, KEY NS 2.1

A related fact can help you find the difference.

$$\begin{array}{r} 8 \\ +6 \\ \hline 14 \end{array}$$

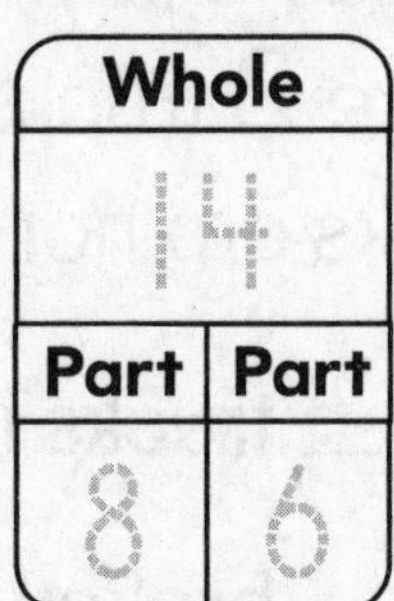

$$\begin{array}{r} 14 \\ -8 \\ \hline 6 \end{array} \qquad \begin{array}{r} 14 \\ -6 \\ \hline 8 \end{array}$$

Add. Then find the difference.

1. $\begin{array}{r} 9 \\ +5 \\ \hline \end{array}$ so $\begin{array}{r} 14 \\ -9 \\ \hline \end{array}$ $\begin{array}{r} 14 \\ -5 \\ \hline \end{array}$

2. $\begin{array}{r} 6 \\ +7 \\ \hline \end{array}$ so $\begin{array}{r} 13 \\ -6 \\ \hline \end{array}$ $\begin{array}{r} 13 \\ -7 \\ \hline \end{array}$

3. $\begin{array}{r} 4 \\ +9 \\ \hline \end{array}$ so $\begin{array}{r} 13 \\ -4 \\ \hline \end{array}$ $\begin{array}{r} 13 \\ -9 \\ \hline \end{array}$

4. $\begin{array}{r} 10 \\ +4 \\ \hline \end{array}$ so $\begin{array}{r} 14 \\ -10 \\ \hline \end{array}$ $\begin{array}{r} 14 \\ -4 \\ \hline \end{array}$

Spiral Review (Chapter 17, Lesson 2) **KEY** NS 2.1, **KEY** NS 2.5

Find the sum.

5. $\begin{array}{r} 6 \\ +7 \\ \hline \end{array}$

6. $\begin{array}{r} 6 \\ +5 \\ \hline \end{array}$

Name ____________________ Date __________

Subtract From 13 and 14

CA Standards
KEY NS 2.2, KEY NS 2.1

Solve.

1. Maria has 4 hats in all.
   1 hat is yellow.
   How many hats are red?

   _____ hats in all

   _____ yellow

   _____ red

2. Ed has 5 toy trucks. He broke 2 trucks. How many trucks are not broken?

   _____ trucks in all

   _____ broken

   _____ not broken

3. Emma had 13 game chips.
   She lost 7 chips.
   How many chips are not lost?

   _____ chips in all

   _____ chips lost

   _____ chips not lost

4. Amed had 14 stickers.
   He gave 9 stickers away.
   How many stickers are left?

   _____ stickers in all

   _____ given away

   _____ left

5. Teri has 14 grapes and 12 apples. She gives Mary 8 grapes. How many grapes does Teri have left?

   _____ grapes in all

   _____ given away

   _____ left

6. Pedro has 16 football cards and 13 baseball cards. He gives 5 baseball cards to Joe. How many baseball cards does Pedro have left?

   _____ baseball cards in all

   _____ given away

   _____ left

Name ________________ Date __________

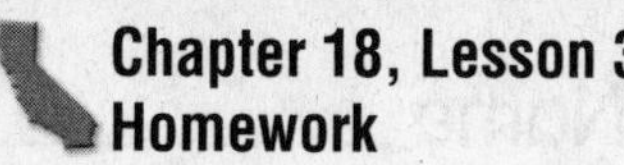

Subtract from 15 and 16

CA Standards
KEY NS 2.2, KEY NS 2.1

You can use an addition fact to help you subtract.

$$\begin{array}{r} 9 \\ +7 \\ \hline 16 \end{array}$$

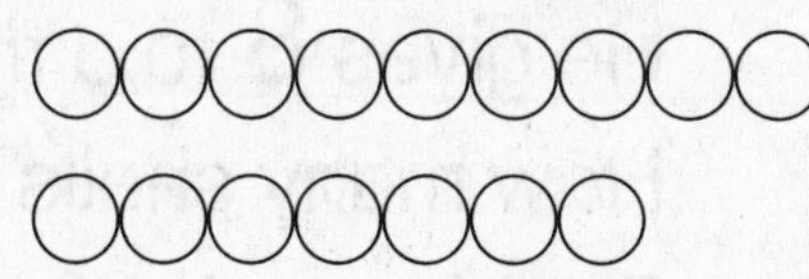

$$\begin{array}{r} 16 \\ -9 \\ \hline 7 \end{array} \qquad \begin{array}{r} 16 \\ -7 \\ \hline 9 \end{array}$$

Add. Then find the difference.

1. $\begin{array}{r} 7 \\ +8 \\ \hline \end{array}$ so $\begin{array}{r} 15 \\ -7 \\ \hline \end{array}$ $\begin{array}{r} 15 \\ -8 \\ \hline \end{array}$

2. $\begin{array}{r} 10 \\ +5 \\ \hline \end{array}$ so $\begin{array}{r} 15 \\ -10 \\ \hline \end{array}$ $\begin{array}{r} 15 \\ -5 \\ \hline \end{array}$

3. $\begin{array}{r} 6 \\ +9 \\ \hline \end{array}$ so $\begin{array}{r} 15 \\ -6 \\ \hline \end{array}$ $\begin{array}{r} 15 \\ -9 \\ \hline \end{array}$

4. $\begin{array}{r} 10 \\ +6 \\ \hline \end{array}$ so $\begin{array}{r} 16 \\ -10 \\ \hline \end{array}$ $\begin{array}{r} 16 \\ -6 \\ \hline \end{array}$

Spiral Review (Chapter 17, Lesson 3) **KEY NS 2.1, MR 1.2**

Show the numbers.
Write the number sentence.

5. Show 10. Show 3 more.

6. Show 10. Show 5 more.

___ ◯ ___ ◯ ___

Name ______________________ Date __________

Subtraction From 15 and 16

CA Standards
KEY NS 2.2, KEY NS 2.1

Solve.

1. Tara picks 16 apples.
She eats 6 of the apples.
How many apples does she have left?

16 − 6 = _____ apples

2. David has 15 shells.
He gives 8 to a friend.
How many shells does David have left?

15 − 8 = _____ shells

3. Lana has 15 round buttons.
She sews 9 of the buttons on a shirt. How many buttons are left?

_____ − _____ = _____
buttons

4. Stan puts 16 plums on a plate. Guests at his party take 8 of the plums from the plate. How many plums are left on the plate?

_____ − _____ = _____
plums

5. Herb has 12 toy cars.
He wants to have 15 toy cars in his collection. How many more does Herb need?

_____ ◯ _____ ◯ _____
toy cars

6. Marta has 4 hair bows. She buys more hair bows at the store. Now she has 16 hair bows. How many did she buy at the store?

_____ ◯ _____ ◯ _____
hair bows

Subtract From 17 Through 20

CA Standards
KEY NS 2.2, **KEY** NS 2.1

Use an addition fact to help you subtract.

$$\begin{array}{r} 19 \\ -9 \\ \hline 10 \end{array}$$

Whole	
19	
Part	Part
○○○○○ ○○○○○	○○○○○ ○○○○

$$\begin{array}{r} 10 \\ +9 \\ \hline 19 \end{array} \qquad \begin{array}{r} 19 \\ -10 \\ \hline 9 \end{array}$$

Add. Then find the difference.

1. $\begin{array}{r} 8 \\ +9 \\ \hline \end{array}$ so $\begin{array}{r} 17 \\ -8 \\ \hline \end{array}$ $\begin{array}{r} 17 \\ -9 \\ \hline \end{array}$

2. $\begin{array}{r} 8 \\ +10 \\ \hline \end{array}$ so $\begin{array}{r} 18 \\ -8 \\ \hline \end{array}$ $\begin{array}{r} 18 \\ -10 \\ \hline \end{array}$

3. $\begin{array}{r} 13 \\ +7 \\ \hline \end{array}$ so $\begin{array}{r} 20 \\ -7 \\ \hline \end{array}$ $\begin{array}{r} 20 \\ -13 \\ \hline \end{array}$

4. $\begin{array}{r} 9 \\ +10 \\ \hline \end{array}$ so $\begin{array}{r} 19 \\ -9 \\ \hline \end{array}$ $\begin{array}{r} 19 \\ -10 \\ \hline \end{array}$

Spiral Review (Chapter 17, Lesson 4) **KEY NS 2.1, MR 1.2**

Make a 10. Find the sum.

5. Show 8 and 8 more.

$8 + 8 =$ ____

6. Show 4 and 9 more.

$4 + 9 =$ ____

Subtract From 17 Through 20

CA Standards
KEY NS 2.2, KEY NS 2.1

Solve.

1. There are 17 children in the room. 8 of the children are boys. How many of the children are girls?

   17 − 8 = _____ girls

   Hint: Remember that
   8 + 9 = 17

2. Lance sees 18 birds at the beach. Then 9 birds fly away. How many birds are on the beach now?

   18 − 9 = _____ birds

   Hint: Remember that
   9 + 9 = 18

3. There are 20 crackers in the bag. Enrique eats 10 of the crackers with lunch. How many crackers are left in the bag?

   _____ crackers

4. There are 17 clay bowls on the shelf. Tamika sells 9 of the bowls. How many bowls are left on the shelf?

   _____ bowls

5. There are 18 frogs and 17 ants on a log. A loud noise makes 7 frogs jump off the log. How many frogs are on the log now?

   _____ frogs

6. Ciara has 19 blue ribbons and 16 red ribbons. She ties 9 red ribbons to balloons. How many red ribbons does Ciara have now?

   _____ red ribbons

Name ______________________ Date __________

Problem Solving: Choose the Operation

CA Standards
NS 2.0, AF 1.1

You can use addition to solve a problem. Use addition when you need to know how many in all.

You can use subtraction to solve a problem. Use subtraction when you need to know how many are left.

Choose the operation to solve.
Write the number sentence.

Draw or write to explain.

1. Mia counts 19 bees buzzing near the hive. She sees 10 bees fly away. How many bees are left at the hive?

   ___ ◯ ___ ◯ ___

   ___ bees

2. Javier reads 7 books. Terri reads 8 books. How many books do they read in all?

   ___ ◯ ___ ◯ ___

   ___ books

Spiral Review (Chapter 17, Lesson 5) **NS 2.7, KEY NS 2.1**

Circle the 2 numbers you added first.
Write the sum.

3.
```
  3
  7
+ 3
---
```

4.
```
  5
  6
+ 4
---
```

Problem Solving: Choose the Operation

CA Standards
NS 2.0, AF 1.1

Solve.

1. There are 12 ants on a log. Then 4 ants leave the log. How many ants are left?

   $12 - 4 =$ ______ ants

2. There are 7 birds in the nest. Then 5 birds join them. How many birds are there in all?

   $7 + 5 =$ ______ birds

3. There are 11 children on the playground. Then 8 children join them. How many children are on the playground now?

   ______ children

4. There are 17 kittens in the pet store. Then 9 kittens find homes. How many kittens are left at the pet store?

   ______ kittens

5. Marissa has 18 stickers. She gives 7 stickers to Carly. Then she gives 6 stickers to Paul. How many stickers does Marissa have left?

   ______ stickers

6. Amed has 9 coins. He finds 6 more coins in his pocket. Then he finds 3 coins on the ground. How many coins does Amed have now?

   ______ coins

Hands On: Fact Families

CA Standard
KEY NS 2.2, NS 2.0

The 4 related facts make a fact family.

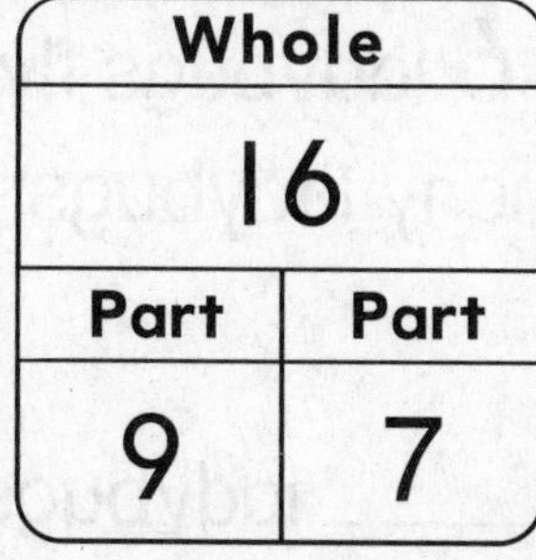

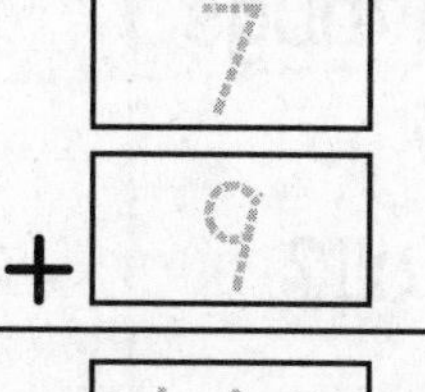

$9 + 7 = 16$ $7 + 9 = 16$ $16 - 9 = 7$ $16 - 7 = 9$

Complete the fact family.

1. Whole 13; Part 8, Part 5

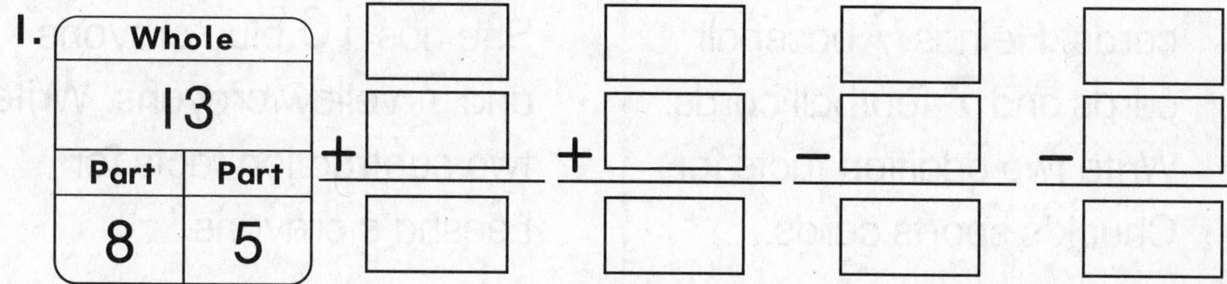

2. Whole 15; Part 9, Part 6

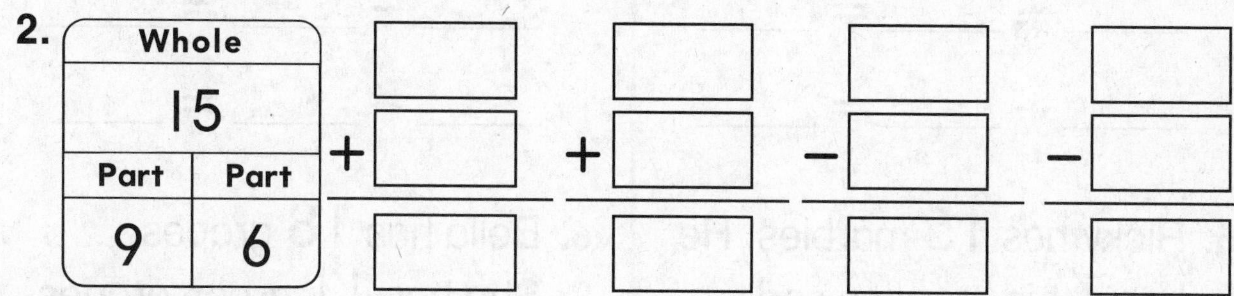

Spiral Review (Chapter 18, Lesson 1) **KEY** NS 2.2, **KEY** NS 2.1

Add. Then subtract.

3. $7 + 7 =$ ____

$14 - 7 =$ ____

4. $9 + 9 =$ ____

$18 - 9 =$ ____

Name ____________________ Date __________

Hands On: Fact Families

CA Standards
KEY NS 2.2, NS 2.0

Solve.

1. Lia finds 8 ladybugs in the trees. She finds 6 ladybugs on the log. How many ladybugs are there in all?

   $8 + 6 =$ _____ ladybugs

2. There are 14 ladybugs in the jar. Then 6 ladybugs fly away. How many ladybugs are left?

   $14 - 6 =$ _____ ladybugs

3. Chuck has 16 sports cards. He has 9 baseball cards and 7 football cards. Write two addition facts for Chuck's sports cards.

   _____ + _____ = _____

   _____ + _____ = _____

4. Leesha has 17 crayons. She has 10 blue crayons and 7 yellow crayons. Write two subtraction facts for Leesha's crayons.

   _____ − _____ = _____

   _____ − _____ = _____

5. Ricky has 15 marbles. He has 7 big marbles and 8 small marbles. Write the fact family for Ricky's marbles.

   _____ ◯ _____ ◯ _____

   _____ ◯ _____ ◯ _____

   _____ ◯ _____ ◯ _____

   _____ ◯ _____ ◯ _____

6. Bella has 18 grapes. She has 11 green grapes and 7 red grapes. Write the fact family for Bella's grapes.

   _____ ◯ _____ ◯ _____

   _____ ◯ _____ ◯ _____

   _____ ◯ _____ ◯ _____

   _____ ◯ _____ ◯ _____

Relate Addition and Subtraction

CA Standard KEY NS 2.2, KEY NS 2.1

You can use an addition fact to find a related subtraction fact.

$9 + 7 = $ 16

$16 - 9 = $ 7 $16 - 7 = $ 9

You can use $9 + 7$ to find $16 - 9$ and $16 - 7$.

Write the missing numbers.

1. $15 - 7 = $ ___ $7 + $ ___ $ = 15$
2. $19 - 6 = $ ___ $6 + $ ___ $ = 19$
3. $18 - 9 = $ ___ $9 + $ ___ $ = 18$
4. $16 - 6 = $ ___ $6 + $ ___ $ = 16$
5. $17 - 7 = $ ___ $7 + $ ___ $ = 17$
6. $15 - 9 = $ ___ $9 + $ ___ $ = 15$

Spiral Review (Chapter 18, Lesson 2) **KEY** NS 2.2, **KEY** NS 2.1

Add.
Then find the difference.

7. $8 + 5$ so $13 - 8$ $13 - 5$

8. $8 + 6$ so $14 - 8$ $14 - 6$

Relate Addition and Subtraction Facts

CA Standards
KEY NS 2.2, KEY NS 2.1

Solve.

1. Micah has 9 grapes. She gets 6 more grapes. How many grapes does she have in all?

   9 + 6 = _____ grapes

2. Chen has 16 cards. He gives 8 to a friend. How many cards does Chen have left?

   16 − 8 = _____ cards

3. Betty has 8 big marbles and 9 small marbles. How many marbles are there in all?

   _____ + _____ = _____ marbles

4. Will picks 10 carrots. Then he picks 8 more carrots. How many carrots did Will pick in all?

   _____ + _____ = _____ carrots

5. Luke has 11 rocks. Conner gives him 7 more rocks. How many does Luke have in all?

   _____ ◯ _____ ◯ _____ rocks

6. Shelly has 12 crayons. She finds 7 more crayons. How many does she have in all?

   _____ ◯ _____ ◯ _____ crayons

Name ____________________ Date __________

Different Ways to Subtract

CA Standards
KEY NS 2.1, NS 2.0

You can subtract in different ways.

Use doubles.

$$\begin{array}{r} 18 \\ -9 \\ \hline 9 \end{array}$$ Think $9 + 9 = 18$

Use an addition fact.

$$\begin{array}{r} 16 \\ -7 \\ \hline 9 \end{array}$$ Think $7 + 9 = 16$

Write each difference.

Circle the fact if it is related to a doubles fact.

1. $\begin{array}{r} 14 \\ -7 \\ \hline \end{array}$

2. $\begin{array}{r} 15 \\ -7 \\ \hline \end{array}$

3. $\begin{array}{r} 17 \\ -10 \\ \hline \end{array}$

4. $\begin{array}{r} 18 \\ -9 \\ \hline \end{array}$

5. $\begin{array}{r} 15 \\ -6 \\ \hline \end{array}$

6. $\begin{array}{r} 18 \\ -6 \\ \hline \end{array}$

7. $\begin{array}{r} 20 \\ -10 \\ \hline \end{array}$

8. $\begin{array}{r} 16 \\ -9 \\ \hline \end{array}$

9. $\begin{array}{r} 14 \\ -7 \\ \hline \end{array}$

10. $\begin{array}{r} 18 \\ -8 \\ \hline \end{array}$

11. $\begin{array}{r} 15 \\ -10 \\ \hline \end{array}$

12. $\begin{array}{r} 16 \\ -8 \\ \hline \end{array}$

Spiral Review (Chapter 18, Lesson 3) **KEY** NS 2.2, **KEY** NS 2.1

Add. Then find the difference.

13. $\begin{array}{r} 9 \\ +6 \\ \hline \end{array}$ $\begin{array}{r} 15 \\ -9 \\ \hline \end{array}$ $\begin{array}{r} 15 \\ -6 \\ \hline \end{array}$

14. $\begin{array}{r} 8 \\ +8 \\ \hline \end{array}$ $\begin{array}{r} 16 \\ -8 \\ \hline \end{array}$ $\begin{array}{r} 16 \\ -8 \\ \hline \end{array}$

Different Ways to Subtract

CA Standards
KEY NS 2.1, NS 2.0

Solve.

1. Gale finds 16 small shells at the beach. She finds 8 large shells. How many more small shells than large shells does Gale find?

   16 − 8 = ________ more small shells

2. There are 15 cards in a box. There are 7 cards in a pack. How many more cards are in a box than in a pack?

   15 − 7 = ________ more cards

3. Kip has 19 model airplanes. He gives 10 models to his grandfather. How many model planes does Kip have left?

   ________ model planes

4. Shayna has 17 marbles. She gives 9 to her sister. How many marbles does Shayna have now?

   ________ marbles

5. Carlos buys a notebook for 75¢ and a pad for 15¢. How much more does he spend on the notebook than the pad?

   ________ ¢

6. Ari has 18 stickers. She gives 5 stickers to a friend. How many stickers does Ari have left?

   ________ stickers

Name ____________________ Date __________

Problem Solving: Comparison Problems

CA Standards
KEY NS 2.1, MR 2.0

Use comparison bars to help solve problems.

Hal collects 9 coins.

When he collects 5 more coins, he will have the same number as Rachel.

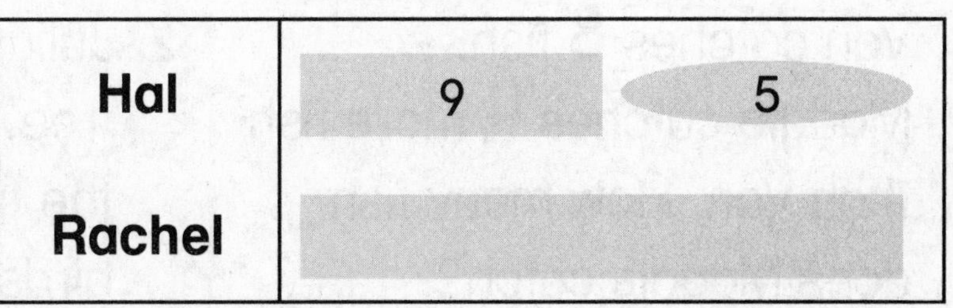

How many coins does Rachel have?

Rachel has __14__ coins.

Use the comparison bars. Solve.

1. Millie has 12 stamps.
   If she gives 3 to a friend, she will have the same amount as Kyle.
   How many stamps does Kyle have?

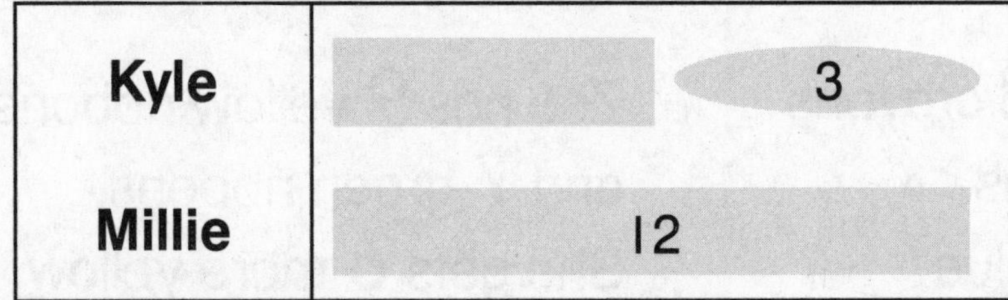

Kyle has _____ stamps.

Spiral Review (Chapter 18, Lesson 3, Lesson 4) **KEY** NS 2.2, **KEY** NS 2.1

Add. Then find the difference.

2. $7 + 9 =$ ___ so $16 - 7 =$ ___ , $16 - 9 =$ ___

3. $8 + 9 =$ ___ so $17 - 8 =$ ___ , $17 - 9 =$ ___

Problem Solving: Comparison Problems

CA Standards
KEY NS 2.1, MR 2.0

Solve.

1. Van catches 8 fish. Maddie catches 4 more fish than Van. How many fish does Maddie catch?

   $8 + 4 =$ _____ fish

2. Julius sees 8 birds in the tree. Joy sees 15 birds in the tree. How many more birds does Joy see than Julius?

   $15 - 8 =$ _____ more birds

3. There are 9 ducks in the pond. Then 7 more swim to the pond. How many ducks are in the pond in all?

   _____ ducks

4. There are 16 cows in the field. There are 18 cows in the barn. How many more cows are in the barn than in the field?

   _____ more cows

5. Jackson has 6 red crayons and 8 blue crayons. He finds 5 more blue crayons. How many more blue crayons does Jackson have than red crayons?

   _____ more blue crayons

6. Zoe has 9 yellow ribbons and 7 green ribbons. She gets 6 more yellow ribbons. How many more yellow ribbons does she have than green ribbons?

   _____ more yellow ribbons

Name ______________________ Date __________

Hands On: Coin Values

CA Standards
NS 1.5, MR 1.2

Different coins can show the same amount.

23¢

Whole
17

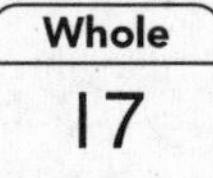   

23¢

Use coins.

Show 2 different ways to pay for the object.

Draw the coins.

1.

2.

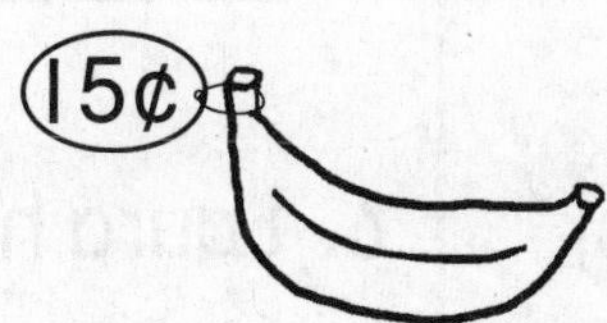

Spiral Review (Chapter 19, Lesson 1) **KEY** NS 2.2, NS 2.0

Complete the fact family.

3.

Whole	
12	
Part	Part
7	5

4.

Whole	
17	
Part	Part
9	8

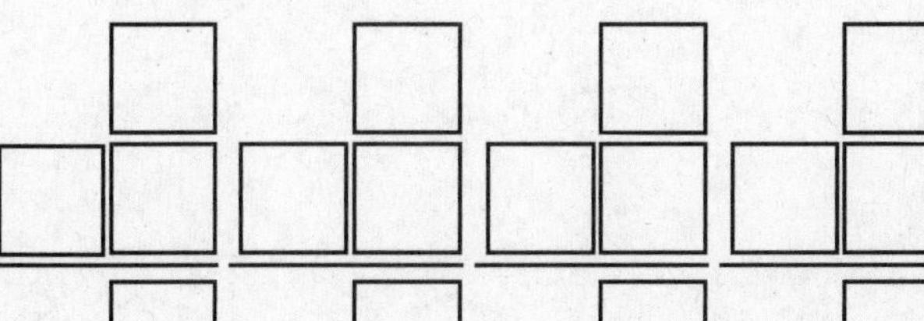

Hands On: Coin Values

CA Standards
NS 1.5, MR 1.2

Solve.

1. Drew has 5¢.
Circle the coin that matches.

2. Hannah has 10¢.
Circle the coin that matches.

3. Amelia has 1 dime and 1 penny. How much money does she have?

_______ ¢

4. Junji has 1 nickel and 2 pennies. How much money does he have?

_______ ¢

5. Bill has 1 dime, 2 nickels, and 3 pennies. How much money does he have?

_______ ¢

6. Laura has 2 dimes, 1 nickel, and 4 pennies. How much money does she have?

_______ ¢

Hands On: Count Nickels

CA Standards
NS 1.5, KEY NS 2.4

Count by 5s. Find the value of the nickels.
Use coins if you wish.

5¢ 10¢ 15¢ 20¢ **Solution:**  ¢

Find the value of the nickels.

1.    

____ ¢ ____ ¢ ____ ¢ ____ ¢ ____ ¢ ____ ¢

2.   

____ ¢ ____ ¢ ____ ¢ ____ ¢

3.      

____ ¢ ____ ¢ ____ ¢ ____ ¢ ____ ¢ ____ ¢ ____ ¢

Spiral Review (Chapter 19, Lesson 2) **KEY** NS 2.2, **KEY** NS 2.1

Write the missing numbers

4. 16 – 9 = ____

9 + ____ = 16

5. 18 – 8 = ____

8 + ____ = 18

Hands On: Count Nickels

CA Standards
NS 1.5, KEY NS 2.4

Solve.
Use coins if you want.

1. Amy has these coins.
How much money does she have?

_____ ¢

2. Hector wants to buy the ball.
How many (nickel) does he need?

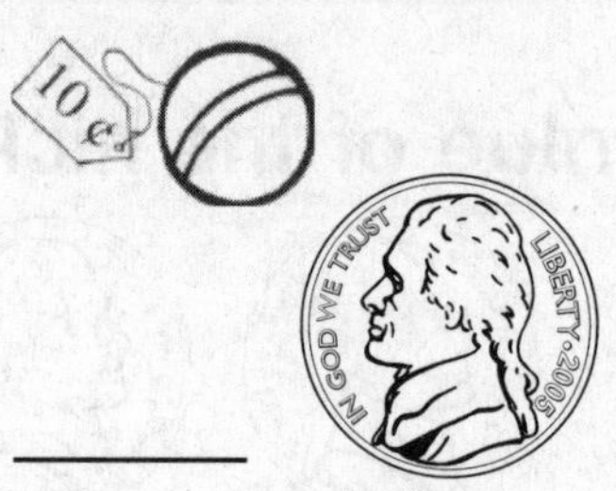

_____

3. Blake has 3 nickels.
His grandma gives him 2 more nickels.
How much money does Blake have now?

_____ ¢

4. Jane counts her money.
She has 40¢.
How many nickels does Jane have?

_____ nickels

5. A pen costs 25¢.
A marker costs 20¢.
Ethan has 9 nickels.
Can he buy both the pen and the marker?

_____

6. Kim has 10 nickels.
She buys a book for 35¢.
She gives 10¢ to her sister.
How much money does Kim have left?

_____ ¢

Hands On: Count Nickels and Pennies

CA Standards
NS 1.5, KEY NS 2.4

When you are counting coins, start with the coins of greatest value.

5 ¢ 10 ¢ 15 ¢ 16 ¢ 17 ¢

17¢

13¢

Spiral Review (Chapter 19, Lesson 3) **KEY** NS 2.2, NS 2.0

Write each difference. Circle the fact if it is related to a doubles fact.

3. 16
− 8
_____

4. 17
− 10
_____

Hands On: Count Nickels and Pennies

CA Standards
NS 1.5, KEY NS 2.4

Solve.

1. Dora has 3 nickels and 1 penny.
How much money does she have?

11¢ 16¢

2. Omar has 4 nickels.
How much money does he have?

20¢ 15¢

3. Kim has some nickels.
She has 30¢.
How many nickels does Kim have?

_____ nickels

4. Derrick has 3 nickels and 4 pennies.
A notebook costs 18¢.
Does Derrick have enough money to buy the notebook?

_____

5. Sasha has 27¢.
Her dad gives her some pennies.
Now Sasha has 35¢.
How many pennies did her dad give her?

_____ pennies

6. Tyrell has 39¢.
He buys an apple for 11¢ and a pretzel for 8¢.
How much money does he have left?

_____¢

Count Dimes

CA Standards
NS 1.5, KEY NS 2.4

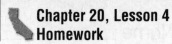

Count by 10s. Find the value of the dimes.

 ¢  ¢  ¢  ¢ **Solution:**  ¢

Find the value of the dimes.

1.      

____¢ ____¢ ____¢ ____¢ ____¢ ____¢ ____¢

2.     

____¢ ____¢ ____¢ ____¢ ____¢ ____¢

Spiral Review (Chapter 19, Lesson 4) **KEY** NS 2.1, MR 2.0

Use the comparison bars. Solve.

3. Rachel has 14 stickers. If she gives 3 to a friend, she will have the same amount as Hal. How many stickers does Hal have?

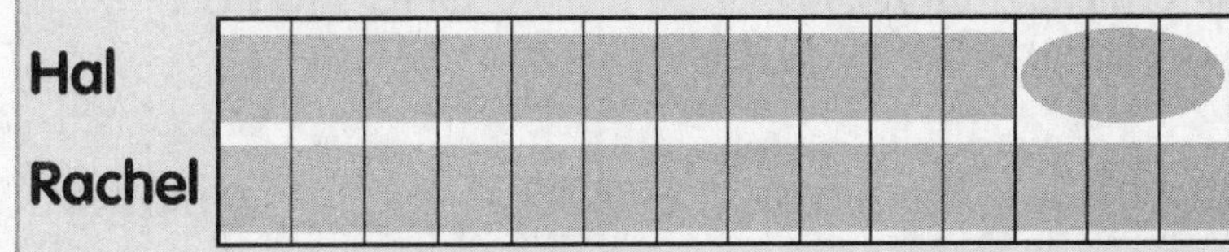

Hal has ____ stickers.

Count Dimes

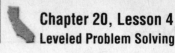

CA Standards
NS 1.5, KEY NS 2.4

Solve.
Use coins if you want.

1. Susan is counting these coins.
What does she say?
Circle the answer.

5¢, 10¢, 15¢
10¢, 20¢, 30¢

2. Hayden has 4 dimes.
How much money does he have?

______ ¢

3. Chen has 5 dimes.
He finds 1 more dime.
How much money does Chen have now?

______ ¢

4. Ella counts her money.
She has 70¢.
How many dimes does Ella have?

______ dimes

5. Matt wants to buy a drink for 40¢ and a bag of popcorn for 50¢.
How many dimes does he need?

______ dimes

6. Tanya has 75¢.
She has 5 nickels.
How many dimes does she have?

______ dimes

Name ______________________ Date __________

Count Dimes and Pennies

CA Standards
NS 1.5, KEY NS 2.4

To find the value of the coins,
count the coin with the greater value first.

10¢ 20¢ 21¢ 22¢ 23¢ 24¢

Count on by tens for dimes. Count on by ones for pennies.

Circle the coins that match each price.

1. 22¢
2. 30¢
3. 15¢

Spiral Review (Chapter 18, Lesson 5) **NS 1.0, AF 1.1**

Choose the operation to solve.
Write the number sentence.

4. Maya counts 17 apples in the tree. She sees 9 apples fall to the ground. How many apples are left in the tree?

___ ◯ ___ ◯ ___

___ apples

5. Chris reads 9 books. Patty reads 9 books. How many books do they read in all?

___ ◯ ___ ◯ ___

___ books

Name ________________ Date __________

Count Dimes and Pennies

CA Standards
NS 1.5, KEY NS 2.4

Solve.

1. Cindy has 3 dimes. She finds 2 pennies. How much money does she have in all?

_____ ¢

2. Rose has 4 dimes and 1 penny. She uses 1 dime to buy an apple. How much money does she have left?

_____ ¢

3. Frank has 7 dimes in his hand. He has 4 pennies in his pocket. How much money does Frank have in all?

_____ ¢

4. Caleb has 3 dimes and 4 pennies. He uses 2 dimes to buy a sticker. How much money does he have left?

_____ ¢

5. An orange costs 35¢. A banana costs 20¢. Jackson has 5 dimes and 4 pennies. Can he buy both the orange and the banana?

_____

6. Vicki has 6 dimes and 3 pennies. She buys a card for 45¢. She gives 15¢ to her brother. How much money does Vicki have left?

_____ ¢

Problem Solving: Create and Solve

CA Standards
AF 1.3, MR 1.0

You can use addition and subtraction to solve problems.

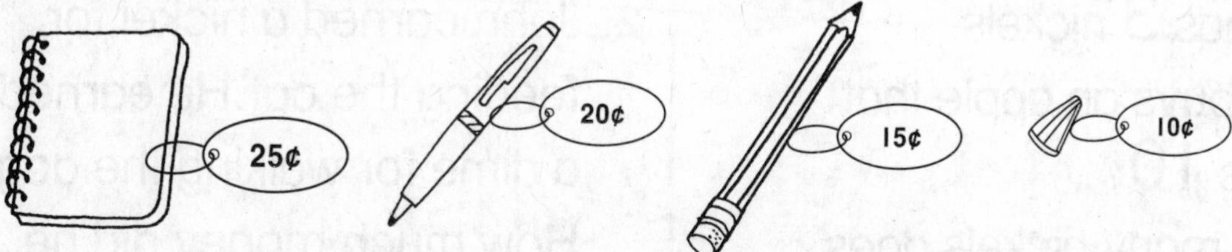

What is the cost of a pencil and a pencil top eraser?

Step 1 The cost of a pencil is 15¢.

The cost of a pencil top eraser is 10¢.

Step 2 Add. 15¢ + 10¢ = 25¢

Solution: The cost is 25¢.

1. Choose 2 school supplies from the picture. How much would they cost together? Complete the addition sentence.

   ____¢ + ____¢ = ____¢

2. Choose 2 school supplies from the picture. Write a subtraction sentence showing which school supply costs more.

   ____¢ − ____¢ = ____¢

Spiral Review (Chapter 19, Lesson 3) **KEY NS 2.1**

Write each difference.
Circle the fact if it is related to a doubles fact.

3. $\begin{array}{r} 19 \\ -9 \\ \hline \end{array}$

4. $\begin{array}{r} 14 \\ -7 \\ \hline \end{array}$

Name ____________________ Date __________

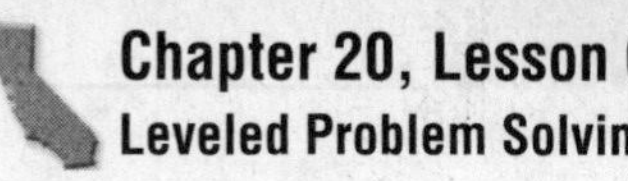

Problem Solving: Create and Solve

CA Standards
AF 1.3, MR 1.0

Solve.

1. Pat has 3 nickels.
She buys an apple that costs 10¢.
How many nickels does she use?

_____ nickles

2. John earned a nickel for feeding the cat. He earned a dime for walking the dog.
How much money did he earn in all?

_____ ¢

3. Kim wants to buy a book for 18¢.
What is the least number of coins she can use?

_____ coins

4. Jake has 4 dimes, 2 nickels, and 3 pennies.
Can he buy a toy for 47¢?

_____

5. Mina has 5 dimes and 3 nickels.
She gets another coin.
Now she has 75¢.
What coin did she get?

____

6. Otis has 7 coins that equal 60¢.
Some are dimes.
Some are nickels.
How many of each coin does Otis have?

_____ dimes _____ nickles

Name ____________________ Date __________

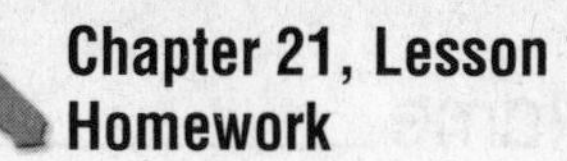

Hands On: Count Coins

CA Standards
NS 1.5, MR 1.2

You can find the value of coins by counting on.

Count dimes first. Count nickels next. Then count pennies.

10¢ __20__ ¢ 25¢ __30__ ¢ __35__ ¢ 36¢ 37¢ __38__ ¢

Find the value of the coins.

1\.

_____ ¢ _____ ¢ _____ ¢ _____ ¢ _____ ¢ _____ ¢

2\.

_____ ¢ _____ ¢ _____ ¢ _____ ¢ _____ ¢ _____ ¢

Spiral Review (Chapter 20, Lesson 1) **NS 1.5, MR 1.2**

Show 2 different ways to pay for the object.
Draw the coins.

3\.

4\.

Hands On: Count Coins

CA Standards
NS 1.5, MR 1.2

Solve.

1. Carlos has 2 dimes, 2 nickels, and 1 penny.
How much money does he have?

31¢ 41¢

2. Aran has 1 dime, 2 nickels, and 2 pennies.
How much money does he have?

17¢ 22¢

3. Crayons cost 45¢.
Janet has 2 dimes, 4 nickels, and 4 pennies.
Can Janet buy the crayons?

______

4. A puzzle costs 50¢.
Lou has 3 dimes, 5 nickels, and 1 penny.
Can he buy the puzzle?

______

5. A pencil costs 30¢.
An eraser costs 25¢.
Jamal has 3 dimes, 4 nickels, and 5 pennies.
Can he buy both the pencil and the eraser?

______

6. Kiki has 3 dimes, 4 nickels, and 3 pennies.
She buys a pen for 25¢.
She gives 15¢ to her mom.
How much money does Kiki have left?

______ ¢

Name ____________________ Date __________

Equal Amounts

CA Standard
NS 1.5

Different coins can show the same amount.
Both groups of coins show 26¢.

_____¢ _____¢ _____¢ _____¢ _____¢

_____¢ _____¢ _____¢ _____¢ _____¢ _____¢

Draw 2 ways to show each amount.

1. 17¢

2. 22¢

Spiral Review (Chapter 20, Lesson 2) **NS 1.5, KEY NS 2.4**

Find the value of the nickels.

3. 

_____¢ _____¢ _____¢ _____¢ _____¢

4. 

_____¢ _____¢ _____¢ _____¢ _____¢ _____¢

Name ____________________ Date __________

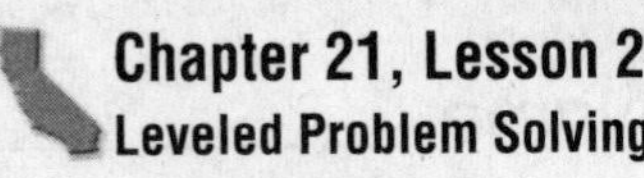

Equal Amounts

CA Standard
NS 1.5

Solve.

1. Kent has these coins.

How much money does he have?

31¢   36¢

2. Rosa has these coins.

How much money does she have?

32¢   52¢

3. Beth has 42¢.
She finds 2 dimes.
How much money does Beth have now?

_____ ¢

4. Jake starts with 58¢.
He spends 3 nickels at the store.
How much money does Jake have left?

_____ ¢

5. Keron has 43¢.
His dad gives him 2 dimes, 3 nickels, and 2 pennies.
How much money does Keron have now?

_____ ¢

6. Marla starts with 75¢.
She spends 3 dimes, 4 nickels, and 5 pennies at the store.
How much money does Marla have left?

_____ ¢

Quarters and Equal Amounts

CA Standards
NS 1.5, KEY NS 2.4

A quarter is equal to 25¢.

These coins make 25¢.

Circle the coins that match the price.

1. 

54¢

2. 

42¢

Spiral Review (Chapter 20, Lesson 3) **NS 1.5, KEY NS 2.4**

Circle the coins to match the price.

3. 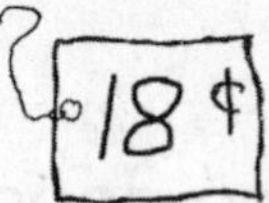

4. 21¢

Quarters and Equal Amounts

CA Standards
NS 1.5, KEY NS 2.4

Solve.

Use coins if you want.

1. Max has 1 quarter.
Which toy can he buy?
Circle your answer.

2. Margo has 2 quarters.
How much money does she have?

______ ¢

3. Juan wants to buy a book that costs 50¢.
He has 1 quarter.
Does he have enough money to buy the book?

______

4. Linda counts her money.
She has 75¢. How many quarters does Linda have?

______ quarters

5. Mark has 3 dimes and 3 nickels. Liz has 1 quarter and 3 dimes. Jen has 2 quarters.
Who has the most money?

______

6. Nancy buys a granola bar for 30¢ and a drink for 25¢. She pays with 3 quarters.
How much change does Nancy get?

______ ¢

Problem Solving: Make a List

CA Standards
NS 1.5, MR 1.0

There are many different ways to show the same amount.
Use coins.
Make a list to show the same amount in different ways.
Draw the coins.

1. 25¢

___

2. 40¢

___

3. 65¢

___

Spiral Review (Chapter 20, Lesson 4) NS 1.5, **KEY** NS 2.4

Find the value of the dimes.

4.   

_____ ¢ _____ ¢ _____ ¢

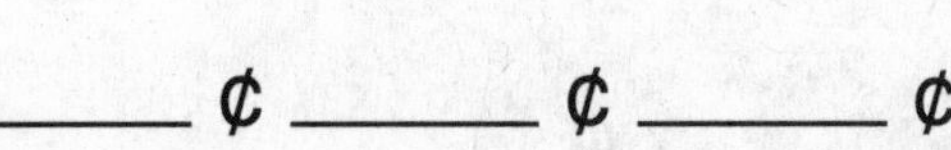

5.    

_____ ¢ _____ ¢ _____ ¢

_____ ¢ _____ ¢ _____ ¢

Name ____________________ Date __________

Problem Solving: Make a List

CA Standards
NS 1.5, MR 1.0

Solve.

1. An apple costs 25¢.
Chet has 1 dime and 1 nickel.
He needs 1 more coin to buy the apple.
What coin does Chet need?

dime nickel

2. Grace uses 1 quarter and 1 nickel to buy a chocolate bar.
How much does the chocolate bar cost?

35¢ 30¢

3. A toy truck costs 40¢.
Jamey has 2 dimes.
How many more dimes does he need to buy the truck?

____

4. A box of crayons is 10¢.
Nancy has 8 nickels.
How many boxes of crayons can she buy?

____

5. Anne has 2 quarters, 1 dime, 3 nickels, and 3 pennies.
She spends 71¢ at the store.
What is the smallest number of coins she uses?

____

6. Alberto buys a stamp for 22¢ and a sticker for 20¢.
He pays with 2 quarters.
How much change should Alberto get back?

_______ ¢

Name ______________________ Date __________

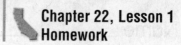

Hands On: Order Events

CA Standards
MG 1.2, MR 1.2

Events happen in an order.

This is what happens when you feed a cat.

Some events happen before.

Some events happen after.

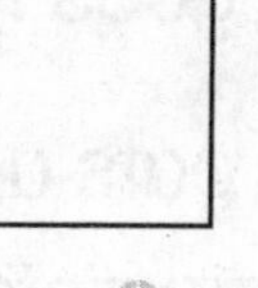

1 ________ 2 ________ 3 ________

1. Write 1, 2, and 3 to show the order.

________ ________ ________

Spiral Review (Chapter 21, Lesson 1) **NS 1.5, MR 1.2**

Find the value of the coins.

2.    

____¢, ____¢, ____¢, ____¢

3.    

____¢, ____¢, ____¢, ____¢

Hands On: Order Events

CA Standards
MG 1.2, MR 1.2

Solve.

1. Eve goes to school. Next, she plays a game. Then she has a snack. Circle what Eve does before she plays a game.

   She goes to school.

   She eats a snack.

2. Hahn brushes her teeth. Next, she reads a book. Then she goes to sleep. Circle what Hahn does after she reads.

   She brushes her teeth.

   She goes to sleep.

3. Sergio gets a piece of paper. Next, he draws a picture. Then he gives the picture to his mom. What does Sergio do after he draws a picture?

   ____

   ____

4. Sari washes her hair. Next, she brushes her hair. Then she puts her hair in a pony tail. What does Sari do before she brushes her hair?

   ____

   ____

5. Maggie brushes her long hair. Next, she goes somewhere. Then Maggie has short hair. Where does Maggie go?

   ____

6. Anton gets a present from a friend. Next, he does something with it. Then he plays with a new ball. What does Anton do with the present?

   ____

Name ______________________ Date ____________

Compare Time

CA Standards
MG 1.2, MR 2.0

It takes less than an hour to do some activities.

It takes longer than an hour to do other activities.

Look at each picture.

Circle the correct word to compare if each activity is shorter or longer than an hour.

1. shorter

   longer

2. shorter

   longer

3. 

   shorter

   longer

4. 

   shorter

   longer

Spiral Review (Chapter 21, Lesson 2) **NS 1.5**

Draw two ways to show each amount.

5. 19 ¢		
6. 21 ¢		

Name ____________________ Date __________

Compare Time

CA Standards
MG 1.2, MR 2.0

Read the problem.

Circle the answer.

1. Ann counts to 10.
About how long does it take?

about 1 minute
about 1 hour

2. Dan reads 20 pages in his book.
About how long does it take?

about 1 minute
about 1 hour

3. The school bus will come in about 1 minute.
Does Kevin have time to make a sandwich?

yes no

4. Shana has about 1 hour before she has to leave for soccer practice.
What can she do in about 1 hour?

clean her room
brush her hair

5. Joey is listening to his favorite CD.
About how long will it take him to listen to it?

about 60 minutes
about 60 hours

6. Lindsay's family is going on a vacation.
About how long will they be gone?

about 10 hours
about 10 days

Name ______________________ Date __________

Hour

CA Standard
MG 1.2

Some clocks show the time with a minute hand and an hour hand. 1 o'clock

Other clocks show the time using only numbers. 1:00

Read the clock.
Write the time two ways.

1. 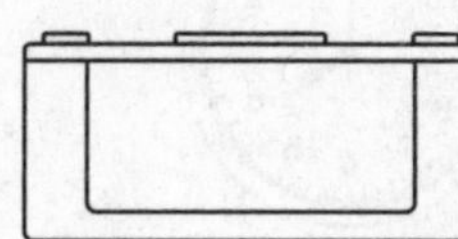

_____ o'clock

2. 

_____ o'clock

3. 

_____ o'clock

4. 

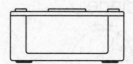

_____ o'clock

Spiral Review (Chapter 21, Lesson 3) NS 1.5, **KEY** NS 2.4

Circle the coins that match the price.

5. 25 ¢    

6. 17 ¢      

Name ____________________ Date __________

Hour

CA Standard
MG 1.2

Solve.

1. Kim goes to bed at 8 o'clock. Which clock shows when Kim goes to bed? Circle the answer.

2. Kele goes to soccer practice at 4 o'clock. Which clock shows when Kele goes to soccer practice? Circle the answer.

3. Betty's piano lesson starts at this time. What time does it start?

__________ o'clock

4. Todd eats dinner at this time. What time does Todd eat dinner?

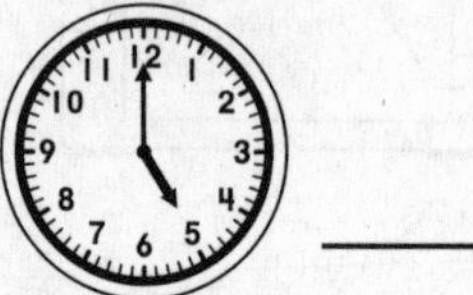

5. The show started 1 hour after Mike bought a ticket. Mike bought a ticket at 6 o'clock. What time did the show start?

____

6. Kyra must sign up for the walk 2 hours before it starts. The walk starts at 1:00. By what time should Kyra sign up?

____

Name ______________________ Date __________

Half Hour

CA Standards
MG 1.2, MR 3.0

An hour is 60 minutes.

3:00
3 o'clock

A half-hour is 30 minutes.

3:30
half past 3

Say and write the time.

1.  half past ______

2.  ______ o'clock

3.  half past ______

4.  ______ o'clock

Spiral Review (Chapter 21, Lesson 4) **NS 1.5, MR 1.0**

Show the amount in 2 different ways. Draw the coins.

5. 

6. 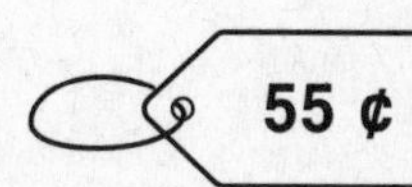

Half Hour

CA Standards
MG 1.2

Solve.

1. Rosa walks her dog at 9:30. Which clock shows when Rosa walks her dog? Circle the answer.

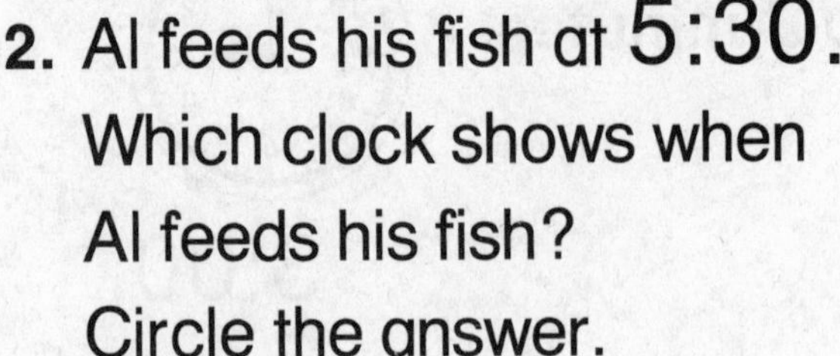

2. Al feeds his fish at 5:30. Which clock shows when Al feeds his fish? Circle the answer.

3. Sara eats lunch at this time. What time does Sara eat lunch?

 half past __________

4. Charles starts his homework at this time. What time does Charles start his homework?

 __________

5. David fell asleep at half past 8. His brother fell asleep at 9 o'clock. Who fell asleep first?

____

6. Mina got to the library at half past 3. Laura got to the library at 3:00. Who got to the library first?

____

Name ____________________ Date __________ | **Chapter 22, Lesson 5 Homework**

Problem Solving: Use a Table

CA Standard
KEY NS 1.1

A table can help you solve problems.
Solve. Use information from the table.

Trail Hiking Schedule

Trail Name	Time
Turtle Trail	7:00
Eagle Way	9:30
Waterfall Springs	1:30
Rabbit Run	3:00

1. Which hike starts $2\frac{1}{2}$ hours after the Turtle Trail hike?

   ____

2. How many hours are there between the Waterfall Springs hike and the Rabbit Run hike? __________

3. Marta arrives for the Eagle Way hike at 8:30. How long must she wait until it begins? __________

Spiral Review (Chapter 21, Lesson 1) **NS 1.5, MR 1.2**

Find the value of the coins

4. 

   ___ ¢ ___ ¢ ___ ¢ ___ ¢

5. 

   ___ ¢ ___ ¢ ___ ¢ ___ ¢

Problem Solving: Use a Table

CA Standards
MG 1.2, SDAP 1.0

Solve.

Picnic Activity Schedule	
Activity	Time
Horseshoe tournament	8:00
Children's races	10:00
Three-legged race	11:00
Magic show	11:30
Lunch	12:30
Egg toss	2:00
Dinner	6:00
Hayride	7:30

1. What activity starts 3 and one-half hours after the horseshoe tournament starts?

   ____

2. What activity starts 5 and one-half hours before dinner begins?

   ____

3. How many hours are there between the magic show and the hayride?

   __________ hours

4. How many hours are there between the children's races and the egg toss?

   __________ hours

5. The children's races last one-half hour. How long after the children's races end does the magic show begin?

   __________ hours

6. The hayride lasts one hour. John arrived at the picnic at 9:00 and left when the hayride ended. How long was John at the picnic?

   __________ hours

Name ____________________ Date __________

Hands On: Add a 2-Digit Number and a 1-Digit Number

CA Standards
NS 2.6, KEY NS 2.5

You can model addition.

14 + 3

Show the greater addend.

Tens Ones

Show 3 more.

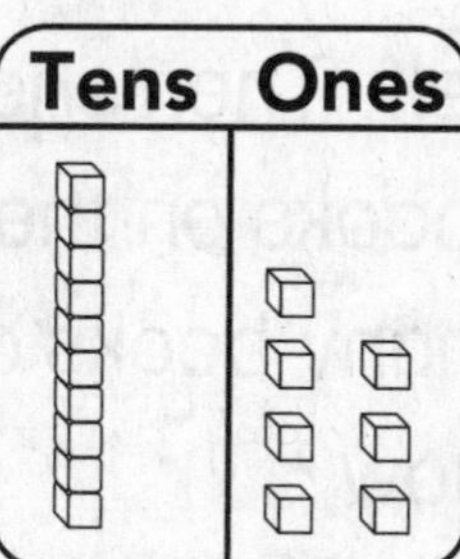

Solution: 14 + 3 = 17

1. 11 + 5 = ________
2. 15 + 2 = ________
3. 13 + 3 = ________
4. 14 + 4 = ________

Add. Count on from the greater addend.

5. 17 + 3 = ____
6. 14 + 3 = ____
7. 12 + 4 = ____
8. 16 + 2 = ____
9. 15 + 4 = ____

Spiral Review (Chapter 22, Lesson 1) **MG 1.2**

10. Write 1, 2, and 3 to show the order.

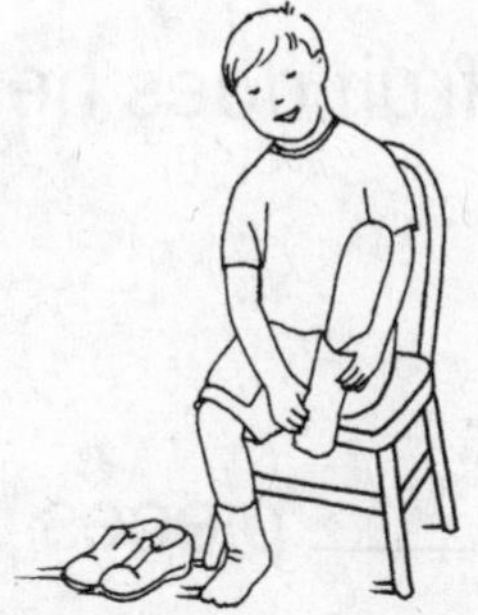

________ ________ ________

Hands On: Add a 2-Digit Number and a 1-Digit Number

CA Standards
KEY NS 2.5, NS 2.6

Solve.

1. Neva puts 12 books on the shelf. Then she puts 3 more books on the shelf. How many books are on the shelf now?

   12 + 3 = ______

2. Justin has 14 marbles. He finds 3 marbles in his pocket. How many marbles does Justin have now?

   14 + 3 = ______

3. Owen counts 15 cherries in the bowl. Then his mom puts 4 more cherries in the the bowl. How many cherries are there now?

   ______ cherries

4. Tonya sees 11 birds in the tree. Then 6 more birds fly to the tree. How many birds are there in all?

   ______ birds

5. Enrique has 10 apples and 5 oranges. Then he gets 4 bananas.How many pieces of fruit does he have in all?

   ______ pieces of fruit

6. Natasha has 12 green crayons and 4 blue crayons. Her friend gives her 4 yellow crayons. How many crayons does Natasha have now?

   ______ crayons

Hands On: Add 2-Digit and 1-Digit Numbers with Regrouping

CA Standards
KEY NS 2.5, NS 2.6

Find 15 + 8.

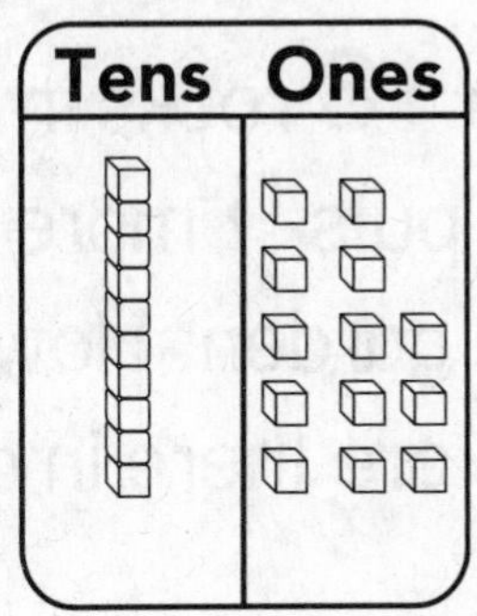

Look to see if you can make another 10.

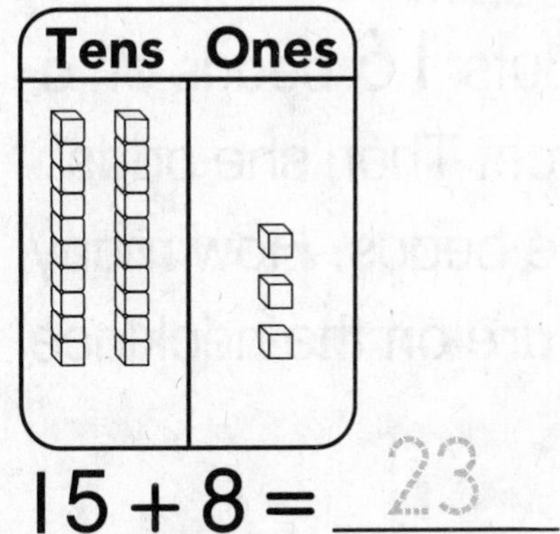

15 + 8 = 23

Find the sum. Model if you wish.
Count on from the greater addend.

1. 17 + 5 = ____
2. 16 + 7 = ____
3. 14 + 7 = ____
4. 18 + 6 = ____
5. 15 + 6 = ____
6. 19 + 4 = ____
7. 14 + 8 = ____
8. 16 + 4 = ____
9. 17 + 9 = ____

Spiral Review (Chapter 22, Lesson 2) **MG 1.2**

Compare to an hour. Circle the correct word.

10. 

shorter longer

11. 

shorter longer

Hands On: Add 2-Digit and 1-Digit Numbers with Regrouping

CA Standards
KEY NS 2.5, NS 2.6

Solve.

1. Anita puts 16 beads on a necklace. Then she adds 5 more beads. How many beads are on the necklace now?

   16 + 5 = ______ beads

2. Hikaru sees 18 rocks in the garden. He puts 4 more rocks in the garden. How many rocks are there in all?

   18 + 4 = ______ rocks

3. Tommy rides his bike for 17 minutes. Then he rides for 8 minutes more. How many minutes does Tommy ride his bike in all?

   ______ minutes

4. Mimi counts 13 flowers in the vase. Her mom adds 9 more flowers to the vase. How many flowers are in the vase now?

   ______ flowers

5. Nancy decorates for the party using 8 red balloons, 9 green balloons, and 10 blue balloons. How many balloons does she use in all?

   ______ balloons

6. Julian has 12 green stickers, 9 yellow stickers, and 7 red stickers. How many stickers does he have in all?

   ______ stickers

Name ______________________ Date __________

Sums to 30

CA Standards
NS 2.6, NS 1.4

Find 18 + 7.

The ones make a basic fact. Add them first. Then add on 10.

18 + 7

10 + 8 + 7

10 + 15 = 25

Circle the basic fact. Then find the sum.

1. Find 15 + 9.

10 + ____ + ____

10 + ☐ = ____

2. Find 22 + 7.

20 + ____ + ____

20 + ☐ = ____

Find the sum.

3. 18 + 5 = ____
4. 16 + 9 = ____
5. 24 + 4 = ____
6. 15 + 7 = ____
7. 21 + 5 = ____
8. 19 + 6 = ____

Spiral Review (Chapter 22, Lesson 3) **MG 1.2**

Read the clock. Write the time.

9.

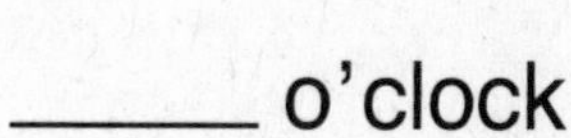

____ o'clock

10.

____ o'clock

Name ______________________ Date __________

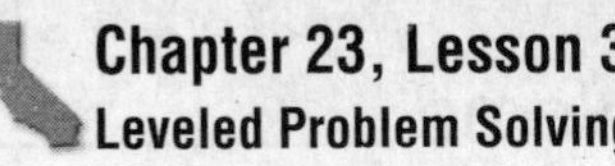

Sums to 30

CA Standards
NS 2.6, NS 1.4

Solve.

1. Tyrone sees 8 ducks in the pond. He sees 4 ducks on the grass. How many ducks does he see in all?

   ______ ducks

2. Randi picks 9 apples from the tree. Danny picks 7 apples. How many apples do they pick in all?

   ______ apples

3. There are 16 books on the shelf. Diane adds 8 books to the shelf. How many books are on the shelf now?

   ______ books

4. There are 18 bees buzzing near the hive. Then 7 more bees join them. How many bees are there in all?

   ______ bees

5. Marshall has 18 red balloons and 19 green balloons. He gets 9 more red balloons. How many red balloons does he have now?

   ______ red balloons

6. Kristi has 17 big shells and 24 small shells in her collection. She finds 6 more small shells at the beach. How many small shells does she have in all?

   ______ small shells

Problem Solving: Guess and Check

CA Standards
NS 2.6, NS 3.1

Jeremy needs 19 bagels for a party.
Which 2 boxes does Jeremy buy?

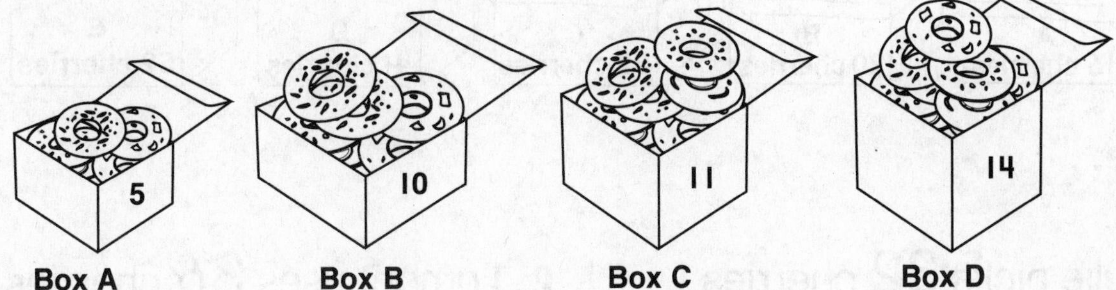

Make a guess. Add to check the guess.

First Guess

Box A 5

Box B + 10

Too few.

Second Guess

Box A 5

Box D + 14

This is the answer.

Guess and check to solve.

1. Saul gets 25 bagels. Which two boxes does he buy?

   Box _____ and Box _____

2. Mrs. Sanchez needs 21 bagels. Which 2 boxes should she buy?

   Box _____ and Box _____

Spiral Review (Chapter 22, Lesson 4) **MG 1.2**

Say and write the time.

3. 

   half past _____ o'clock

4. 

   half past _____ o'clock

Name ______________________ Date __________

Problem Solving: Guess and Check

CA Standards
NS 2.6, NS 3.1

Solve.

1. Julie picks 32 cherries. Which box belongs to Julie?

   Box ______

2. Lamont uses 36 cherries to make a tart. Which boxes does he use?

   Box ______ and Box ______

3. Arnitra needs 48 cherries to make a pie. Which two boxes does she buy?

   Box ______ and Box ______

4. Michael picks 61 cherries to take home. Which boxes belong to Michael?

   Box ______ and Box ______

5. Jenny is making 2 cherry pies for a bake sale. She will use 36 cherries in each pie. Which boxes should she buy?

   Box ______ and Box ______

6. Samuel is making 2 cherry tarts for the bake sale. He will use 24 cherries in each tart. Which boxes should he use?

   Box ______ and Box ______

Hands On: Model Addition to 50

CA Standards
NS 2.6, KEY NS 2.5

Find 34 + 7. Show each number 34 + 7.

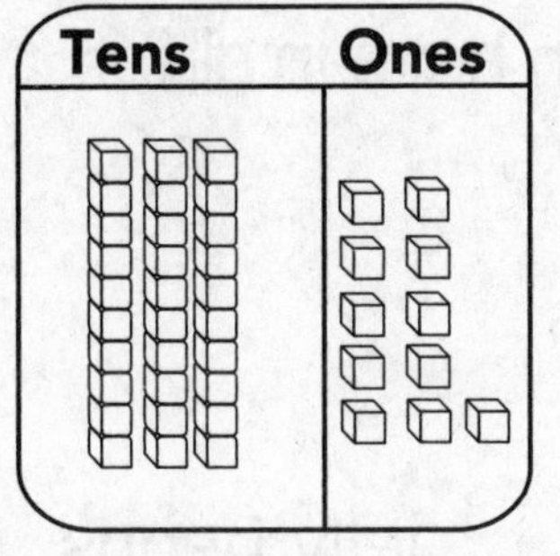

Regroup by trading 10 ones for 1 ten.

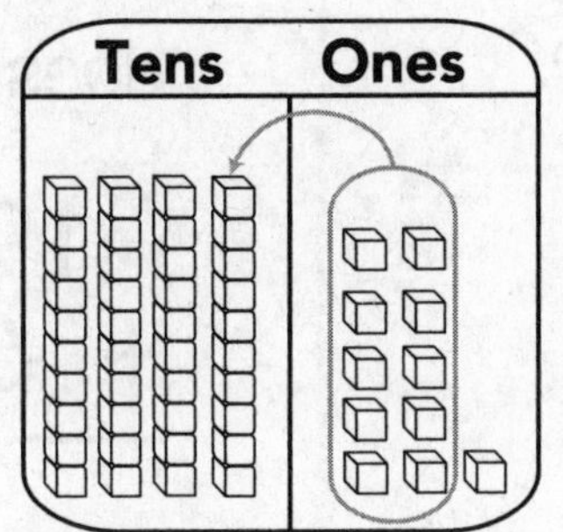

Write the sum.

34 + 7 = 41

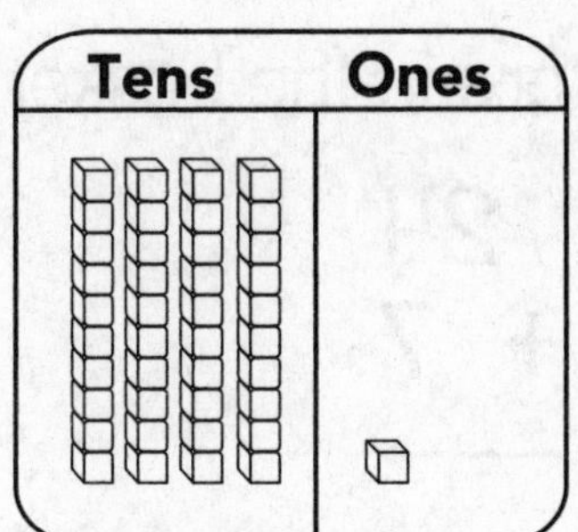

Regroup. Write the sum.

1. 32 + 9 = ________
2. 27 + 6 = ________
3. 19 + 7 = ________
4. 22 + 8 = ________
5. 28 + 4 = ________
6. 35 + 7 = ________

Spiral Review (Chapter 23, Lesson 1) **KEY** NS 2.5, NS 2.6

Add. Count on from the greater addend.

7. 11 + 4 = ____
8. 17 + 2 = ____

Name ________________ Date __________

Hands On: Model Addition to 50

CA Standards
NS 2.6, KEY NS 2.5

Solve.

1. There are 24 flowers in the basket. Then Mona adds 7 flowers. How many flowers are in the basket now?

$$\begin{array}{r} 24 \\ +\ 7 \\ \hline \end{array}$$

_____________ Flowers

2. Allison has 19 jelly beans. Shelly gives her 6 more jelly beans. How many jelly beans does Allison have in all?

$$\begin{array}{r} 19 \\ +\ 6 \\ \hline \end{array}$$

_____________ jelly beans

3. Jarrius does his math homework for 18 minutes. Then he does his science homework for 9 minutes. How many minutes does it take for Jarrius to do his homework?

_____________ minutes

4. Julia has 26 coins. She finds 8 more coins in her pocket. How many coins does Julia have in all?

_____________ coins

5. Mark counts 18 red ants and 24 black ants on the sidewalk. He counts 8 black ants on a leaf. How many black ants are there in all?

_____________ black ants

6. Cindy has 24 big marbles and 21 small marbles. Her friend gives her 7 more big marbles. How many big marbles does Cindy have in all?

_____________ big marbles

Name ______________________ Date __________

Sums to 50

CA Standard
KEY NS 2.6, NS 2.0

Add the ones first. Regroup if you have enough to make another ten.

32 + 9 = 41 **Can I make another 10?**

2 + 9 = 11

Rule: Add 7

In	Out
1. 24	
2. 36	
3. 29	
4. 17	
5. 25	
6. 19	

Rule: Add 8

In	Out
7. 35	
8. 28	
9. 33	
10. 39	
11. 21	
12. 26	

Spiral Review (Chapter 23, Lesson 2) **KEY** NS 2.5, NS 2.6

Find the sum. Model if you wish.
Count on from the greater addend.

13. 16 + 5 = ________

14. 18 + 7 = ________

Sums to 50

CA Standards
NS 2.6, NS 2.0

Solve.

1. There are 32 chickens on the farm. Then 9 chicks are born. How many chickens are on the farm now?

$$\begin{array}{r} 32 \\ +\ 9 \\ \hline \end{array}$$

__________ chickens

2. Ramon has 17 cherries. Terri gives him 8 more cherries. How many cherries does Ramon have in all?

$$\begin{array}{r} 17 \\ +\ 8 \\ \hline \end{array}$$

__________ cherries

3. Lukas rides his bike for 27 minutes in the morning. Then he rides his bike for 9 minutes in the afternoon. How many minutes does Lukas ride in all?

__________ minutes

4. There are 34 children at the park. Then 8 more children join them. How many children are at the park now?

__________ children

5. Josh counts 24 nickels and 27 pennies in his bank. He adds 7 pennies to the bank. How many pennies are there in all?

__________ pennies

6. Olivia has 38 big shells and 21 small shells in her collection. She finds 6 more big shells at the beach. How many big shells are in Olivia's collection now?

__________ big shells

Hands On: Model Addition to 100

CA Standards
KEY NS 2.5, NS 2.6

Find 65 + 8. Show each number.	Regroup by trading 10 ones for 1 ten.	Write the sum. 65 + 8 = 73
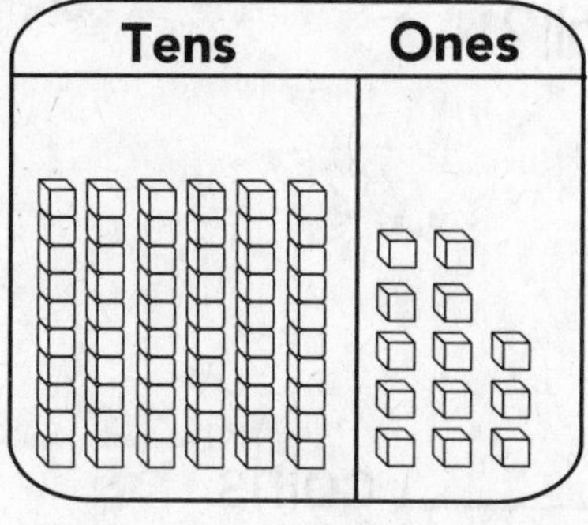	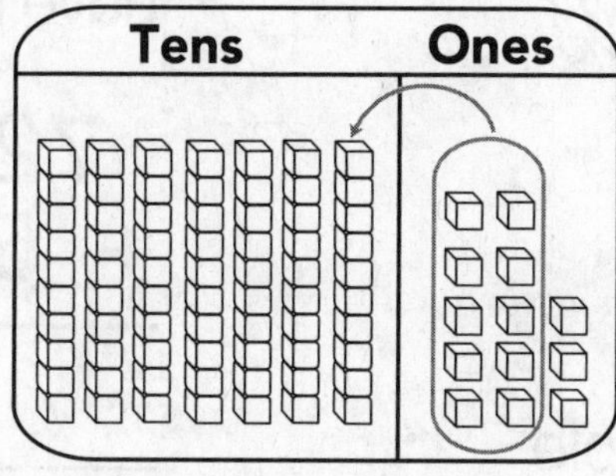	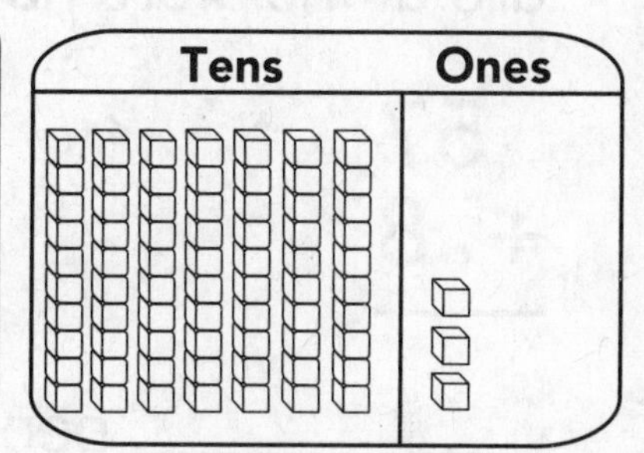

Regroup. Write the sum.

1. 74 + 8 = ________
2. 68 + 5 = ________
3. 57 + 6 = ________
4. 82 + 9 = ________
5. 77 + 8 = ________
6. 65 + 7 = ________

Spiral Review (Chapter 23, Lesson 3) **NS 2.6, NS 1.4**

Find the sum.

7. 18 + 6 = ________
8. 17 + 9 = ________

Name ____________________ Date __________

Hands On: Model Addition to 100

CA Standards
KEY NS 2.5, NS 2.6

Solve.

1. There are 57 people at the store. Then 8 more people arrive. How many people are at the store now?

$$\begin{array}{r} 57 \\ +\ 8 \\ \hline \end{array}$$

__________ people

2. Lamont has 72 coins. Mom gives him 5 more coins. How many coins does Lamont have in all?

$$\begin{array}{r} 72 \\ +\ 5 \\ \hline \end{array}$$

__________ coins

3. Anna counts 72 fish in the tanks at the pet store. Then 9 more fish are added to the tanks. How many fish are in the tanks now?

__________ fish

4. There are 67 animals in the zoo. Then 7 more animals join them. How many animals are in the zoo now?

__________ animals

5. Josh counts 59 black beans in the jar and 67 red beans in the pan. Then his mom adds 9 black beans to the jar. Are there more black beans or red beans now?

__________ beans

6. Maria has 82 stickers in her red book and 89 stickers in her blue book. She adds 8 more stickers to her red book. Which book has the most stickers now?

__________ book

Name ________________________ Date ____________

Sums to 100

CA Standards
NS 2.6, NS 2.0

When you add to a 2-digit number, you may or may not need to regroup.

64 + 7 = 71

Sometimes you have enough ones to make another 10.

53 + 6 = 59

Sometimes you do not have enough ones to make another 10.

Solve. Regroup if you need to.

1. 78 + 7 = ________
2. 62 + 6 = ________
3. 55 + 4 = ________
4. 84 + 7 = ________
5. 67 + 7 = ________
6. 54 + 4 = ________

Spiral Review (Chapter 23, Lesson 4) **NS 3.1, NS 2.6**

Guess and check to solve.

7. Marty wants to get 25 apples. Which 2 bags should he buy?

   Bag ______ and Bag ______

8. Vera wants 20 apples. Which 2 bags should she buy?

   Bag ______ and Bag ______

Name ____________________ Date __________

Sums to 100

CA Standards
NS 2.6, NS 2.0

Solve.

1. Bonnie has 73 coins. Dad gives her 5 more coins. How many coins does Bonnie have now?

$$\begin{array}{r} 73 \\ +\ 5 \\ \hline \end{array}$$

_________ coins

2. Riley has 52 cards. Jody gives her 9 more cards. How many cards does Riley have in all?

$$\begin{array}{r} 52 \\ +\ 9 \\ \hline \end{array}$$

_________ cards

3. Carlos runs laps on the track for 84 seconds. Then he walks on the track for 9 seconds. How long is Carlos on the track?

_________ seconds

4. Vera counts 73 flowers in the garden. Then Vera finds 4 more. How many flowers are there in all?

_________ flowers

5. Maggie puts 56 big books and 63 small books on the shelves in the library. Then she puts 8 more small books on the shelf. How many small books are on the shelves now?

_________ small books

6. Don puts 65 big marbles and 47 small marbles into a jar. Then he adds 7 big marbles to the jar. How many big marbles are there in all?

_________ big marbles

Name ______________________ Date __________

Problem Solving: Find a Pattern

CA Standards
KEY NS 2.4, MR 2.0

You can use the pattern in the table to solve problems.

Find the pattern. Complete the table.
Then use the table to answer the questions.

Number of Ducks	Number of Feet
1	2
2	4
3	6
4	8
5	10
6	12
7	14
8	16

1. Tori visits the duck pond. She sees 14 feet waddling to the water. How many ducks does she see? ________ ducks

2. How many feet do 3 ducks have? ________ feet

3. How many feet do 6 ducks have? ________ feet

Spiral Review (Chapter 23, Lesson 1) **KEY NS 2.5, NS 2.6**

Add. Count on from the greater addend.

4. $\begin{array}{r} 16 \\ +\ 3 \\ \hline \end{array}$

5. $\begin{array}{r} 11 \\ +\ 8 \\ \hline \end{array}$

Problem Solving: Find a Pattern

CA Standards
KEY NS 2.4, MR 2.0

Solve.

1. There are 2 bags on the table. Each bag has 3 apples in it. How many apples are there in all?

   3 + 3 = _____ apples

2. There are 4 boxes on the floor. Each box has 2 balls in it. How many balls are there in all?

   2 + 2 + 2 + 2 = _____ balls

3. Kim is packing sandwiches for a class picnic. She needs 5 sandwiches in each basket. She has 4 baskets. How many sandwiches does Kim need?

   _____ sandwiches

4. Keron is making cupcakes for the picnic. Each pan will hold 10 cupcakes. He has 3 pans. How many cupcakes is Keron making?

   _____ cupcakes

5. Randi finds 6 buckets of rocks. Each bucket has the same number of rocks. There are 48 rocks in all. How many rocks are in each bucket?

   _____ rocks

6. Caleb counts 9 groups of stickers. Each group has the same number of stickers. There are 45 stickers in all. How many stickers are in each group?

   _____ stickers

Name ____________________ Date __________

Hands On : Subtract a 1-Digit Number from a 2-Digit Number

CA Standards
KEY NS 2.5, NS 2.6

Find 37 − 6.

Subtract the ones.

Tens	Ones
3	7
−	6
	1

Subtract the tens.

Tens	Ones
3	7
−	6
3	1

Subtract. Write the difference.

1.

Tens	Ones
2	7
−	2

2.

Tens	Ones
2	5
−	3

3.

Tens	Ones
3	9
−	8

4.

Tens	Ones
2	6
−	6

5.

Tens	Ones
5	7
−	6

6.

Tens	Ones
4	6
−	3

7.

Tens	Ones
6	8
−	4

8.

Tens	Ones
5	4
−	2

Spiral Review (Chapter 24, Lesson 1) NS 2.6 **KEY** NS 2.5

Regroup. Write the sum.

9. 33 + 8 = _____

10. 28 + 5 = _____

Hands On: Subtract a 1-Digit Number from a 2-Digit Number

CA Standards
KEY NS 2.5, NS 2.6

Solve.

1. There are 27 apples in the tree. 4 apples fall to the ground. How many apples are left in the tree?

$$\begin{array}{r} 27 \\ -\ 4 \\ \hline \end{array}$$

____

2. Bruce has 39 marbles. He gives 6 marbles to Alex. How many marbles does Bruce have now?

$$\begin{array}{r} 39 \\ -\ 6 \\ \hline \end{array}$$

____

3. Trina counts 43 geese at the park. She watches 2 geese fly away. How many geese are still at the park?

____

4. The clown brings 28 balloons to the party. He pops 3 balloons. How many balloons are left?

____

5. Raul has 28 green markers and 39 blue markers. He gives 7 blue markers to Nancy. How many blue markers does Raul have left?

____

6. Yolanda makes 36 cookies and 30 cupcakes for the bake sale. She gives 4 cookies to Mary. Does Yolanda have more cookies or cupcakes now?

____

CA Standards
KEY NS2.5, NS2.6

Hands On: Subtract from Numbers to 50

Find 46−8.

Step 1 Show 46.

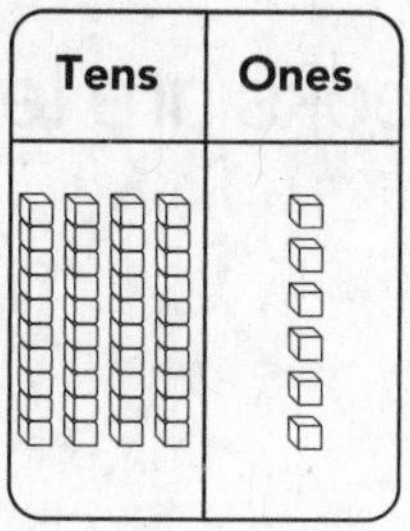

Tens	Ones
4	6

Step 2 Regroup if needed.

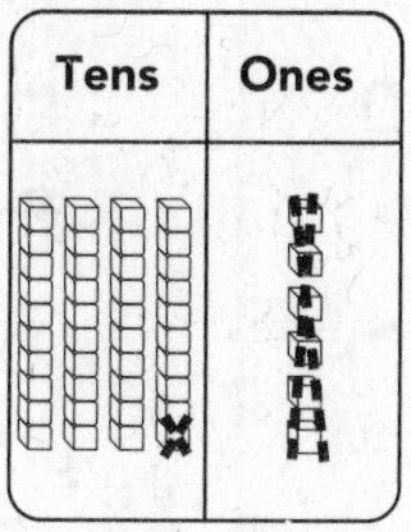

Tens	Ones
3	16
~~4~~	~~6~~
	8

Step 3 Subtract.

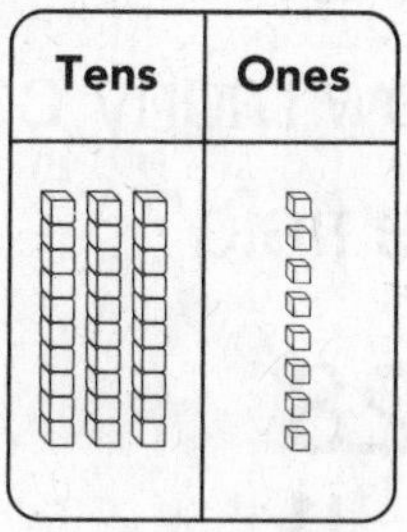

Tens	Ones
4	6
	8
3	8

46−8 = 38

Regroup if needed.

Subtract. Write the difference.

1. 42 − 5 = ____
2. 39 − 7 = ____
3. 37 − 9 = ____
4. 44 − 6 = ____
5. 49 − 9 = ____
6. 35 − 8 = ____

Spiral Review (Chapter 24, Lesson 2) NS 2.6, NS 2.0

Add to complete the chart.

7.

Rule: Add 6	
In	Out
27	
36	

8.

Rule: Add 7	
In	Out
29	
38	

Hands On: Subtract from Numbers to 50

CA Standards
KEY NS 2.5, 2.6

Solve.

1. There are 28 cows in the field. Then 4 cows go in to the barn.
How many cows are left in the field?

$$\begin{array}{r} 28 \\ -\ 4 \\ \hline \end{array}$$

____

2. There are 46 books on the shelf. Jenny takes 6 books off the shelf.
How many books are left on the shelf?

$$\begin{array}{r} 46 \\ -\ 6 \\ \hline \end{array}$$

____

3. There are 34 children playing in the park. Then 8 children go home.
How many children are left in the park?

____

4. There are 43 cars in the lot. Then 8 cars drive away.
How many cars are left in the lot?

____

5. Kinslee has 38 red stickers and 47 green stickers. She gives 9 green stickers to Molly. How many green stickers does Kinslee have left?

____

6. Jamal has 45 red grapes and 39 green grapes. He eats 8 red grapes.
How many red grapes does Jamal have left?

____

Hands On: Model Subtraction from Numbers to 100

CA Standards
KEY NS 2.5, NS 2.6

Find 74 – 7.

Step 1
Show 74.

	Tens	Ones
	7	4
–		7

Step 2
Regroup if needed.

	Tens	Ones
	6	14
	7	4
–		7

Step 3
Subtract.

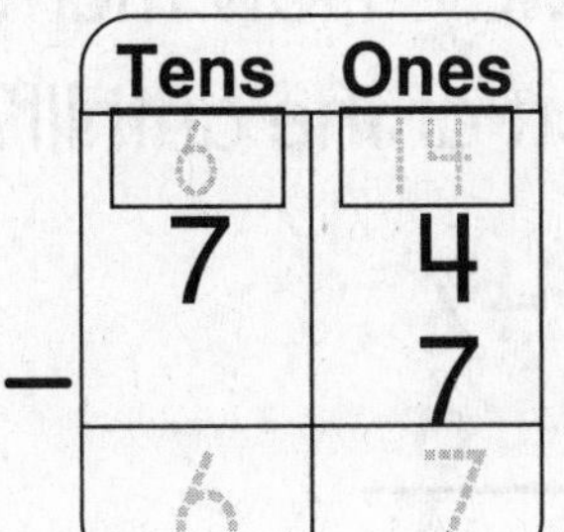

74 – 7 = 67

Regroup if needed. Subtract.

1.

	Tens	Ones
	7	6
–		9

2.

	Tens	Ones
	8	4
–		7

3.

	Tens	Ones
	6	8
–		6

4.

	Tens	Ones
	5	3
–		8

Spiral Review (Chapter 24, Lesson 3) NS 2.6, **KEY** NS 2.5

Regroup. Write the sum.

5. 75 + 8 = ________

6. 63 + 8 = ________

Hands On: Model Subtraction from Numbers to 100

CA Standards
KEY NS 2.5, NS 2.6

Solve.

1. There are 47 ants at the anthill. Then 6 ants crawl away. How many ants are left at the anthill?

$$\begin{array}{r} 47 \\ -\ 6 \\ \hline \end{array}$$

____

2. There are 54 bees in the hive. Then 6 bees fly to a flower. How many bees are left in the hive?

$$\begin{array}{r} 54 \\ -\ 6 \\ \hline \end{array}$$

____

3. Lionel has 78 stamps in his collection. He gives 9 stamps to a friend. How many stamps does Lionel have left?

____

4. MaryBeth collects 63 cans for the food drive. She packs 8 cans in a box. How many cans does MaryBeth have left to pack?

____

5. Carla has 64 big shells and 72 small shells in her collection. She gives 9 small shells to Maria. Does Carla have more big shells or small shells now?

____

6. Kevin has 85 big marbles and 78 small marbles in his collection. He gives 8 big marbles to Danny. Does Kevin have more big marbles or small marbles now?

____

Name ______________________ Date __________

Subtract from Numbers to 100

CA Standards
NS 2.6, NS 2.0

Subtract.

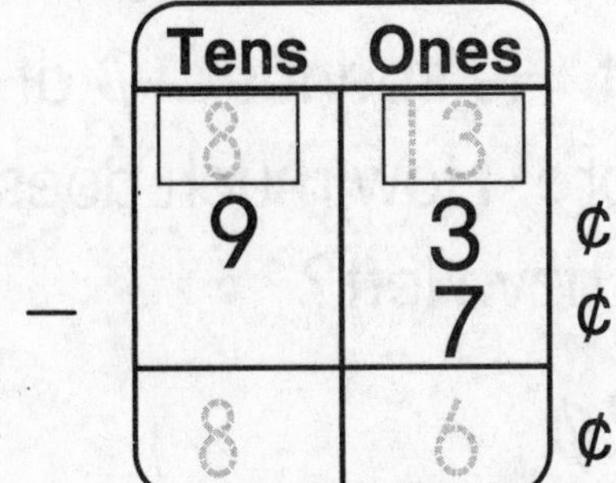

There are not enough ones.

I regroup.

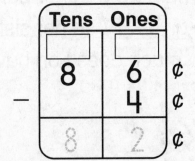

Tens Ones
8 6 ¢
– 4 ¢
8 2 ¢

There are enough ones.

I don't regroup.

Look at the problem. Circle do or don't. Subtract.

1. I do / don't regroup

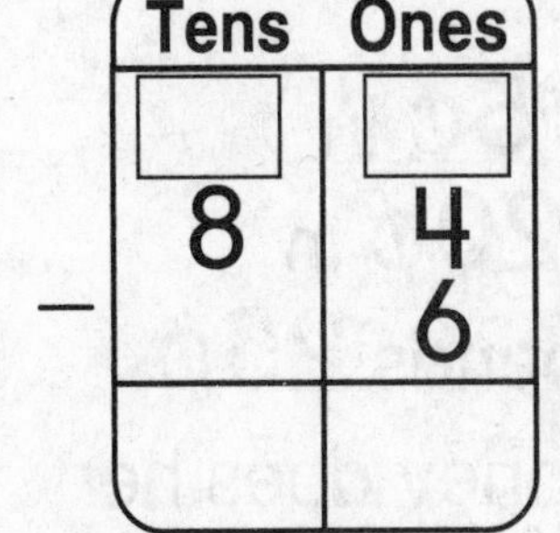

2. I do / don't regroup

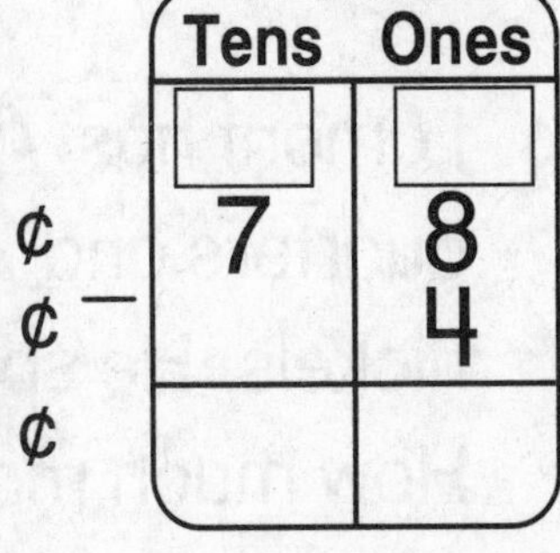

3. I do / don't regroup

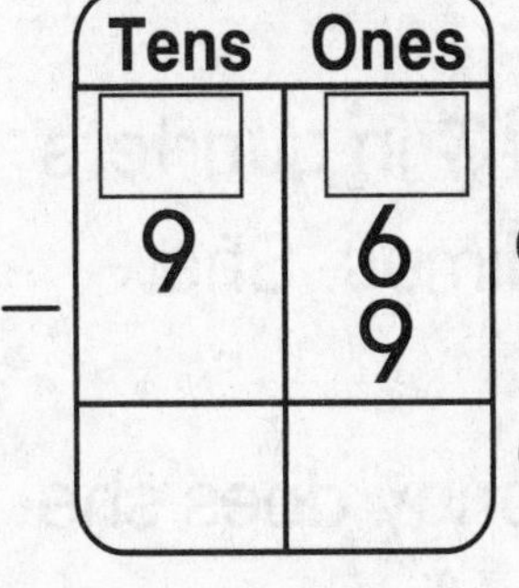

4. I do / don't regroup

Tens Ones
6 9 ¢
– 5 ¢
¢

Spiral Review (Chapter 24, Lesson 4) NS 2.6, NS 2.0

Solve. Regroup if you need to.

5. 68 + 7 = ______

6. 82 + 6 = ______

Subtract from Numbers to 100

CA Standards
NS 2.6, NS 2.0

Solve.

1. Lori has 56¢ in her bank. She gives 4¢ to her sister. How much does Lori have left?

   56¢
   − 4¢

   ____

2. Pedro has 62¢ in his pocket. He spends 5¢ at the store. How much does Pedro have left?

   62¢
   − 5¢

   ____

3. Jim has 74¢ in his pocket. He spends 8¢ on gum. How much does Jim have left?

   ____

4. Carol has 98¢ in her purse. She gives 9¢ to her brother. How much does Carol have left?

   ____

5. Tasha has 50¢ in quarters and 20¢ in dimes. She spends 15¢. How much money does she have left?

   ____

6. Lamont has 75¢ in quarters and 20¢ in nickels. He spends 25¢. How much money does he have left?

   ____

Name ______________________ Date __________

Hands On: Position Words

CA Standards
MG 2.3, MG 2.4

Some position words are **above, below, between, left,** and **right.**

Complete the sentence using above, below, between, left, and right.

1. The [dog] is __________ the tree.

2. The [boy] is to the ______ of the [tree].

3. The [sun] is __________ the tree.

4. The [girl] is to the ______ of the tree.

Spiral Review (Chapter 25, Lesson 1) **KEY** NS 2.5, NS 2.6

Subtract. Write the difference.

5.

	Tens	Ones
	3	8
−		5

6.

	Tens	Ones
	5	9
−		8

Name ______________________ Date ______________

Hands On: Position Words

CA Standards
MG 2.3, MG 2.4

Use the clues to solve.

1. Dan is to the left of the pear. What is Dan's fruit?

apple orange

2. Amie is to the right of the orange. What is Amie's fruit?

pear peach

3. Carol is below the table. What is Carol's fruit?

____

4. James is between the banana and the peach. What is his fruit?

____

5. Rosa is 2 places to the left of the peach. What is Rosa's fruit?

____

6. Kyle is 4 places to the left of the peach. What is Kyle's fruit?

____

Name ____________________ Date __________

More Position Words

CA Standards
MG 2.3, MG 2.4

You can use more position words to tell where things are. Some of these words are **behind, in front of, far from, next to, near, up, and down.**

Circle the answer that completes the sentence.

1. The cat goes

_____________ the stairs.

up   down

2. The rabbit is _____________ the carrot.

far from   near

3. The mountain is _____________ the cloud.

in front of   behind

4. The baby is _____________ the carriage.

next to   far from

Spiral Review (Chapter 25, Lesson 2) **KEY NS 2.5, NS 2.6**

Regroup if needed.
Subtract. Write the difference.

5. $52 - 7 =$ _____________

6. $39 - 4 =$ _____________

More Position Words

CA Standards
MG 2.3, MG 2.4

Help Max find his things.

1. Where is Max's cat?

climbing up the tree

climbing down the tree

2. Where is Max's bike?

behind the garage

in front of the garage

3. Where is Max's dog?

far from the doghouse

near the doghouse

in the doghouse

4. Where is Max's soccer ball?

far from the bush

above the bush

below the bush

5. Look at Max's soccer ball. Use position words to tell where it is in relation to the doghouse.

____

____

____

6. Look at the tree. Use position words to tell where it is in relation to the garage.

____

____

____

Name ______________________ Date __________

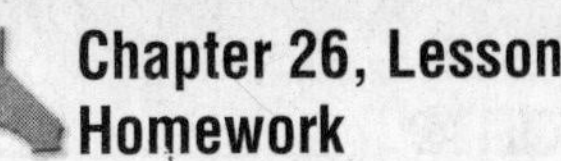

Plane Figures

CA Standard
MG 2.1, MG 2.0

Answer the questions.
Color the figures on the truck.

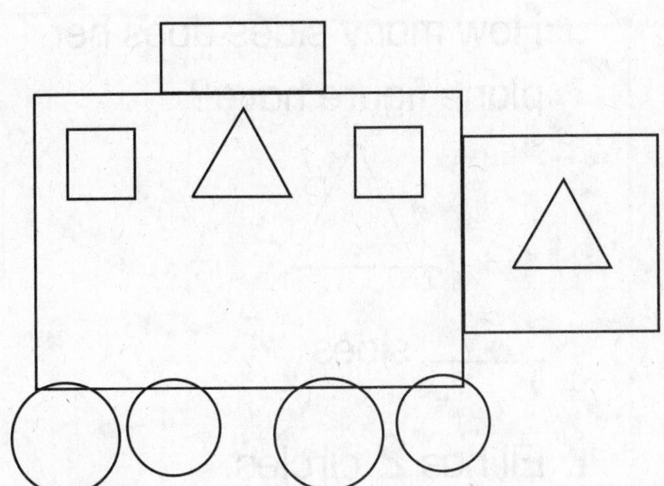

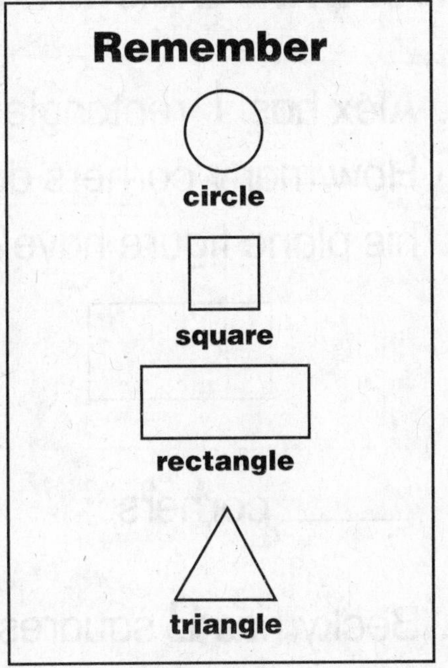

1. How many figures have 0 sides? _____
   Color them Blue.

2. How many figures have 3 sides? _____
   Color them Yellow.

3. How many figures have 4 sides that are not all the same size? _____
   Color them Red.

4. How many figures have 4 sides that are all the same? _____
   Color them Green.

Spiral Review (Chapter 25, Lesson 3) **KEY** NS 2.5, NS 2.6

Regroup if needed. Subtract.

5.

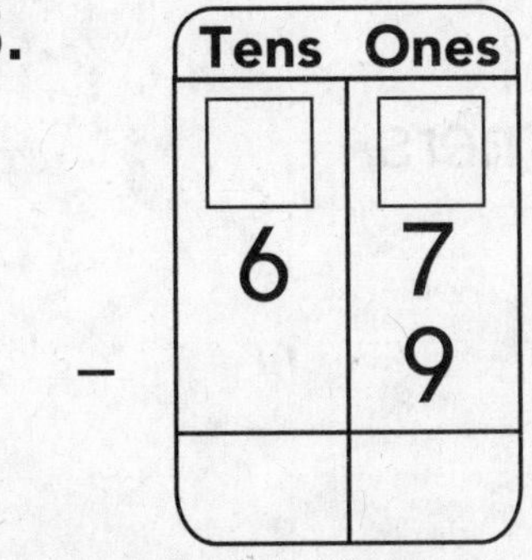

Tens	Ones
6	7
−	9

6.

Tens	Ones
8	8
−	8

Name ______________________ Date ____________

Plane Figures

CA Standards
MG 2.1, MG 2.0

Solve. Draw a picture to help.

1. Alex has 1 rectangle.
How many corners does his plane figure have?

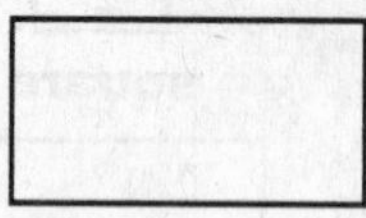

_____ corners

2. Sara has 1 triangle.
How many sides does her plane figure have?

_____ sides

3. Becky has 2 squares.
How many corners do her plane figures have in all?

_____ corners

4. Eli has 2 circles.
How many sides do his plane figures have in all?

_____ sides

5. Abby has 5 circles and 3 triangles.
How many sides do her plane figures have in all?

_____ sides

6. Mandy has 2 triangles and 2 rectangles.
How many corners do her plane figures have in all?

_____ corners

Sort Plane Figures

CA Standard
MG 2.2, SDAP 1.1

Some figures have 3 or 4 corners.

corner

Some figures have 3 or 4 sides.

side

Circle the figures that follow the rule.

1. 3 sides

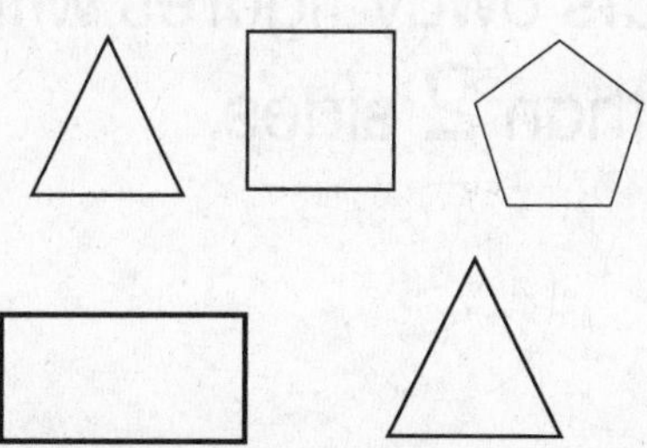

2. **4 sides the same**

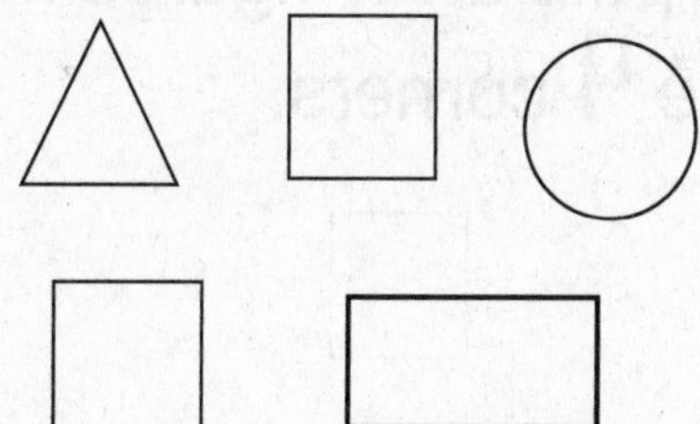

Spiral Review (Chapter 25, Lesson 4) **NS 2.6, MR 2.2**

Look at the problem. Circle do or don't. Subtract.

3. I do / don't regroup.

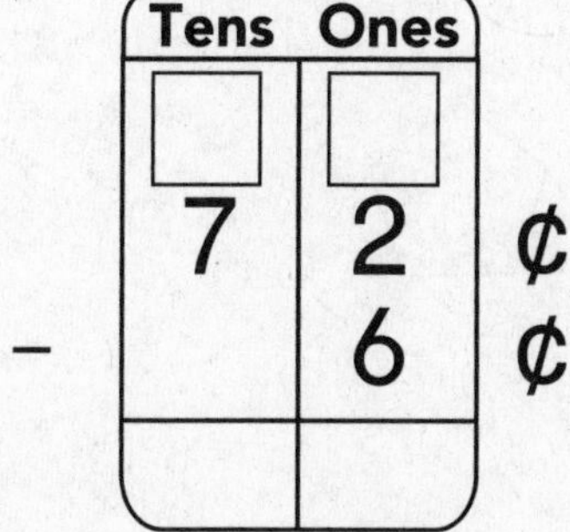

Tens	Ones	
7	2	¢
–	6	¢

4. I do / don't regroup.

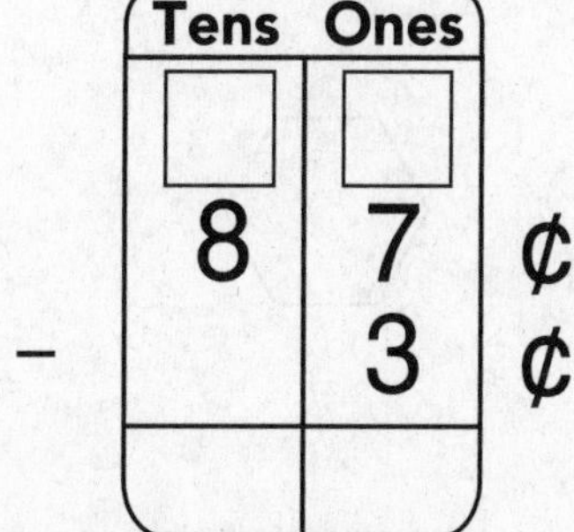

Tens	Ones	
8	7	¢
–	3	¢

Name ________________ Date __________

Sort Plane Figures

CA Standards
MG 2.2, MG 2.1, SDAP 1.1

Circle the figures that follow the sorting rule.

1. Austin puts away figures that have no corners.

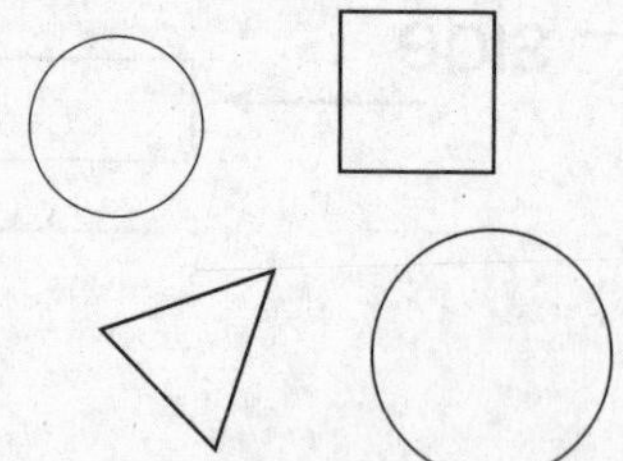

2. Teela puts away figures with 3 sides.

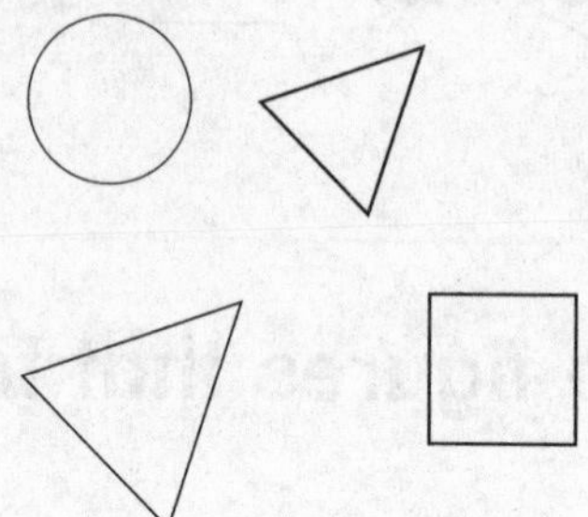

3. Tad puts away figures that have 4 corners.

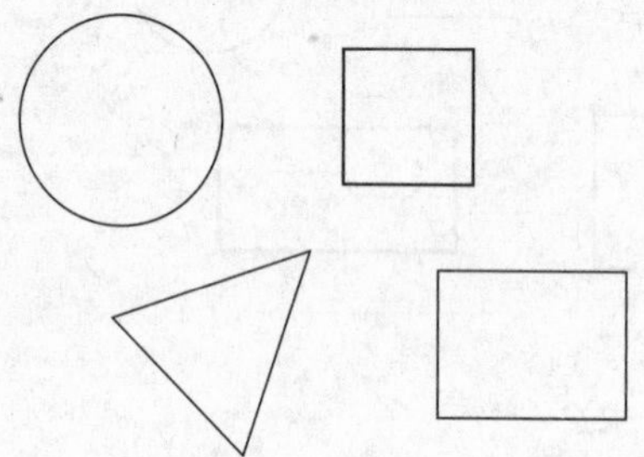

4. Lyn puts away figures with more than 2 sides.

5. Emma puts away figures with more than 4 sides and less than 7 sides.

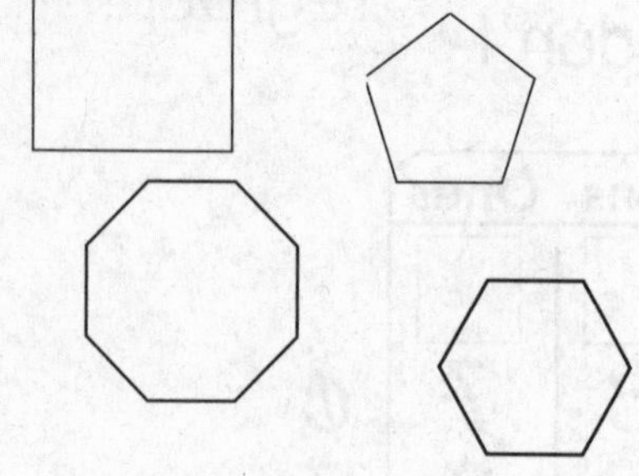

6. Luis puts away figures with more than 3 corners and less than 6 corners.

Problem Solving: Find a Pattern

CA Standard
KEY SDAP 2.1

Sometimes you need to look for a pattern to solve a problem.

Greg sees this pattern on the computer screen:

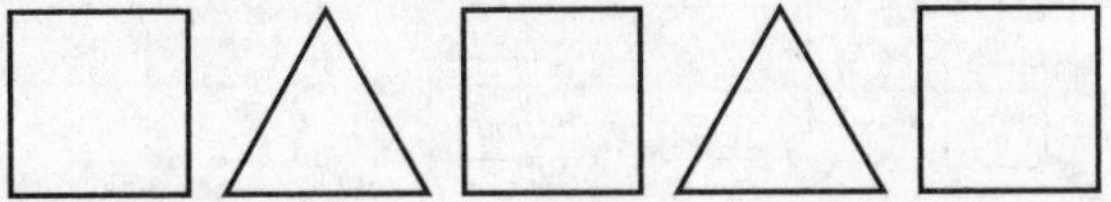

What shape comes next?

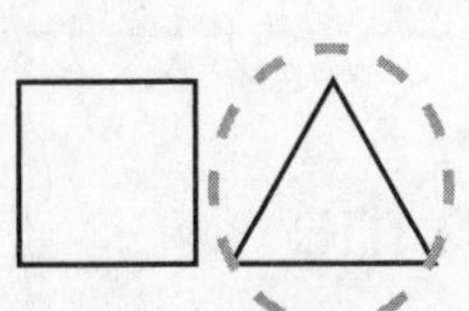

You need to find the next shape in the pattern. Look for the pattern. Circle the shape that comes next.

Solution: The triangle comes next in the pattern.

Find the pattern to solve.

1. Deana sees this pattern on a quilt.
   Circle the one that comes next.

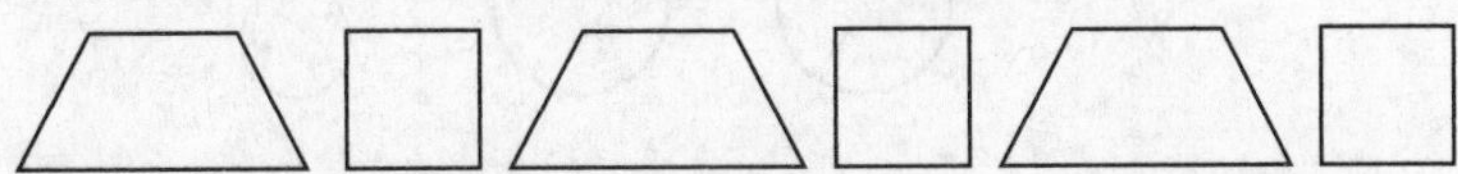

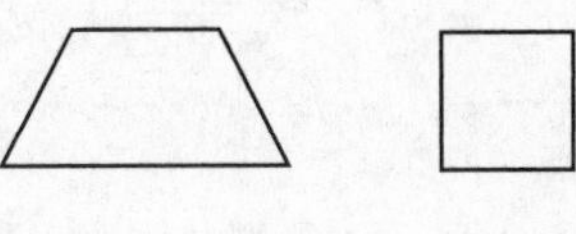

2. Alan sees this pattern on a magazine.
   Circle the one that comes next.

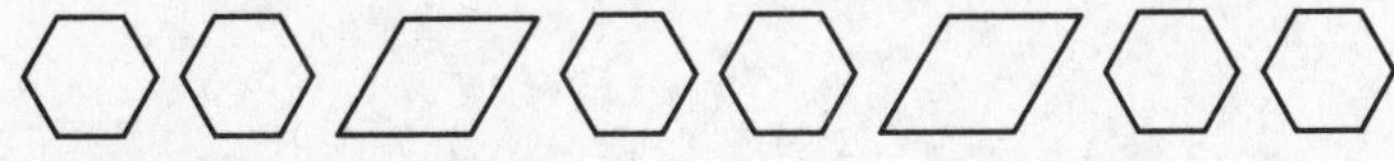

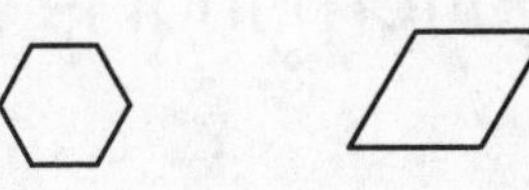

Spiral Review (Chapter 24, Lesson 2; Chapter 25, Lesson 2) **NS 2.6, MR 1.0**

Decide if you need to add or subtract.
Solve.

3. Franklin has 25 coins. Then he finds 7 more coins. How many coins does Franklin have now?

   _____ coins

4. Joy has 34 stickers. She gives 8 stickers to Tasha. How many stickers does Joy have left?

   _____ stickers

Name ____________________ Date __________

Problem Solving: Find a Pattern

CA Standard
KEY SDAP 2.1

Solve.

1. Barry makes this pattern.

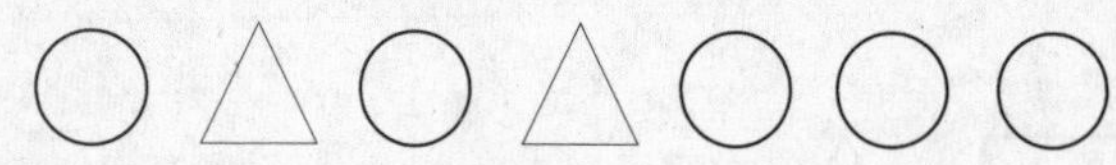

Circle the shape in the pattern that is wrong.

2. Lea makes this pattern.

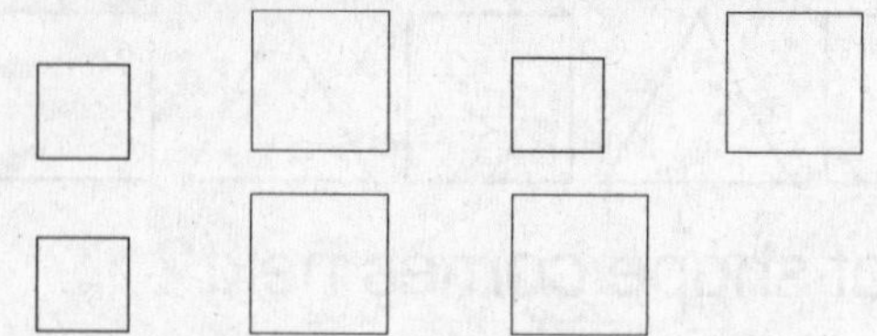

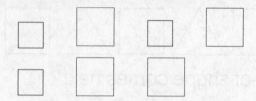

Circle the shape in the pattern that is wrong.

3. Mimi makes this pattern.

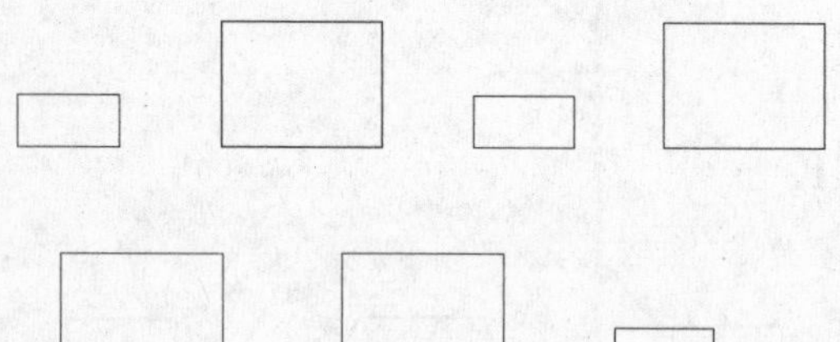

Circle the shape in the pattern that is wrong.

4. Junji makes this pattern.

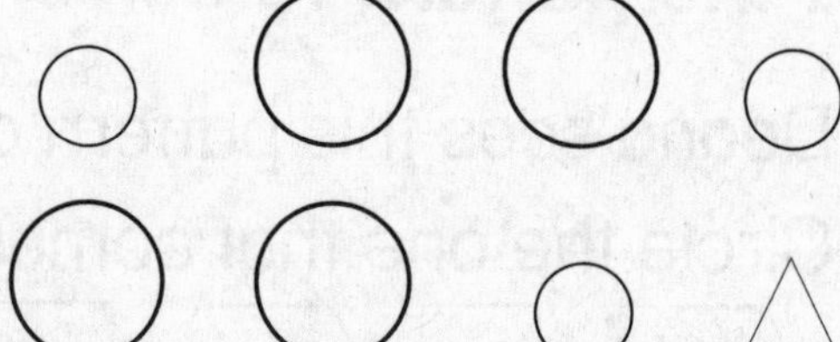

Circle the shape in the pattern that is wrong.

5. Ian makes this pattern.

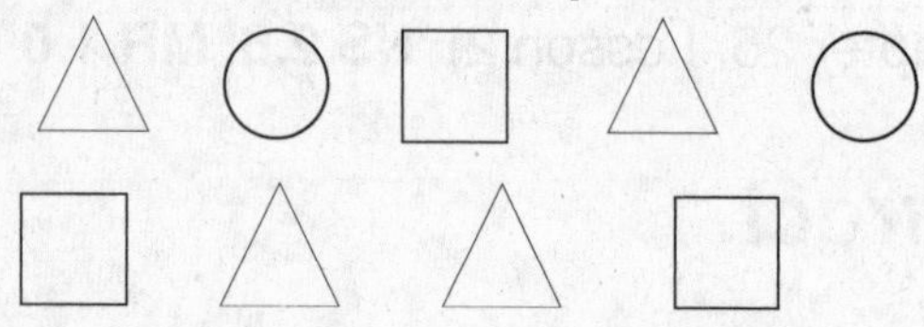

Circle the shape in the pattern that is wrong.

Draw the shape it should be.

6. Cindy makes this pattern.

Circle the shape in the pattern that is wrong.

Draw the shape it should be.

Hands On: Sort Solid Figures

CA Standards
MG 2.2, SDAP 1.1

Solid shapes have special names.

cube

cone

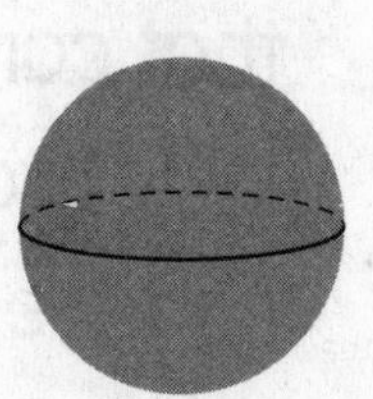
sphere

rectangular prism

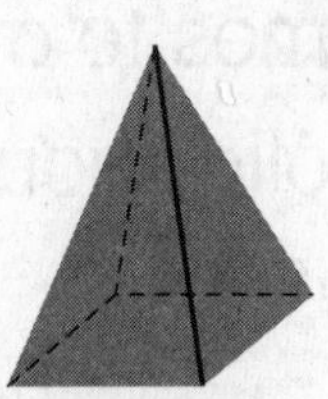
pyramid

cylinder

Solids can move.

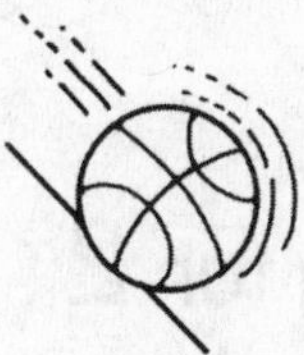
Roll

Slide

Stack

Find how each solid can move.
Complete the table.

	Slide	Stack	Roll
1.			
2.			
3.			

Spiral Review (Chapter 26, Lesson 1) **MG 2.3, MG 2.4**

Read the directions. Draw the object.

4. Write an **X** below the .

5. Write an **L** to the left of the .

Name ____________________ Date __________

Hands On: Sort Solid Figures

CA Standards
MG 2.2, SDAP 1.1

Solve. Circle the solids that follow the rule.

1. Emma is looking for 1 solid that comes to a point. What solid should she choose?

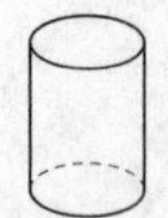  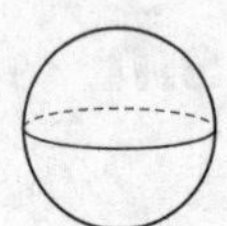

2. Tad is looking for 1 solid that can roll. What solid should he choose?

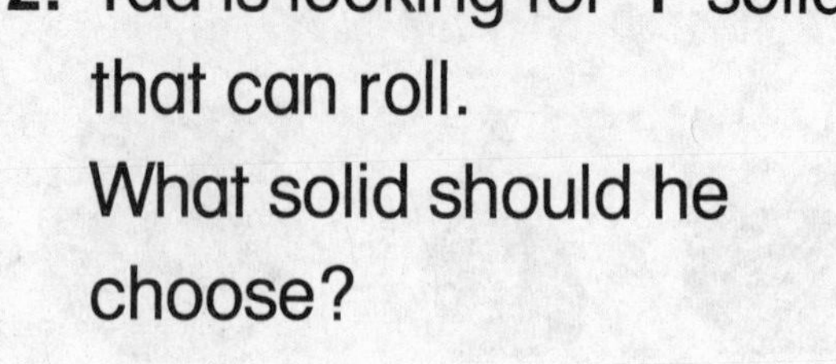 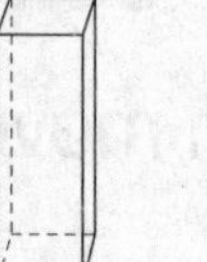

3. Ian is looking for 2 solids that have 8 corners. Which solids should he choose?

 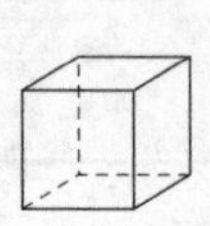 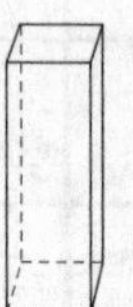

4. Anna is looking for 2 solids that have 1 or more curved surfaces. Which solids should she choose?

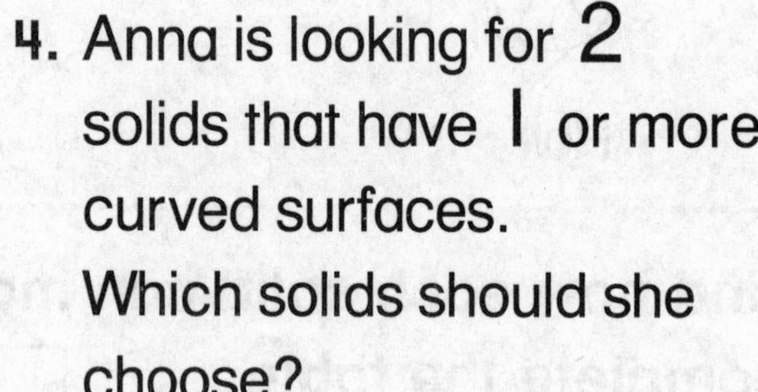

5. Deb is looking for 1 solid that has 1 square surface and 4 triangular surfaces. Name the solid that fits her rule.

____

6. Raul is looking for 1 solid that has no corners and no flat surfaces. Name the solid that fits his rule.

____

Name ______________________ Date __________

Solid Figures

CA Standards
MG 2.2, SDAP 1.1

There are many ways to sort solid figures.
Read the sorting rule.
Circle the figures that follow the rule.

1. Figures with corners

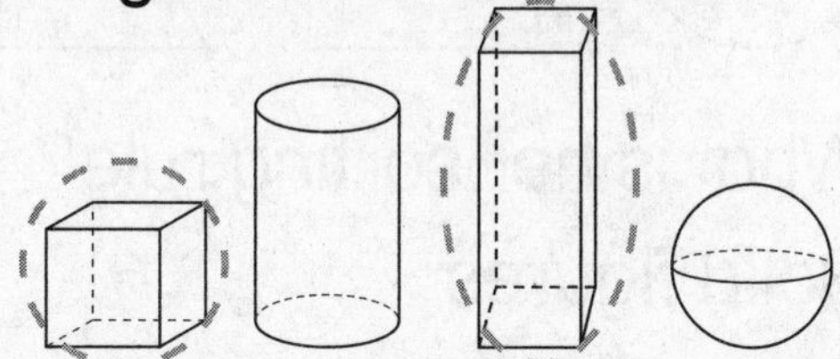

2. Figures with all flat surfaces

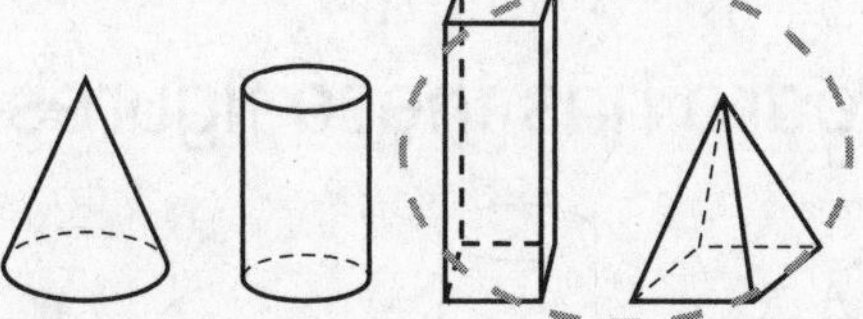

3. Figures with curved surfaces

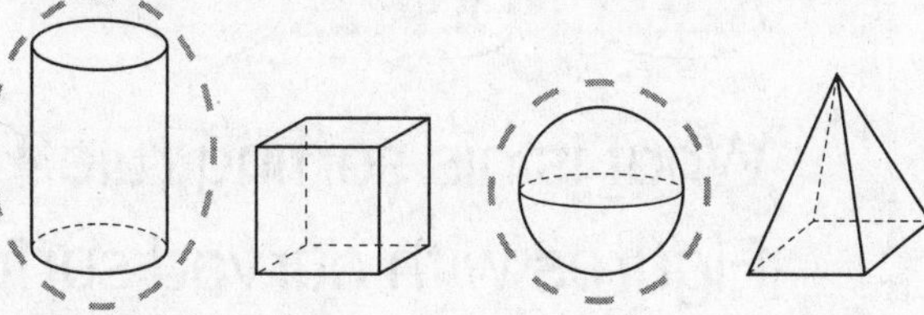

Spiral Review (Chapter 26, Lesson 2) **MG 2.3, MG 2.4**

4. Draw a ◯ **far from** the △.

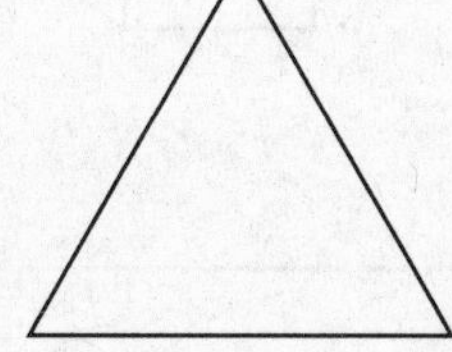

5. Draw a □ **next to** the ▭.

Solid Figures

CA Standards
MG 2.2, SDAP 1.1

Solve.

1. Mike has these figures.

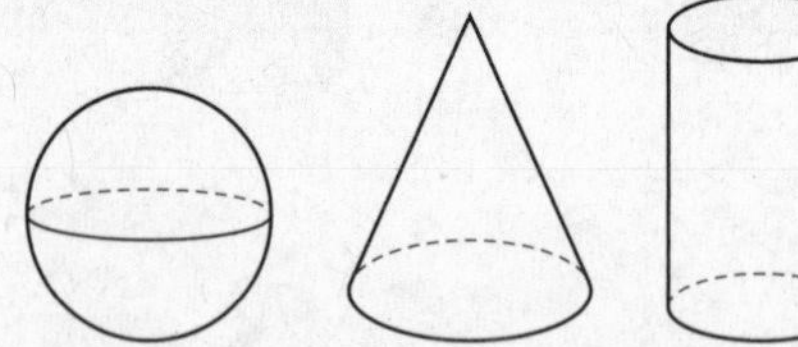

What is his sorting rule?
Figures that roll
Figures with flat surfaces

2. Lara has these figures.

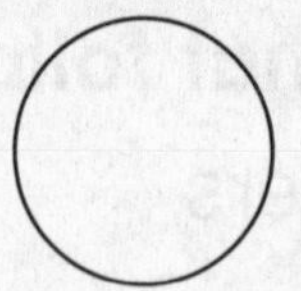
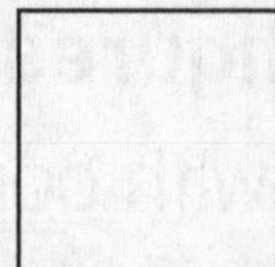
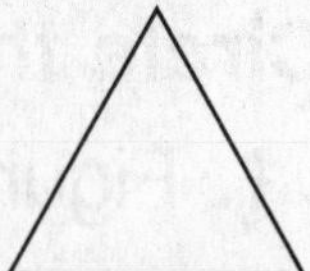

What is her sorting rule?
Solid figures
Plane figures

3. Marge has these figures.

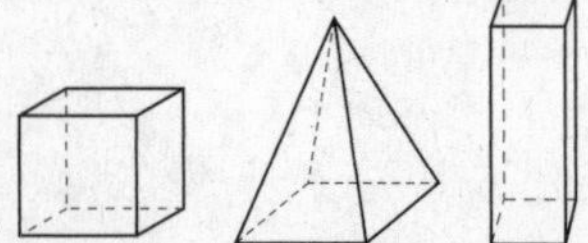

What is her sorting rule?
Figures with corners
Figures with curved surfaces

4. Pedro has these figures.

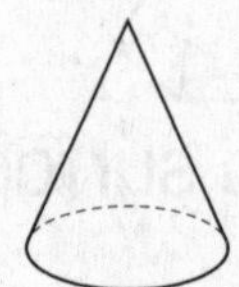
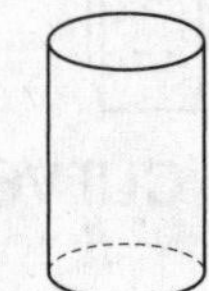
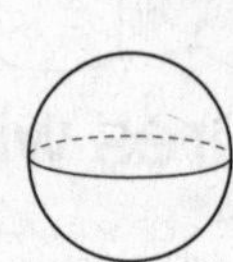

What is his sorting rule?
Figures with curved surfaces
Figures that stack

5. Rosa has these figures.
What is her sorting rule?

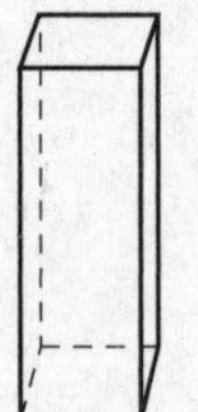
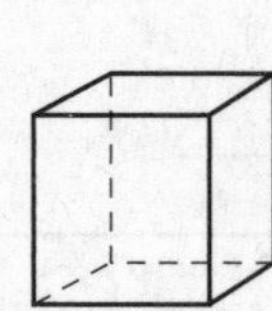
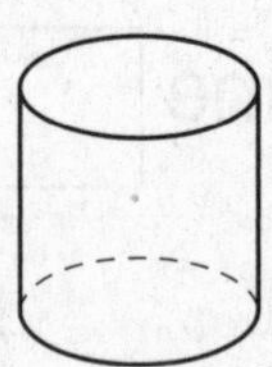

____

____

____

6. Jack has these figures.
What is his sorting rule?

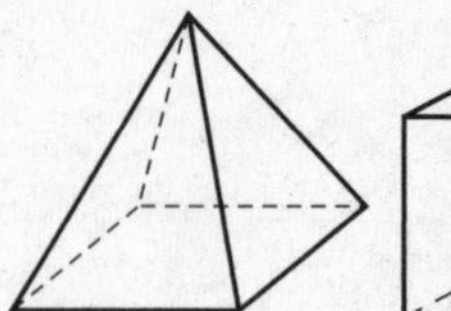
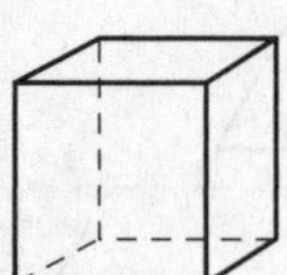

____

____

____

Name ____________________ Date __________

Identify Faces of Solid Figures

CA Standards
MG 2.1, MG 2.0

The face of a solid is a plane figure. The face is flat.

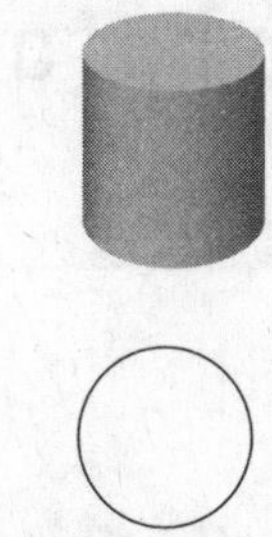

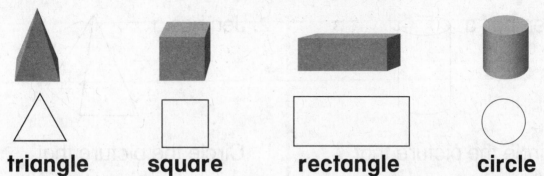

triangle **square** **rectangle** **circle**

Look at the plane figure. Circle the solid with a face like it.

1.

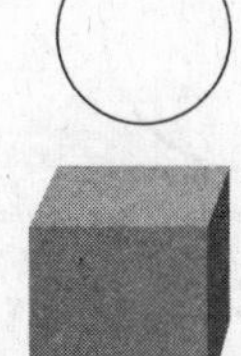

2.

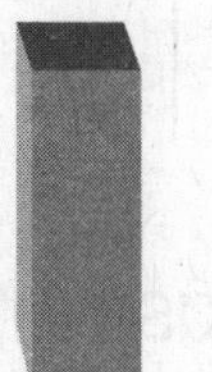

3.

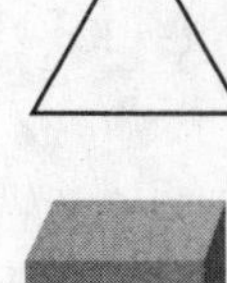

4.

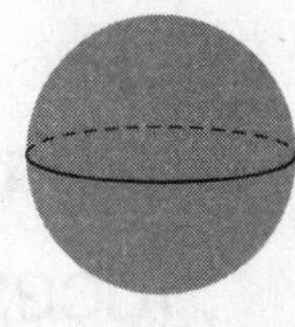

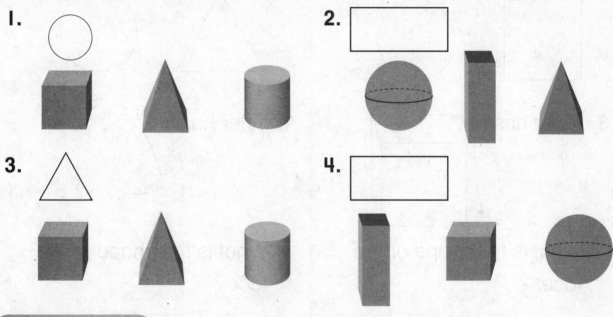

Spiral Review (Chapter 26, Lesson 3) **MG 2.1, MG 2.0**

5.

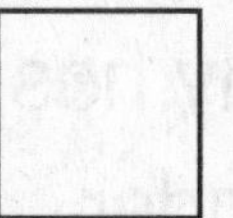
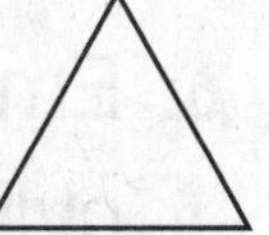

Circle the figures that have 4 sides that are the same.
How many figures have 4 sides that are the same?

______

6.

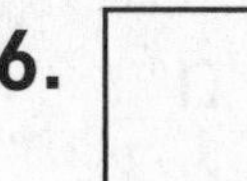

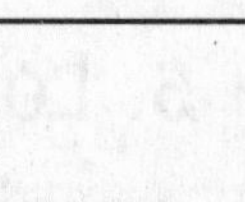

Circle the figures that have 3 sides.
How many figures have 3 sides?

______

Identify Faces of Solid Figures

CA Standards
MG 2.1, MG 2.0

Solve.

1. Ben has a 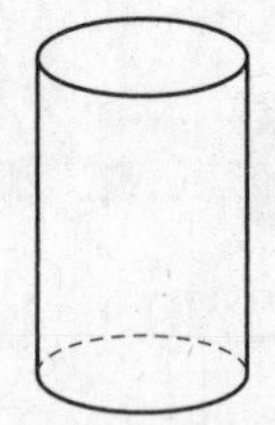 .

Circle the picture that shows a face of his solid.

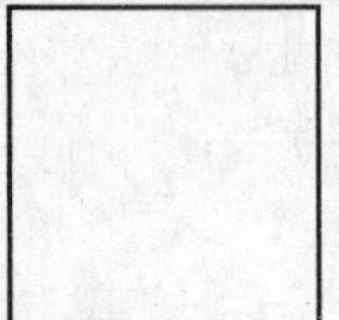 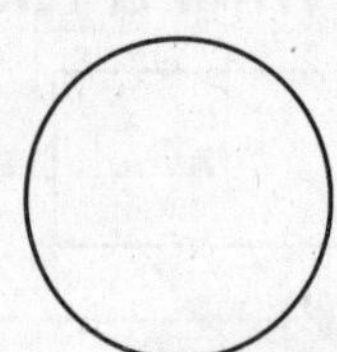

2. Jen has a 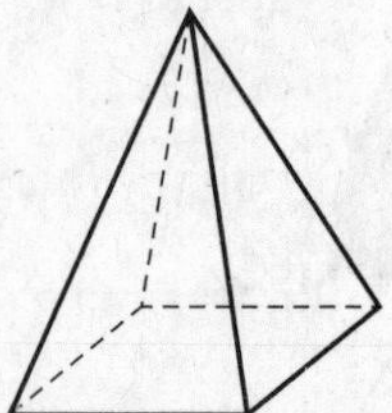 .

Circle the picture that shows a face of her solid.

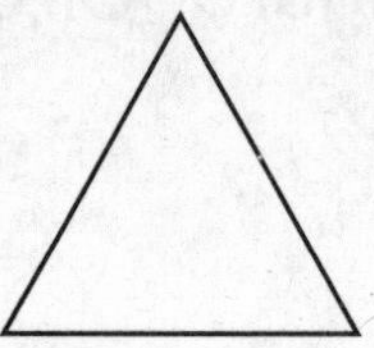 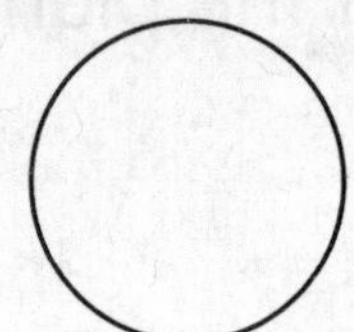

3. Anita has a 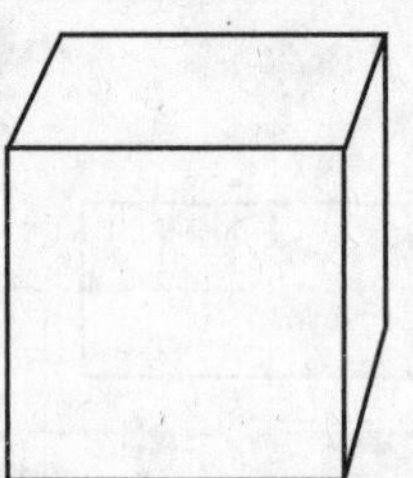 .

What is the shape of the faces?

____

4. Tyler has a 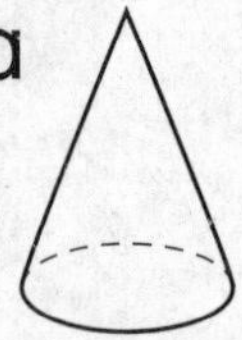 .

What is the shape of the face?

____

5. Lalo has a cube and a rectangular prism.
What is the shape of a face that they both have?

____

6. Emily has a cone and a cylinder.
What is the shape of the face that they both have?

____

Problem Solving: Make a Table

CA Standards
KEY NS 2.4, SDAP 1.0

Complete the table.

Quinn is using blocks to make towers.
He is going to make 6 towers like the one shown.

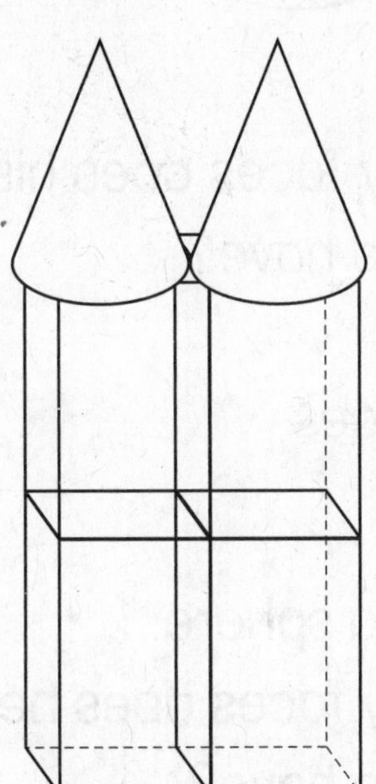

Number of Towers	Number of Rectangular Prisms	Number of Cones
1	4	2
2	8	4
3		
4		

Spiral Review (Chapter 26, Lesson 4) **MG 2.2, SDAP 1.1**

Read the sorting rule. Circle the figures that follow the rule.

1. More than 3 sides

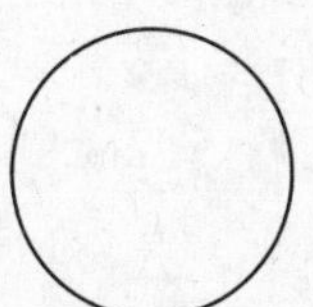
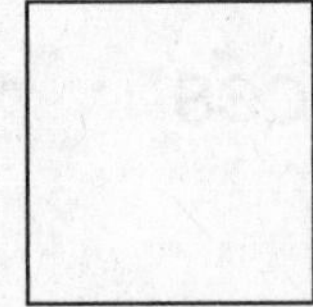
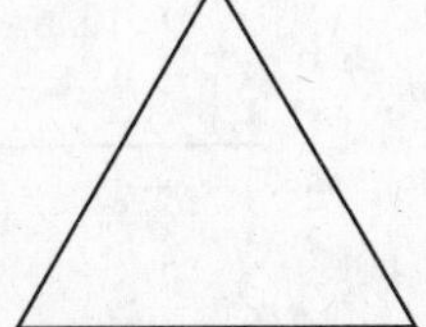

2. No corners

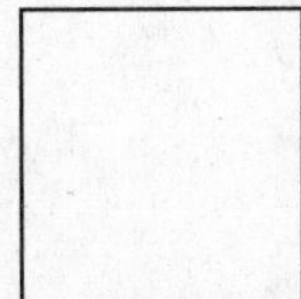
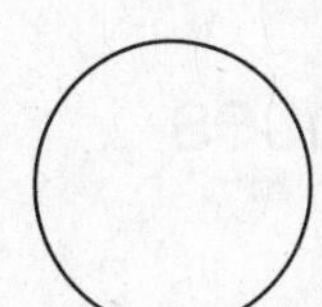
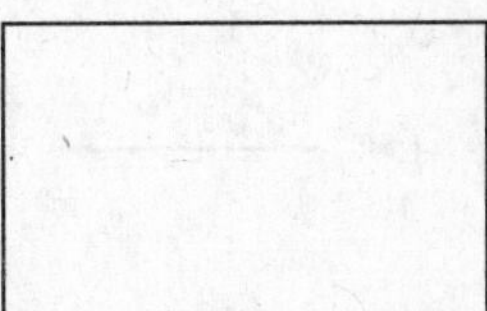

Problem Solving: Make a Table

CA Standards
KEY NS 2.4, SDAP 1.0

1. Dora has a 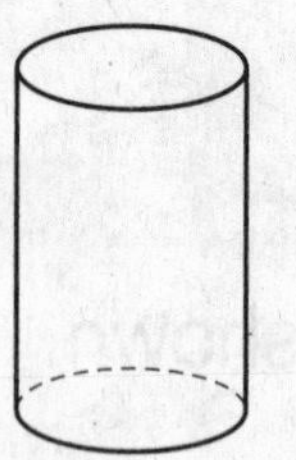 .

   How many faces does her solid figure have?

   ______ faces

2. Ray has a 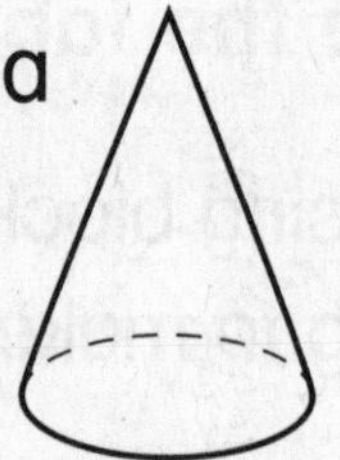 .

   How many faces does his solid figure have?

   ______ faces

3. Ken has a cube.
   How many faces does his solid figure have?

   ______ faces

4. Sofia has a sphere.
   How many faces does her solid figure have?

   ______ faces

5. Marty has a cube and a cone. How many faces do his solid figures have in all?

   ______ faces

6. Pam has a rectangular prism and a cylinder. How many faces do her solid figures have in all?

   ______ faces

Hands On: Compare Length and Height

CA Standard
MG 1.1, MG 1.0

Use taller and shorter when you compare height.

Use longer and shorter when you compare length.

Is the object longer or shorter than your hand? Circle.

1. 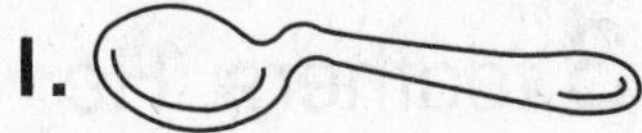

longer shorter

2.

longer shorter

3. 

longer shorter

4.

longer shorter

Spiral Review (Chapter 27, Lesson 1) **MG 2.2, SDAP 1.1**

Find how each figure can move.
Complete the table. Write Yes or No.

		Slide	Stack	Roll
5.				
6.				

Hands On: Compare Length and Height

CA Standards
MG 1.1, MG 1.0

Solve.

1. Mack and Mike each have a new pencil. Mike's pencil is longer. Circle Mike's pencil.

2. Jen and Luz each have a new hair ribbon. Jen's hair ribbon is shorter. Circle Jen's hair ribbon.

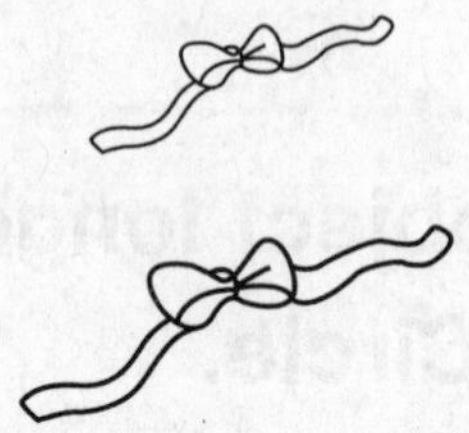

3. Tam has 3 pieces of string. She wants to use the longest piece. Circle the string Tam should use.

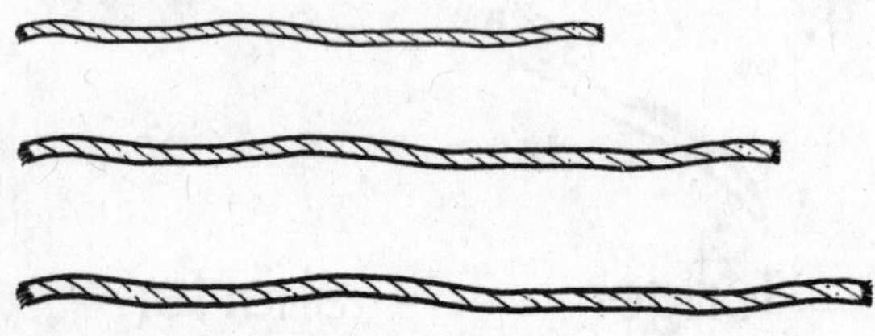

4. Nick finds 3 feathers. He gives the shortest feather away. Circle the feather Nick gives away.

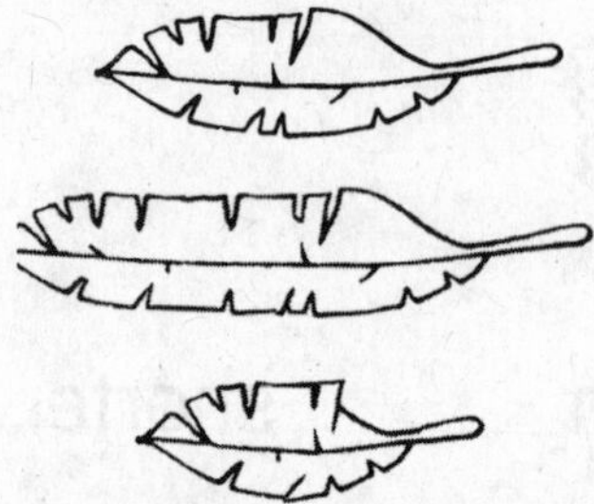

5. Sam is shorter than Pedro. Bess is taller than Ann. Ann is taller than Pedro. Who is the tallest?

____

6. The yellow ribbon is longer than the green ribbon. The blue ribbon is longer than the red ribbon. The red ribbon is shorter than the green ribbon. Which ribbon is the shortest?

______ ribbon

Name ______________ Date ________

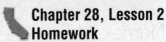

Hands On: Nonstandard Units

CA Standards
MG 1.1, MG 1.0,

You can measure length with different units.

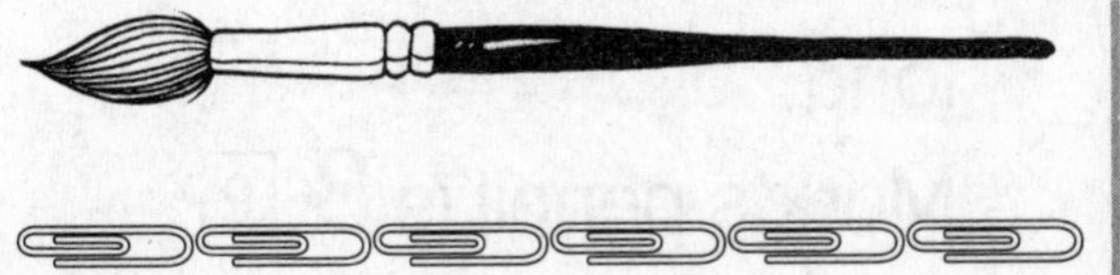

The paintbrush is about
6 paper clips long.

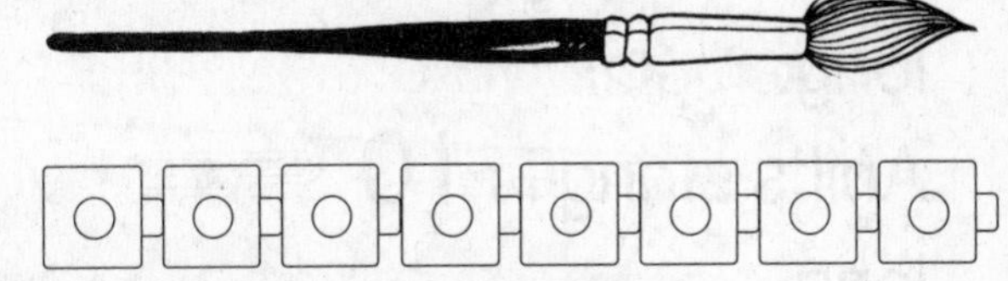

The paintbrush is about
8 cubes long.

Write the number of units.

1. About how many teaspoons long is your kitchen table?

   My kitchen table is about ________ teaspoons long.

2. About how many toothpicks long is a pen?

   A pen is about ________ toothpicks long.

3. About how many napkins long is your bed?

   My bed is about ________ napkins long.

Spiral Review (Chapter 27, Lesson 2) **MG 2.2, SDAP 1.1**

Read the sorting rule.
Circle the figures that follow the rule.

4. Corners

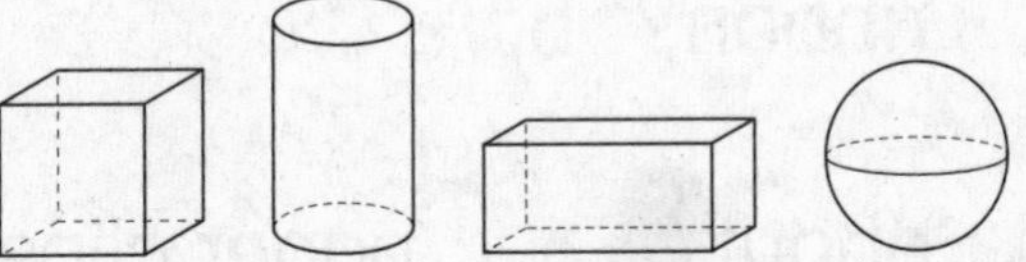

5. Curved surfaces

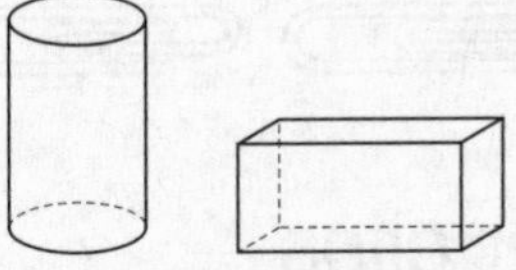
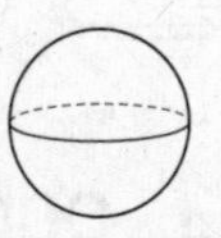
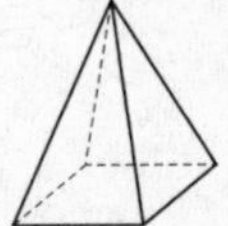

Hands On: Nonstandard Units

CA Standards
MG 1.1, MG 1.0

Solve.

1. Brian's string is 18 paper clips long.
Anil's string is 10 paper clips long.
Who has the longer string?

____

2. Susan's pencil is 12 cubes long.
Mark's pencil is 8 cubes long.
Who has the shorter pencil?

____

3. Larry draws a bug that is about 1 paper clip long.
Circle Larry's bug.

4. Dora draws a rope that is about 5 cubes long.
Circle Dora's rope.

5. Jake lines up 4 crayons end to end. How long is the line of crayons?

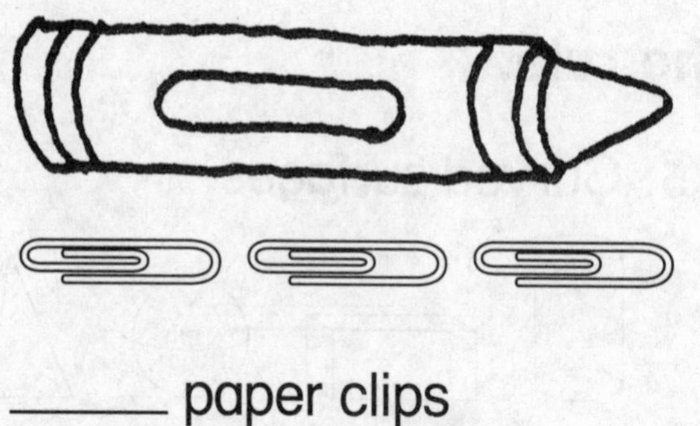

_____ paper clips

6. Maya's ribbon is about 8 paper clips long. Zach's ribbon is about 5 paper clips long. About how many paper clips longer than Zach's ribbon is Maya's ribbon?

about _____ paper clips

Hands On: Compare Weight

CA Standards
MG 1.1, MG 1.0

Find the object. Circle the heavier object.

1. 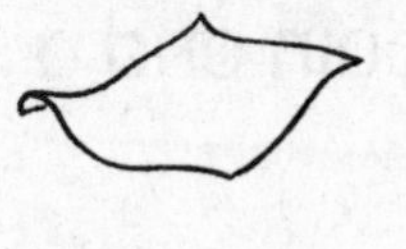 

2. 

3.  

Circle the lighter object.

4.  

5.  

6.  

Spiral Review (Chapter 27, Lesson 3) **MG 2.1, MG 2.0**

Look at the two-dimensional figure.
Circle the three-dimensional with a face like it.

7. 

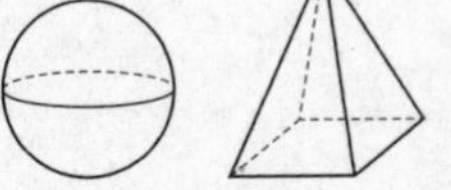

8. 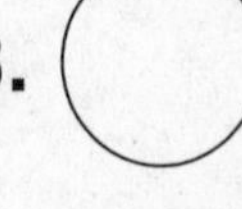

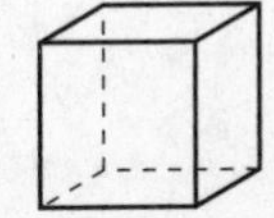 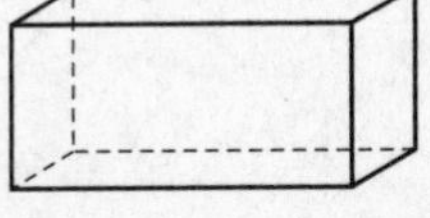 

Hands On: Compare Weight

CA Standards
MG 1.1, MG 1.0

Solve.

1. Jamal has a pencil and a book.
Circle the heavier object.

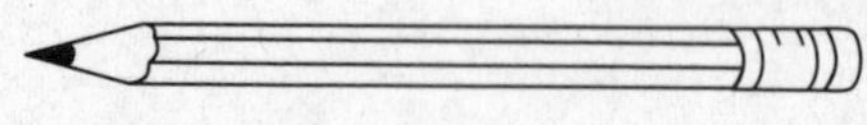

2. Sandy has a coin and a purse.
Circle the heavier object.

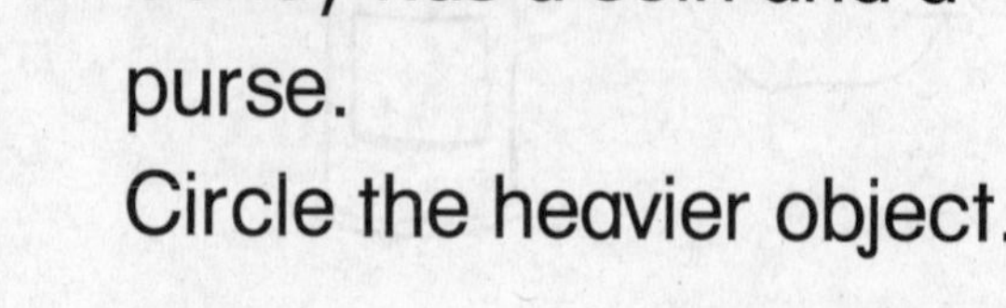

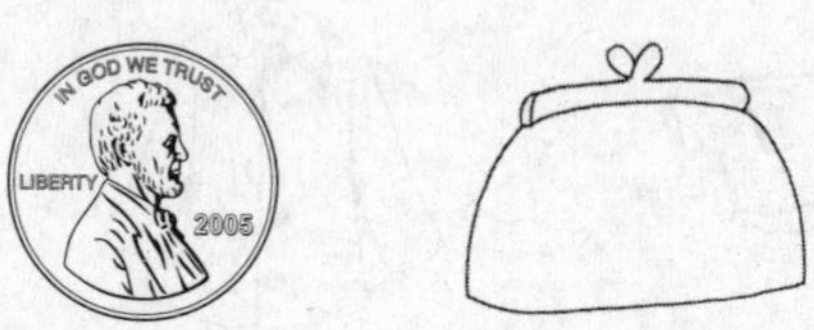

3. Abby has an apple and a grape.
Which is the heavier piece of fruit?

____

4. Mike has an orange and a watermelon.
Which is the heavier piece of fruit?

____

5. Carmen has a bottle of water, a paper clip, and a crayon.
Which is the heaviest object?

____

6. Owen has a pencil, a pair of shoes, and a toy car.
Which is the heaviest object?

____

Name ____________________ Date __________

Hands On: Compare Volume

CA Standard
MG 1.1, MG 1.0

Compare containers.
Fill one container. Pour it into the other.

The glass is full and the pitcher is not empty.
The pitcher holds more.

Circle the container that can hold more.

1. 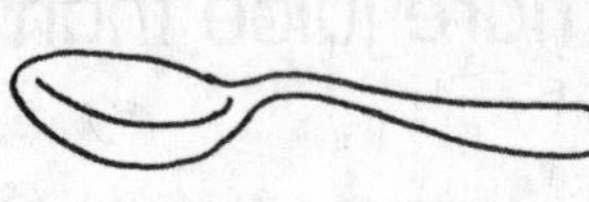 

2.  

Circle the container that can hold less.

3.  

4. 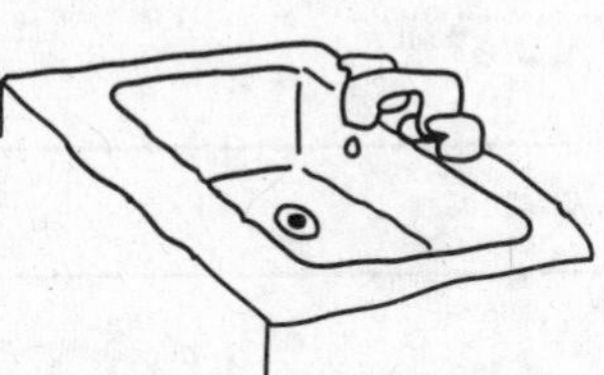 

Spiral Review (Chapter 27, Lesson 4) **KEY** NS 2.4, SDAP 1.0

Look at the table. Solve.

Number of Towers	Number of Cubes
1	10
2	20
3	30

5. How many cubes does it take to build 3 towers?
______ cubes

6. Look at the pattern. How many cubes will you need to build 4 towers? ______ cubes

Name ______________________ Date __________

Hands On: Compare Volume

CA Standards
MG 1.1, MG 1.0

Solve.

1. Beth wants a container that will hold more than this fish bowl.
Circle the container Beth should get.

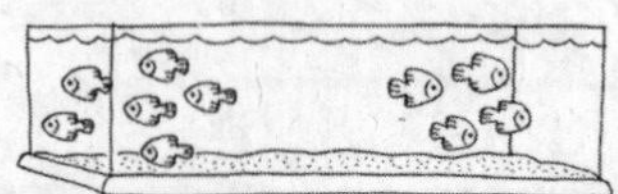

2. Kwan wants a container that holds less than this jar.
Circle the container Kwan should get.

3. Ned needs a container that will hold more than this bowl.
Name something that can hold more than his bowl.
____
____
____

4. Iris needs a container that will hold more juice than this one.
Name something that can hold more than her glass.
____
____
____

5. Luis wants a container that will hold 5 glasses of juice.
Name a container that he can use.
____
____
____

6. Sandra wants a container that will hold enough water for her to sit in.
Name a container that she can use.
____
____
____

Name ______________________ Date ____________

Problem Solving: Use a Graph

CA Standards
SDAP 1.2, MG 1.1

This graph shows how long the objects are.
Use the graph to solve.

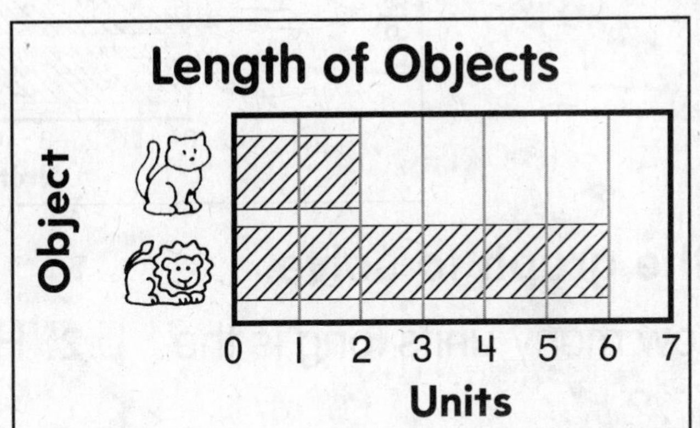

How many units long is the cat?

2 Units

Use the graph to solve.

1. How many units long is the lion?
   ______ Units
2. How many more units long is the lion than the cat?
   ______ more Units
3. How many units long are the cat and the lion in all?
   ______ Units in all

Spiral Review (Chapter 27, Lesson 1) **MG 2.2, SDAP 1.1**

Find how each figure can move.
Complete the table. Write Yes or No.

		Slide	Stack	Roll
4.				
5.				

Name ______________________ Date __________

Problem Solving: Use a Graph

CA Standards
SDAP 1.2, MG 1.1

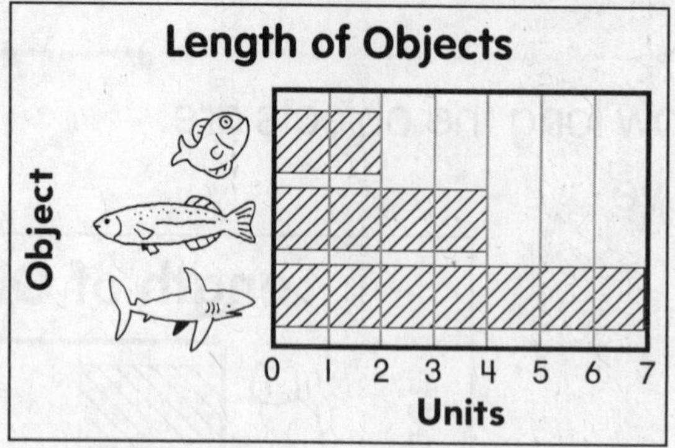

Use the graph to solve.

1. How many units long is the ?

   _____ units

2. How many units long is the ?

   _____ units

3. How many units long are the and in all? Write the number sentence.

   _____ ◯ _____ ◯ _____

   units in all

4. How many more units long is the than the ? Write the number sentence.

   _____ ◯ _____ ◯ _____

   more units

5. How many more units long is the than the and combined? Write the number sentence.

   _____ ◯ _____ ◯ _____

   more units

6. The grows 3 units. The grows 2 units. Now how many units long are the and in all? Write the number sentence.

   _____ ◯ _____ ◯ _____

   units in all